Principles of

IONIC ORGANIC REACTIONS

Principles of

IONIC

ORGANIC REACTIONS

ELLIOT R. ALEXANDER

Assistant Professor of Chemistry
in the University of Illinois

NEW YORK · JOHN WILEY & SONS, INC.
LONDON · CHAPMAN & HALL, LIMITED

PREFACE

It is becoming increasingly apparent that it is possible to break down a very large number of organic reactions into different sequences of a few basic transformations, the nature of which does not change regardless of the process being carried out. Such a sequence is commonly called a *reaction mechanism*. To many organic chemists, however, a reaction mechanism is more often regarded merely as a pleasant form of retrospection not useful for stimulating research or for implementing the chemical intuition for which all synthetic chemists strive.

To a certain extent this attitude is understandable. For many years organic chemists have been trained to think in terms of the reactions of functional groups, and it is often very difficult to see the thread of continuity connecting a number of transformations in which the similarities are only those of electronic distribution or behavior. Even the way organic formulas are written obscures the electrons in a molecule and minimizes their importance in understanding chemical reactions. Frequently, since it is not always clear that the individual steps of a mechanism are of a general nature, the mechanisms themselves are more difficult to remember than the starting materials and the end products. Nomenclature has also proved to be a stumbling block to the assimilation of organic chemical theory. It is always exasperating to find unfamiliar terms used to describe phenomena which may be well known in other situations. Finally, to the despair of organic chemists, the physical rather than the chemical aspects of organic theory have been stressed. Occasionally rather unimportant organic reactions have been studied and discussed in great detail because they could be treated experimentally in a precise quantitative fashion, while other more important reactions, for which there is only qualitative information, have been omitted from discussion. Obviously such information does not belong in books dealing with the physical nature of organic chemistry, but it is of considerable importance to us for whom these reactions are the tools of our profession.

Accordingly, in writing this book for advanced undergraduates and first-year graduate students, the objective has been twofold. First an attempt has been made to present from the point of view of an organic chemist the mechanisms which seem to be most reasonable for a number

v

of organic reactions together with the pertinent data which support them. It is well known that while our interpretation of data may change in the light of later experimental work, the facts themselves do not change. Second, I have attempted to present the material in a sequence that will stress the *similarities* rather than the differences between seemingly diverse organic reactions. In the first six chapters are discussed the fundamental intermediates and types of reactions from which most ionic transformations can be constructed. The remaining chapters of the book are concerned with a more detailed discussion of individual organic reactions.

Such a book as this could not have been written without the aid of a great many people, most of whom cannot be properly credited in these pages. This I regret because my debt to them is very real. It is a pleasure to acknowledge my indebtedness to the students and the staff of the University of Illinois not only for many stimulating discussions but also for much practical help in the preparation of the manuscript. Foremost among them are Dr. Elizabeth Harfenist, Dr. and Mrs. R. E. Heckert, and Dr. L. E. Miller. It was Dr. Miller who read and constructively criticized the manuscript in detail while it was still only in the form of a rough draft. My thanks are also due to the trustees of the Jewett Fellowships for the opportunity to spend a year in study and research in the field of organic theory.

Finally no acknowledgment of indebtedness could be considered complete without mentioning the assistance and continuous encouragement I received from my wife. It was she more than anyone else who bore the brunt of book writing.

ELLIOT R. ALEXANDER

Urbana, Illinois
April, 1950

CONTENTS

CHAPTER 1

INTRODUCTION

In general a covalent bond between two atoms, for example X and Y, results from a process of electron sharing. One electron is furnished by X, the other by Y, and the two interact to form a covalent bond.

$$X\cdot + \cdot Y \rightarrow X:Y \text{ (a covalent bond)} \qquad (1)$$

Such a covalent bond can break in one of two ways, giving rise to two separate and fundamentally different mechanisms by which organic molecules undergo reaction. Either it can break so that one electron goes to X and one to Y, or in the cleavage the electron pair which was shared by X and Y can become associated with only one of them:

$$X:Y \rightarrow X\cdot + \cdot Y \text{ (homolytic cleavage—free radicals)} \qquad (2)$$

$$X:Y \rightarrow [\overset{\oplus}{X}] + [:\overset{\ominus}{Y}] \text{ (heterolytic cleavage—ions)} \qquad (3)$$

When the bond breaks so that each fragment acquires one electron, $X\cdot$ and $Y\cdot$ are known as *free radicals*. Since they often have the same electronic structure in their outermost valence shell, the process is known as a *homolytic cleavage*. When Y usurps both electrons, however, X loses the electron which it furnished to make the covalent bond (equation 1) and it thus acquires a unit positive charge. Conversely, the ion $[Y:]\ominus$, although it has two unshared electrons, actually has acquired only one more electron than it had originally (equation 1) and it now carries a unit negative charge. Since the two ions produced have different electronic structures, this type of fission is known as a *heterolytic cleavage*.

In heterolytic cleavage the fragments formed are electrically charged and subject to the usual laws of electrostatic attraction and repulsion. When free radicals are formed, highly reactive species are present, but the fragments have no formal charge. Clearly, therefore, such reactions

1

will not be subject to the same laws or principles that govern ionic transformations.

In discussing mechanisms, therefore, it is of the utmost importance to know the process by which bond rupture occurs. Frequently this is very difficult, but often an indication of the nature of a reaction may be obtained by an examination of the characteristics of the transformation and a study of the experimental conditions favorable for the process. In Table 1 the characteristics of free radical and ionic reactions are compared

TABLE 1

CHARACTERISTICS OF FREE RADICAL AND IONIC REACTIONS

Free Radical Reactions	Ionic Reactions
1. Catalyzed by light, high temperatures, or the decomposition of substances known to produce other free radicals.	1. Unaffected by light, the presence of free radicals or peroxides. Frequently catalyzed by acids or bases.
2. Inhibited by substances such as hydroquinone and diphenylamine which are known to react readily with other free radicals.	2. Unaffected by free radical acceptors.
3. Proceed in vapor phase or in nonpolar solvents.	3. Rarely occur in vapor phase. Affected in a characteristic way by solvents (Chapter 4).
4. Frequently autocatalytic and exhibit an induction period before reaction commences.	4. Usually follow first- or second-order kinetics.
5. Aromatic substitution proceeds abnormally insofar as orientation rules are concerned.	5. Aromatic substitution follows orientation rules.

Thus, to mention only a few examples, oxidations, electrolytic reductions, most polymerizations, reactions utilizing organic peroxides as catalysts, reactions of aromatic diazonium salts in which nitrogen is lost, and photochemical or hot-tube processes are probably free radical transformations. The Friedel-Crafts reaction, the alkylation of acetoacetic ester, aromatic substitutions, dehydrations, and the aldol or Claisen condensations appear to involve transitory ionic intermediates.

There are instances in which the mode of fission and therefore reaction mechanism changes with the environment or experimental conditions. This can be illustrated with the dissociation of hexaphenylethane, the bromination of bromobenzene, and the reactions of diazonium ions:

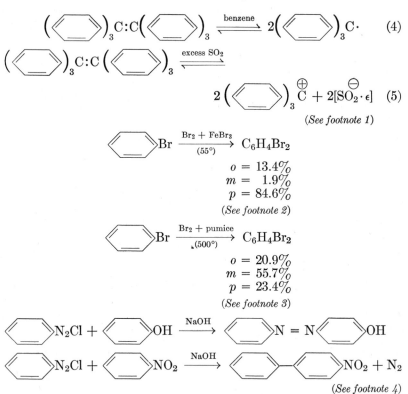

$$\left(\langle\rangle\right)_3 C:C\left(\langle\rangle\right)_3 \underset{\text{benzene}}{\rightleftharpoons} 2\left(\langle\rangle\right)_3 C\cdot \qquad (4)$$

$$\left(\langle\rangle\right)_3 C:C\left(\langle\rangle\right)_3 \underset{\text{excess } SO_2}{\rightleftharpoons}$$

$$2\left(\langle\rangle\right)_3 \overset{\oplus}{C} + 2[\overset{\ominus}{SO_2}\cdot\epsilon] \qquad (5)$$

(See footnote 1)

$$\langle\rangle Br \xrightarrow[(55°)]{Br_2 + FeBr_3} C_6H_4Br_2$$

$$o = 13.4\%$$
$$m = 1.9\%$$
$$p = 84.6\%$$

(See footnote 2)

$$\langle\rangle Br \xrightarrow[(500°)]{Br_2 + pumice} C_6H_4Br_2$$

$$o = 20.9\%$$
$$m = 55.7\%$$
$$p = 23.4\%$$

(See footnote 3)

$$\langle\rangle N_2Cl + \langle\rangle OH \xrightarrow{NaOH} \langle\rangle N=N\langle\rangle OH$$

$$\langle\rangle N_2Cl + \langle\rangle NO_2 \xrightarrow{NaOH} \langle\rangle-\langle\rangle NO_2 + N_2$$

(See footnote 4)

The question of mechanisms is complicated further by the existence of free radicals which are themselves charged. Thus in the reduction of duroquinone (tetramethylbenzoquinone) there is both potentiometric and magnetometric evidence (paramagnetism) that an intermediate is formed which is at once an ion and a free radical.[5] Such intermediates

[1] Early investigators believed that solutions of hexaphenylethane in liquid sulfur dioxide contained both triphenylmethyl cations and triphenylmethyl anions [$C_6H_5)_3C: \ominus$]. That equation 5 represents the correct nature of the dissociation has been demonstrated by the work of Anderson (*J. Am. Chem. Soc.*, **57**, 1674 [1935]). He has shown that the absorption curves of hexaphenylethane and triphenylmethyl bromide in liquid sulfur dioxide are almost identical and that in dilute solution the same number of triphenylmethyl cations is obtained from one mole of hexaphenylethane as from two moles of triphenylmethyl bromide.

[2] Van der Linden, *Rec. trav. chim.*, **30**, 376 (1911).

[3] Wibaut, van de Lande, and Wallagh, *ibid.*, **52**, 805 (1933).

[4] Bachmann and Hoffman, in Adams, *Organic Reactions*, Vol. II, p. 224, John Wiley and Sons, New York, 1944.

[5] Michaelis, Schubert, Reber, Kuck, and Granick, *J. Am. Chem. Soc.*, **60**, 1678 (1938).

are called *semiquinones*. They are formed by the gain or loss of one elec-

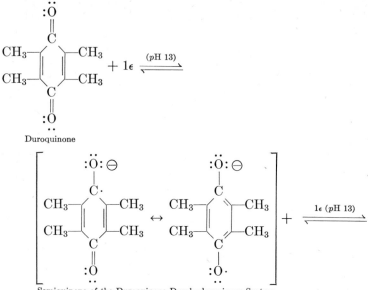

Duroquinone

Semiquinone of the Duroquinone-Durohydroquinone System

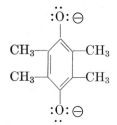

Anion of Durohydroquinone

tron in those oxidation-reduction systems which require the gain or loss of two electrons for completion of the reaction.

In the subsequent chapters, we shall concern ourselves almost exclusively with the reactions which proceed by ionic mechanisms.

CHAPTER 2

FACTORS INFLUENCING DISTRIBUTION AND MOBILITY OF ELECTRONS

There are at least five factors to be considered in a discussion of the distribution and the mobility of electrons within organic molecules. They are:

1. The permanent polarization of single bonds (I_s).
2. The polarizability of single bonds (I_D).
3. Resonance (M).
4. The polarizability of double bonds or conjugated systems (E).
5. Hyperconjugation.

Since it is possible for some of these factors to operate in opposition to each other, it is necessary to be able to evaluate, qualitatively at least, both the direction in which they operate and their relative magnitudes.

PERMANENT POLARIZATION OF SINGLE BONDS

The permanent polarization of single bonds, or induction-static (I_s), as it is often called, originates whenever there is a covalent bond between atoms which are electrically dissimilar. In a cova-
lent bond between two like atoms the shared electron pair is midway between the two nuclei, and the valence electrons of each atom completely neutralize the positive charge of each atomic kernel (Fig. 1). In a covalent bond between two atoms such as carbon and chlorine, however, chlorine has a greater affinity for electrons than carbon. Consequently the shared pair, together with the valence electrons of the carbon atom, is attracted towards chlorine, and the electrical centers of the valence electrons and the atomic kernels no longer coincide

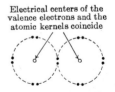

Electrical centers of the valence electrons and the atomic kernels coincide

FIG. 1. Electron distribution of a symmetrical covalent bond.

5

(Fig. 2). Electrical dipoles are thus created, the overall effect of which places a fractional negative charge $(-\delta)$ on the chlorine atom and a fractional positive charge $(+\delta)$ on the carbon atom. By analogy with the extreme case in which chlorine captures both shared electrons and forms an electrovalent ion pair [e.g., $\text{Na}:\text{Cl} \rightarrow (\text{Na})\oplus + (:\text{Cl})\ominus$], such a covalent bond is said to have *partial ionic character.*

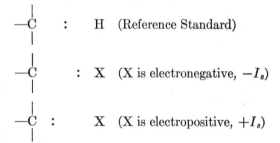

Electrical centers of the valence electrons

$+\delta$ $-\delta$

Electrical centers of the atomic kernels

Fig. 2. Electron distribution of an unsymmetrical covalent bond.

An atom or group is sometimes defined as *electronegative* $(-I_s)$ if the electron pair which it shares with a carbon atom is farther from the carbon atom to which it is connected than the shared pair of a carbon-hydrogen bond is from the carbon atom. Conversely, an atom or group is said to be *electropositive* $(+I_s)$ if the shared electron pair is closer to the carbon atom with which it is connected than the shared electron pair of a carbon-hydrogen bond is to that carbon atom. The convention may be diagrammed as follows:

$$\overset{|}{\underset{|}{-\text{C}}} \quad : \quad \text{H} \quad \text{(Reference Standard)}$$

$$\overset{|}{\underset{|}{-\text{C}}} \quad : \quad \text{X} \quad (\text{X is electronegative, } -I_s)$$

$$\overset{|}{\underset{|}{-\text{C}}} : \quad \text{X} \quad (\text{X is electropositive, } +I_s)$$

Useful as this notation may be, it is nevertheless often confusing. By this definition a quaternary nitrogen atom becomes electronegative and an alcoholate oxygen atom becomes electropositive. Since the terms *electron attracting* and *electron repelling* are much more easily grasped, they will be used throughout this book whenever reference is made to the permanent polarization of a single bond.

It is apparent that the effect of the electrical dipole between the carbon and the chlorine atom will be felt upon other atoms of the carbon chain. The very fact that there is a positive charge developed upon the atom connected to chlorine means that it will have a greater affinity for electrons than the next carbon atom of the skeleton, and again the electrical center of the valence electrons will not quite coincide with that of the atomic kernel (Fig. 3). Thus in the vicinity of an electron-attracting atom or group there is an electrostatic force exerted upon the valence electrons of the near-by carbon atoms, and fractional positive charges are *induced* at these points. The effect will be greatest for a charged atom, intermediate for dipoles resulting from semipolar or double bonds, and smallest for unsymmetrical covalences. Thus, other things

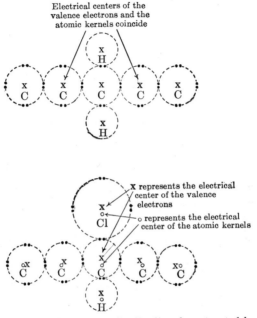

Fig. 3. A comparison of the electron distribution of a saturated hydrocarbon with that of a chloroalkane.

being equal, the fractional positive charge on the tertiary carbon atom in the following series increases from the sulfide to the sulfonium salt:

$$R_3C\text{---}S\text{---}R' < \left[\begin{matrix} O \\ | \\ R_3C\text{---}S\text{---}R' \end{matrix} \quad \text{or} \quad \begin{matrix} O \\ \| \\ R_3C\text{---}S\text{---}R' \end{matrix} \right] < R_3C\text{---}\overset{\oplus}{S}\diagdown\begin{matrix} R'' \\ R' \end{matrix}$$

(*See footnote 1*)

Furthermore, since permanent polarization is due to the inherent affinity an atom has for electrons, it is to be expected that the induced charge on an adjacent atom will become larger as the electron affinity of an attached group increases. This happens in moving from left to right across

[1] For a discussion of the nature of the sulfur-oxygen bond in sulfoxides, see Philips, Hunter, and Sutton, *J. Chem. Soc.*, **1945**, 146; Fehnel and Carmack, *J. Am. Chem. Soc.*, **71**, 231 (1949).

a row in the periodic table or in ascending a given group. The following sequences are then obtained again with respect to the electron density at the tertiary carbon atom (Table 1).

TABLE 1

DECREASING ORDER OF ELECTRON DENSITY AT R_3C—

$R_3C—I > R_3C—Br > R_3C—Cl > R_3C—F$

$R_3C—CR_3 > R_3C—NR_2 > R_3C—OR > R_3C—F$

$R_3C—Na > R_3C—MgX$

In discussing the permanent polarization of single bonds we cannot help wondering how far along a carbon chain this factor exerts its influence. From an examination of the ionization constants of the aliphatic chloroacids we see (Table 2) that two methylene groups interposed between the carboxyl group and the carbon to which the chlorine atom is attached almost destroy the effect of the permanent polarization of the carbon-chlorine bond upon the carboxyl group.

TABLE 2

IONIZATION CONSTANTS OF ALIPHATIC ACIDS

(Data from Robinson, *J. Chem. Soc.*, **1947**, 1289)

Acid	$K \times 10^{-5}$
$CH_3(CH_2)_7COOH$	1.4
$CH_3(CH_2)_6COOH$	1.4
$CH_3(CH_2)_5COOH$	1.4
$CH_3(CH_2)_4COOH$	1.5
$\overset{\text{Cl}}{\underset{\vert}{C}}H_2(CH_2)_3COOH$	2.0
$\overset{\text{Cl}}{\underset{\vert}{C}}H_2(CH_2)_2COOH$	3.0
$CH_3\overset{\text{Cl}}{\underset{\vert}{C}}HCH_2COOH$	8.9
$CH_3CH_2\overset{\text{Cl}}{\underset{\vert}{C}}HCOOH$	139.0

Similarly, if we agree that withdrawal of electrons from an aromatic ring favors *meta* substitution (see Chapter 13), the nitration of the quaternary salts of certain phenylalkyl amines indicates that two methylene groups are sufficient to block the effect of the permanent polarization of the carbon-nitrogen bond from the aromatic ring (Table 3).

TABLE 3

PERCENTAGE OF META ISOMER OBTAINED IN THE NITRATION OF
QUATERNARY ARALKYLAMINES

I. $C_6H_5\overset{\oplus}{N}(CH_3)_3 \xrightarrow[100°]{HONO_2\ (d\ =\ 1.5)} m\text{-}O_2NC_6H_4\overset{\oplus}{N}(CH_3)_3$ (100%)

II. $C_6H_5CH_2\overset{\oplus}{N}(CH_3)_3 \xrightarrow[-5°]{HONO_2\ (d\ =\ 1.5)} m\text{-}O_2NC_6H_4CH_2\overset{\oplus}{N}(CH_3)_3$ (88%)

III. $C_6H_5CH_2CH_2\overset{\oplus}{N}(CH_3)_3 \xrightarrow[-5°]{HONO_2\ (d\ =\ 1.5)} m\text{-}O_2NC_6H_4CH_2CH_2\overset{\oplus}{N}(CH_3)_3$ (19%)

IV. $C_6H_5CH_2CH_2CH_2\overset{\oplus}{N}(CH_3)_3 \xrightarrow[-15°]{HONO_2\ (d\ =\ 1.5)}$

$m\text{-}O_2NC_6H_4CH_2CH_2CH_2\overset{\oplus}{N}(CH_3)_3$ (5 ± 2%)

Sources. I: Voländer and Siebert, *Ber.*, **52**, 294 (1919). II and III: Goss, Hanhart, and Ingold, *J. Chem. Soc.*, **1927**, 250. IV: Ingold and Wilson, *ibid.*, 810.

We observe, however, that the effect is small after the introduction of only one methylene group. It is for this reason that when other factors are in operation the influence of a permanent polarization is generally considered almost negligible at a point more distant than one saturated carbon atom.[2]

It is interesting that the presence of a charged atom in a molecule induces a fractional charge not only on the other atoms of the chain but also on those atoms which are near by in space. Thus if the electrostatic attraction were "conducted" only through the carbon skeleton of a molecule, we should expect to find the dissociation constants of fumaric and maleic acids to be identical. In actual fact the first dissociation constants are somewhat similar, but there is a considerable difference in the second dissociation constants. A possible explanation of this phenomenon is that in the case of the mono acid salts of maleic acid, the near-by negative charge on the carboxylate group hinders the removal of the second proton.

$$
\begin{array}{c}
H\text{—}C\text{—}CO\overset{\ominus}{O} \\
\parallel \\
H\text{—}C\text{—}COOH
\end{array}
\rightleftharpoons
\begin{array}{c}
H\text{—}C\text{—}CO\overset{\ominus}{O} \\
\parallel \\
H\text{—}C\text{—}CO\overset{\ominus}{O}
\end{array}
+ \overset{\oplus}{H}
\qquad (1)
$$

$$K_2 = 2.6 \times 10^{-7} (K_1 = 15 \times 10^{-3})$$

[2] See, for example, Dostrovsky, Hughes, and Ingold, *J. Chem. Soc.*, **1946**, 189.

$$\overset{\ominus}{O}OC-C-H \atop H-C-COOH \rightleftharpoons \overset{\ominus}{O}OC-C-H \atop H-C-CO\overset{\ominus}{O} + \overset{\oplus}{H} \tag{2}$$

$$K_2 = 300 \times 10^{-7}(K_1 = 1 \times 10^{-3})$$

When the carboxylate group is in the more distant *trans* position (fumaric acid), the effect is weaker.

THE POLARIZABILITY OF SINGLE BONDS

If we think of electrons as negatively charged particles, it is to be expected that the outermost valence electrons of an atom will be attracted or repelled by a charge brought into their vicinity. The displacement which these electrons undergo when a unit charge is brought up is a measure of *polarizability*. This factor is given the symbol I_D, which de-

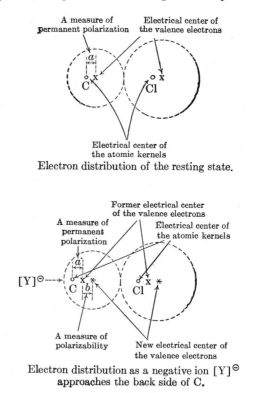

Electron distribution of the resting state.

Electron distribution as a negative ion $[Y]^{\ominus}$ approaches the back side of C.

FIG. 4. The polarizability of a single bond.

notes induction-dynamic. It is different from permanent polarization in that when the charge is removed the electrons again resume their old positions. In the oversimplified diagrams shown (Fig. 4), a is a measure of the permanent polarization (I_s), and b is a measure of the polarizability (I_D).

The ease with which the valence electrons are displaced from their resting position depends to a very large extent on the attraction the atomic kernel of X has for electrons. The greater affinity for electrons it has, the closer it holds them to itself, and the more difficult it is for an approaching ion to displace them. Consequently, polarizability decreases in moving across a row in the periodic table, and the following series of decreasing bond polarizabilities is observed:

$$C—C > C—N > C—O > C—F$$

Similarly as the atomic kernel of X becomes larger, the electrostatic control which the nucleus is able to exert upon its valence electrons becomes smaller, and bond deformation becomes easier as we descend within a group of the periodic table:

$$C—I > C—Br > C—Cl > C—F$$

This is the order of reactivity of alkyl halides in displacement reaction which is familiar to all organic chemists. Although it might not have been predicted, the polarizability factor almost always appears to outweigh the permanent polarization factor in reactions of saturated molecules.

It is interesting that as a carbon atom becomes more highly branched, it behaves more and more as if it were repelling electrons towards the next atom. Thus the reactions of *saturated* molecules suggest that the electron density at Z decreases in the order:

$$R_3C—Z > R_2CH—Z > RCH_2—Z > CH_3—Z$$

The origin of this electron-repelling tendency has not been clearly determined. Since much of the evidence for it has been obtained from displacement reactions (Chapter 4), it seems very reasonable that the sequence is not due principally to electron release but rather to the fact that the more bulky groups hinder the approach of an attacking ion. However, a similar order is observed with the ionization constants of the branched chain aliphatic acids which does indeed indicate the presence of a small permanent polarization (Table 4). Since branched chain saturated hydrocarbons have no dipole moment, the electron-repelling tendency of an alkyl group in a saturated molecule must be small unless it is attached to an electron-attracting atom.

TABLE 4

DISSOCIATION CONSTANTS OF BRANCHED CHAIN ALIPHATIC ACIDS

	$K \times 10^{-5}$
CH_3COOH	2.1
CH_3CH_2COOH	1.4
$(CH_3)_2CHCOOH$	1.5
$(CH_3)_3CCOOH$	1.0

The argument has been advanced that it is a polarizability factor which is responsible for the selective nitration of the most highly branched carbon atom in a saturated hydrocarbon.[3,4] For example, 2-methyl-2-nitropropane is obtained in 99 per cent purity by the nitration of isobutane at 150°.[5]

$$(CH_3)_3CH \xrightarrow[\text{Sealed Tube}]{\text{HONO}_2 \text{ at } 150°} (CH_3)_3C-NO_2 \quad (99\% \text{ purity}) \quad (3)$$

The point of view that such selectivity is due to a polarizability factor may be correct, but, as it was pointed out in Chapter 1, such gas phase or heterogeneous systems as these are not ideal for drawing conclusions concerning ionic mechanisms.

RESONANCE

Most organic chemists would state the general principle of resonance somewhat like this:

If for any given compound two or more structures can be written differing only in the distribution of electrons, the properties of that compound will not be those to be expected of any of the formulas but rather they will be those to be expected of a hybrid of them all. An ion or a molecule in which resonance can occur will always be more stable than one in which it cannot.

It is obvious that when the principle is stated in such general terms no attempt has been made to explain the phenomenon, but rather the conditions have been described for recognizing its occurrence. Furthermore, since each covalent bond may have a certain amount of partial ionic character, different electronic structures may actually be written for every chemical compound. The problem with which we are con-

[3] Ingold, *J. Chem. Soc.*, **1933**, 1125.

[4] Remick, *Electronic Interpretation of Organic Chemistry*, 2nd Ed., p. 94, John Wiley and Sons, New York, 1949.

[5] Hass, Hodge, and Vanderbilt, *Ind. Eng. Chem.*, **28**, 342 (1936). See also Hass and Riley, *Chem. Revs.*, **32**, 378 (1942).

cerned in discussing resonance, then, is one of deciding which forms will contribute significantly towards making up the hybrid.

For example, the ethane molecule might be considered to have the structures I, II, or III, in which the positions of the atomic kernels in

$$
\begin{array}{ccc}
\text{H} \quad \text{H} & \text{H} \quad \text{H} & \text{H} \quad \text{H} \\
| \quad | & -\delta| \quad |+\delta & +\delta-\delta| \quad | \\
\text{H} : \text{C} : \text{C} : \text{H} & \text{H} : \text{C} : \text{C} : \text{H} & \text{H} : \text{C} : \text{C} : \text{H} \\
| \quad | & | \quad | & | \quad | \\
\text{H} \quad \text{H} & \text{H} \quad \text{H} & \text{H} \quad \text{H} \\
\text{I} & \text{II} & \text{III}
\end{array}
$$

the different formulas are assumed to be very nearly the same.

Since only the distribution of electrons in the molecule has been changed, our principle suggests that the properties of ethane should not correspond to those expected of any one of the formulas, but rather should be those to be expected of a hybrid of them all. Experimentally it has been found that formula I adequately represents the nature of ethane so that forms II and III are customarily neglected. Nevertheless, even such forms as these are considered in discussions of absorption spectra.

Similarly, the carbonyl group may be written as in IV or V, but here

$$
\begin{array}{cc}
-\text{C}::\text{O}: & \overset{\oplus}{-}\overset{\ominus}{\text{C}}:\overset{..}{\text{O}}: \\
| \quad \overset{..}{} & | \quad \overset{..}{} \\
\text{IV} & \text{V}
\end{array}
$$

resonance is important since dipole moment studies indicate a **47 per cent** contribution of form V,[6] and the deviation of the actual properties of the carbonyl group from those to be expected of form IV (or V) is large. In discussing the location of electrons within a molecule, we must always consider this tendency of molecules to assume an electron distribution intermediate between two or more different *electronic* structures which can be written. It is particularly important in unsaturated molecules, and it is most commonly called the *resonance* or *mesomeric* factor (*M*).

In even the very simplest molecules almost chemical intuition is required to be able to judge whether a resonance form contributes much or little to the structure of a compound. The following generalizations are by no means laws, but they may prove helpful.

(1) *Resonance involves only the movement of electrons over the same atomic skeleton.* Thus the keto and enol forms of acetoacetic ester are *not*

[6] Pauling, *The Nature of the Chemical Bond*, p. 75, Cornell University Press, Ithaca, N. Y., 1939.

resonance structures although each form itself is better represented as a hybrid of two electronic structures. For the keto form they are VI and VII. For the enol form they are VIII and IX.

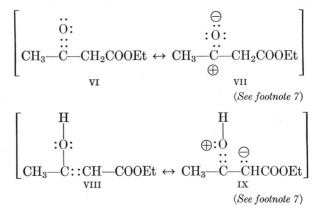

VI   VII

(*See footnote 7*)

VIII   IX

(*See footnote 7*)

(2) *Whenever electrically dissimilar atoms are connected by a double bond, there will be a contribution of a structure apparently formed by one of the bonds remaining intact and the other acquiring a certain amount of partial ionic character.*

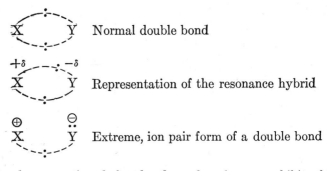

As has been mentioned already, the carbonyl group exhibits this type of resonance. The hybrid can be written as in X:

X

which implies that there has been a drift of one electron pair of the

---

[7] A double-headed arrow indicates that a compound is a hybrid of the electronic formulas shown. It should not be confused with the notation, $\rightleftharpoons$, employed for equilibrium.

double bond towards the oxygen atom and that both the carbon and the oxygen atoms have acquired fractional charges. Other common examples of this class of double bonds are:

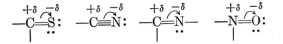

In each functional group partial polarization takes place toward the more electronegative atom, and the contribution of these forms becomes more and more important as the atoms become more electrically dissimilar.

(3) *Whenever an atom with an unshared electron pair is connected to a carbon-carbon double bond, there will be a tendency for that pair to form a double bond with the carbon atom to which it is attached and for the original double bond to become abnormally polarized in the direction away from that atom.* This is undoubtedly one of the most difficult principles of resonance with which to become familiar because such an atom can at the same time attract electrons by a permanent polarization of the single bond. Consider, for example, the structure of vinyl chloride. There are two resonance structures of the double bond which must be considered (XI and XII). Experience has shown that the contribution of

these forms is small for isolated double bonds, and this is indeed true for form XII. In form XI, however, it will be observed that there is a carbon atom with an incomplete valence shell adjacent to a neutral atom having an unshared electron pair. It now seems to be almost conclusively established that whenever this opportunity presents itself, a *partial double bond* is formed between these two atoms, and the resulting extreme form (XIV),

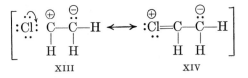

will contribute significantly towards the actual electron distribution of the molecule. The sequence XI, XIII, XIV can conveniently be abbreviated as in XV:

XV

The arrow in the center of the bond between the carbon and the chlorine atom indicates a permanent polarization towards chlorine, and the curved arrows represent a process of double bond formation and of polarization.

(4) *In the halogen group of the periodic table resonance becomes decreasingly important as the atomic weight increases.* This order of electron release

$$F > Cl > Br > I$$

is rather surprising, and its physical significance is not well understood. Intuitively we would suppose that as the atoms become larger, the valence electrons should be less subject to nuclear control and should enter into double bond formation more easily. There can be little doubt, however, that the sequence shown is correct. Highly refined dipole moment studies [8] indicate that, although the differences are not large, the order is unmistakable. The dissociation constants of *para* halogenated benzoic [9] phenylacetic,[10] and phenyl boric [10] acids as well as the dissociation constants of the corresponding anilines [11] all support this order.

(5) *Whenever one of the groups mentioned in (1) is conjugated with a double bond, only that polarized form of the double bond is significant which will permit partial double bond formation with the positive atom.* Thus, for acrolein, we might write the resonance forms XVII and XVIII, which involve only the carbon-carbon double bond. Of the two only XVIII will contribute significantly to the resting state of the molecule since

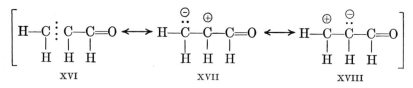

XVI   XVII   XVIII

this double-bond polarization is further intensified by the fact that a partial double bond can be formed between the negatively charged α-

[8] For a discussion of this work, see Remick, *Electronic Interpretations of Organic Chemistry*, 2nd Ed., p. 103, John Wiley and Sons, New York, 1949.

[9] Dippy, Watson, and Williams, *J. Chem. Soc.*, **1935**, 349.

[10] Bettman, Branch, and Yabroff, *J. Am. Chem. Soc.*, **56**, 1866 (1934).

[11] Baddeley, Bennett, Glasstone, and Jones, *J. Chem. Soc.*, **1935**, 1828.

carbon atom and the positively charged carbon atom of the carbonyl group.

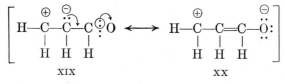

XIX   XX

The extreme electronic structure is then XX, but the resonance hybrid can be indicated as in XXI.

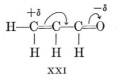

XXI

(6) *Whenever a conjugated system is present, all the partial ionic structures of the double bonds which permit partial double bond formation become important.* Thus for 1-chloro-1,3,5-hexatriene we have the structures XXII, XXIII, and XXIV. It will be observed that we must consider

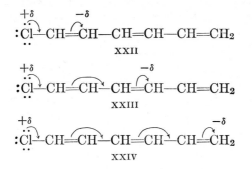

fractional negative charges on the second, fourth, and sixth carbon atoms as contributing to the resting structure of the molecule. It is usually not possible to predict in advance which of the structures will be the most important for controlling chemical reactions. With chlorobenzene, for example, the fact that substitution occurs in both the *ortho* and *para* positions indicates independent reaction through the partial ionic forms of chlorobenzene corresponding to XXII, XXIII, and XXIV. The operation of one shift produces a negative charge in the *ortho* position (XXV); of two, a charge in the *para* position (XXVI); and three shifts operating over the complete conjugated system return the negative charge to the other *ortho* position (XXVII).

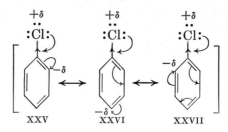

XXV   XXVI   XXVII

The substitutions reactions of furan, however, show an almost selective orientation for the α-position.[12] In this particular system the form resulting from the formation of only one partial double bond (XXVIII) does not seem to contribute as much as one in which two partial double bonds are formed (XXIX).

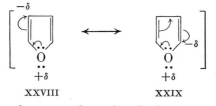

XXVIII   XXIX

It is significant, however, that when both α-positions are occupied substitution will occur in the β-position as structure XXVIII suggests.[13]

(7) *Whenever an atom with an unshared electron pair is attached to a carbon atom of a double bond which is conjugated with a group such as those discussed in (1), the resonance contribution of the ionic forms becomes particularly important.* This generalization follows from (2) and (3) since the resonance factors of such a combination act to reinforce each other.

A classical example of such a system is *p*-nitroaniline. The nitro group has a partial polarization in the direction

and the amino group contains an atom with an unshared electron pair attached to a double bond conjugated with the nitro group. Conse-

[12] Morton, *Chemistry of Heterocyclic Compounds*, p. 4, McGraw-Hill Book Co., New York, 1946.

[13] The orientation of aromatic substitution reactions and chemical reactivities in general actually do not measure the effect of resonance alone upon a resting system but rather the combined operation of resonance and the polarizability of double bonds or conjugated systems (p. 28). For many reactions it is not necessary to consider each separately since polarizability simply intensifies the contribution of certain resonance structures. (For example, see p. 156.)

quently the form **XXXI** will make an important contribution to the structure and reactivity of the *p*-nitroaniline molecule. For example, it can be seen that the electron pair normally present on the nitrogen atom is unavailable for combination with a proton. Consequently, it is a weaker base than aniline.[14] For the same reason *p*-nitrodimethyl-aniline forms quaternary salts only with difficulty.[15] (See p. 80.)

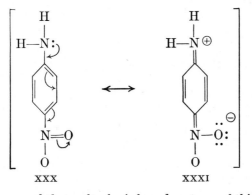

XXX   XXXI

Perhaps a more subtle result of reinforced systems of this kind can be illustrated with *p*-dimethylaminobenzaldehyde. When an atom having an unshared electron pair (in this case a dimethylamino group) is conjugated with a carbonyl group, the fractional positive charge which is usually found on the carbon atom of the carbonyl group is reduced. Thus *p*-dimethylaminobenzaldehyde will not undergo the Cannizzaro reaction (p. 168) nor the benzoin condensation (p. 194), presumably because the fractional positive charge on the carbonyl carbon atom which appears to be necessary for these reactions has been relayed to the nitrogen atom by the contribution of structure **XXXIII**.

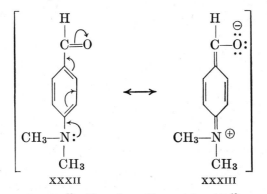

XXXII   XXXIII

[14] K_b aniline $= 4.6 \times 10^{-10}$. K_b *p*-nitroaniline $= 1.2 \times 10^{-12}$.
[15] Zaki and Fahim, *J. Chem. Soc.*, **1942**, 270.

(8) *Resonance in a molecule occurs only when all of the atoms lie in the same plane.* This can be seen most easily when functional groups enter into resonance with a benzene ring. Consider, for example, the resonance forms XXXIV and XXXV for benzaldehyde:

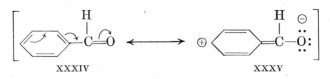

XXXIV   XXXV

An examination of models shows that in **XXXIV** there can be free rotation between the aromatic ring and the carbonyl carbon atom. At times, then, the oxygen atom may lie out of the plane of the ring (**XXXVI**):

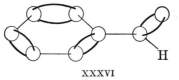

XXXVI

In structure **XXXV**, however, the tetrahedral arrangement of the valence bonds of the carbonyl carbon atom requires that the oxygen atom must fall in the same plane with the benzene ring (**XXXVII**):

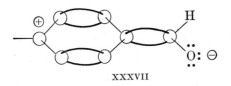

XXXVII

Consequently if form **XXXV** is to contribute to the structure of benzaldehyde, all the atoms of the resonating system must be in the same plane.

(9) *Any structural modification which tends to destroy coplanarity inhibits resonance.* The introduction of alkyl groups *ortho* to a dialkylamino, an acyl, or a nitro group hinders the formation of a structure like **XXXV**, and as a result these substituted derivatives resemble their aliphatic analogs more closely. In addition to arguments based upon dipole moments,[16] molecular refractivity,[17] and ultraviolet absorption spectra,[18] there is other chemical evidence which indicates the *steric in-*

---

[16] Birtles and Hampson, *J. Chem. Soc.*, **1937**, 10. Ingham and Hampson, *ibid.*, **1939**, 981. Kadesch and Weller, *J. Am. Chem. Soc.*, **63**, 1310 (1941).

[17] Thompson, *J. Chem. Soc.*, **1944**, 404, 408.

[18] Philips, *J. Org. Chem.*, **12**, 337 (1947). Buu Hoi and Cagniant, *J. chim. phys.*, **42**, 131 (1945).

*hibition of resonance.** In a study of the replacement reaction of a number of dichloronitrobenzenes, Holleman [19] found that the chlorine in 2,6-dichloronitrobenzene (XLII) was less readily replaced by methoxide ion than that in the 2,3, the 2,5, the 3,4, or the 2,4 isomers (XXXVIII to XLI, Table 5).

TABLE 5

RELATIVE RATE CONSTANTS (HOURS^{-1}) FOR THE REACTION OF
DICHLORONITROBENZENES WITH SODIUM METHYLATE AT 85°

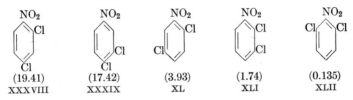

(19.41)	(17.42)	(3.93)	(1.74)	(0.135)
XXXVIII	XXXIX	XL	XLI	XLII

Similarly the reactivity of 2-nitro-5-bromo-*m*-xylene (XLIII),

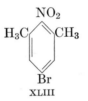

XLIII

towards piperidine [20] was lower than would be expected.

These data are in agreement with the point of view that resonance of the nitro group with the benzene ring is sterically inhibited by the bulk of two *ortho* methyl groups. Hence the fractional positive charge which is normally present at the seat of reaction as a result of a contribution of a form such as XLIV is absent and the approach of the negatively

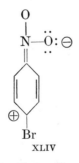

XLIV

charged methoxide ion is not aided.   (See Chapter 4.)

* See footnote 13.
[19] Holleman and De Mooy, *Rec. trav. chim.*, **35**, 19 (1915).
[20] Wheland and Spitzer, *J. Am. Chem. Soc.*, **62**, 2995 (1940).

An indication of the importance of the steric inhibition of resonance in aromatic substitution reactions has been gained by a study of the exchange reaction of dialkylanilines with deuterium oxide.[21]   With dimethylaniline, for example, the *ortho* and *para* hydrogen atoms equilibrate readily with deuterium oxide. This reaction, like most aromatic substitution reactions (see Chapter 13), is believed to proceed by the attack of a positively charged fragment (in this case a hydrogen or deuterium ion) at a point of high electron density. Consequently, the ease with which equilibration occurs can be taken as an approximate measure of the contribution of forms such as XLV or XLVI to the structure of the

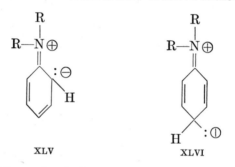

XLV   XLVI

substituted aniline molecule.*

Under conditions such that the exchange of the *meta* and *para* isomers was essentially complete, *o*-bromo and *o*-chlorodimethylaniline did not exchange with deuterium and the exchange of *o*-fluorodimethylaniline was incomplete. An examination of molecular scale models shows that these results would have been predicted from a consideration of the bulk of the atoms involved.

The condensation reactions of di- and trinitro mesitylene and *m*-xylene also indicate that nitro groups lose their characteristic activating influence when they are flanked by two methyl groups. In the presence of piperidine, 4,6-dinitro-*m*-xylene (XLVII) and 2,4,6-trinitro-*m*-xylene (XLVIII) will condense with benzaldehyde [22] (equations 4 and 5). When

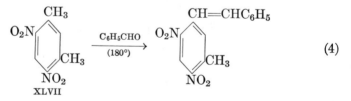

$$\tag{4}$$

XLVII

---

* See footnote 13.

[21] Brown, Widiger, and Letang, *J. Am. Chem. Soc.*, **61**, 2598 (1939).
[22] Borsche, *Ann.*, **386**, 351 (1912).

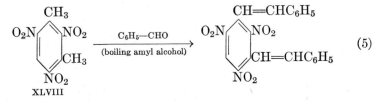

(5)

XLVIII

each nitro group has two methyl groups in the ortho positions, as in the case of dinitro- and trinitromesitylene (XLIX and L), reaction does not take place.

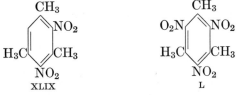

XLIX   L

If resonance cannot include the nitro group, presumably the equilibrium

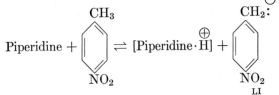

LI

lies so far to the left that reactions which proceed through intermediates, such as LI (see Chapters 6 and 9), do not occur. When the nitro group does resonate with the aromatic ring as in LII, the characteristic sta-

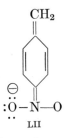

LII

bilization of LI and LII displaces the equilibrium to the right and condensation occurs readily. The fact that the sodium salt of tri-p-nitrophenylmethane (LIII) is stable towards aqueous dioxane, methanol, or ethanol while the sodium salt of tri- (3,5-dimethyl-4-nitrophenyl)-methane (LIV) hydrolyzes rapidly [23] illustrates the importance of an un-

[23] Wheland and Danish, *J. Am. Chem. Soc.*, **62**, 1125 (1940).

hindered nitro group in stabilizing ions of this type.

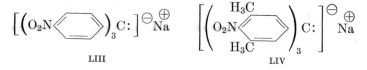

LIII   LIV

Acid-base equilibria also can be used to measure the steric inhibition of resonance. If we write the equilibrium

$$A{:}H \rightleftharpoons \overset{\ominus}{A}{:} + \overset{\oplus}{H}$$

or

$$B{:} + \overset{\oplus}{H} \rightleftharpoons B\overset{\oplus}{H}$$

it is evident that if resonance can occur more readily in one species than another, equilibrium will be displaced towards that particular side of the equation as a result of the increased stability which always accompanies resonance (p. 12). A typical example of such a displaced equilibrium is to be found in a comparison of the acid strength of phenol and the corresponding alcohol, cyclohexanol. For both hydroxy compounds the following equilibria exist:

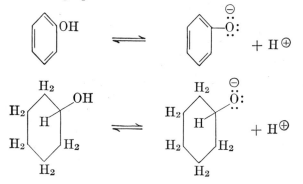

With phenol, however, the equilibrium is displaced farther to the right as a result of the increased stability of the phenolate ion which is actually a resonance hybrid of the forms LV, LVI, and LVII:

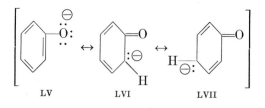

LV   LVI   LVII

True, similar forms, such as LIX and LX, can be written for undis-

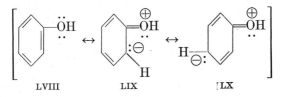

LVIII   LIX   ⌐LX

sociated phenol but, important as they are to the resting state of the molecule, LVI and LVII contribute much more to the structures of the phenolate ion than LIX and LX contribute to the structure of phenol. The resonance structures for phenol involve the development of a positive charge on the oxygen atom which tends to restore the molecule to LVIII. In the structures written for the phenolate ion there is no electrostatic restoring force exerted on the negative charge.

With aniline, however, the equilibrium is displaced to the left in comparison to cyclohexyl amine because resonance stabilizes the nonprotonated molecule (LXI to LXIII) and not the anilinium ion (LXIV).

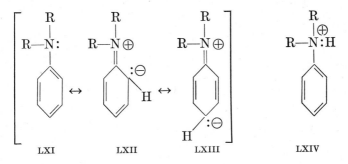

LXI   LXII   LXIII   LXIV

In the light of these considerations, the phenol which would be expected to be the strongest acid will be the one in which resonance operates most effectively in the phenolate ion. *p*-Nitrophenol is a stronger acid than phenol because of the important contribution of the form LXV to the *p*-nitrophenolate ion. *p*-Nitroaniline is a weaker base than

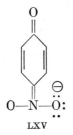

LXV

aniline because of the contribution of LXVI to the structure of the neutral molecule.

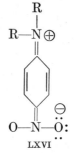

LXVI

In a study of mononitro-*m*-xylenols, Wheland [24] has found that while *m*-2-xylenol (LXVII) and *m*-5-xylenol (LXVIII) are of about the same acidity, the corresponding *para* nitro derivatives, LXIX and LXX, dif-

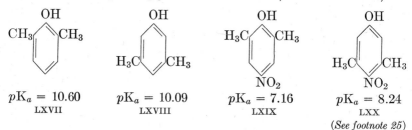

| $pK_a = 10.60$ | $pK_a = 10.09$ | $pK_a = 7.16$ | $pK_a = 8.24$ |
| LXVII | LXVIII | LXIX | LXX |

(*See footnote 25*)

fer considerably. Here again the presence of two groups *ortho* to a nitro group seems to hinder the operation of resonance.

Aromatic amines offer a more complex situation. From the values shown in LXXI to LXXIV,[26] we see that one methyl group in the *ortho*

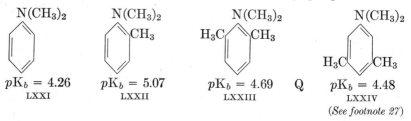

| $pK_b = 4.26$ | $pK_b = 5.07$ | $pK_b = 4.69$ Q | $pK_b = 4.48$ |
| LXXI | LXXII | LXXIII | LXXIV |

(*See footnote 27*)

[24] Wheland, *The Theory of Resonance*, p. 185, John Wiley and Sons, New York, 1944.

[25] $pK_a = -\log\left(\dfrac{[(\text{solvent} \cdot \overset{\oplus}{H})][\text{phenolate ion}]}{[\text{phenol}]}\right)$, a low value indicates a strong acid.

[26] Thompson, *J. Chem. Soc.*, **1946**, 1114.

[27] $pK_b = -\log\left(\dfrac{[\text{amine}][(\text{solvent} \cdot \overset{\oplus}{H})]}{[(\text{amine} \cdot H) \oplus]}\right)$, a high value indicates a strong base.

position (LXXII) increases the basicity but that a second one in the other *ortho* position (LXXIII) decreases the basicity almost to that of dimethylaniline (LXXI). Furthermore, dimethyl-*m*-5-xylidene (LXXIV) (in which both nuclear methyl groups are *meta* to the dimethylamino group and no steric inhibition of resonance can arise) does not have a basicity very different from that of dimethyl-*m*-2-xylidine (LXXIII). From dipole moment data [16] it seems quite certain that two *ortho* groups do indeed almost completely suppress resonance of the dimethylamino group with the benzene ring. As Thompson has pointed out, however, the fact that the basicities of LXXIII and LXXIV are so close to each other emphasizes that resonance does not completely determine the strength of aromatic amines.

In concluding these remarks on the steric inhibition of resonance, it should be pointed out that all the examples which have been mentioned involve the displacement of a group from the plane of a benzene ring. There may be at least one instance of the inhibition of resonance by the deformation of the aromatic ring itself. Prelog and coworkers [28] have found that the absorption spectra of compounds of the type LXXV re-

$(CH_2)_n$ HO—⟨ ⟩—NO_2 ($n = 5, 6, 7, 9$–$15, 17, 18$, and 27)

LXXV

semble that of *p*-nitrophenol, but that the maxima are shifted somewhat toward the visible range. As the size of the bridge decreases, the maximum is shifted more and more toward the longer wavelengths. In passing from the six- to the five-membered ring, however, the maximum absorption is abruptly shifted to a wave length even shorter than that for *p*-nitrophenol. This would be the expected result if in some manner resonance were inhibited at this point. An examination of scale molecular models reveals that a strainless model can be constructed with a seven-membered bridge, but that models with a five- or six-membered methylene bridge cannot be made without considerable strain or even a puckering of the benzene ring. A careful study of the physical and chemical properties of the pentamethylene homolog has revealed that it is a substituted cyclohexadienone.

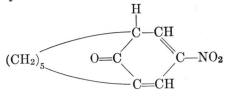

---

[28] Prelog and Wiesner, *Helv. Chim. Acta*, **30**, 1465 (1947); Prelog, Wiesner, Ingold, and Häfliger, *ibid.*, **31**, 1325 (1948).

(10) *Any structural modification which aids coplanarity facilitates res-onance.* In the series LXXVI, LXXVII, and LXXVIII [21] the hydrogen atoms of LXXVI equilibrate faster with deuterium oxide than those of LXXVII, but with both compounds the rate is faster than that of di-methylaniline. The hydrogen atoms of LXXVIII, in which it is difficult for the methylene chain and the N-methyl group ever to be in the same plane with the benzene ring, exchange very slowly. In the light of the discussion on p. 22, this information can be interpreted to mean that resonance of the amino group with the aromatic ring is enhanced by LXXVI and inhibited by the noncoplanarity of LXXVIII.

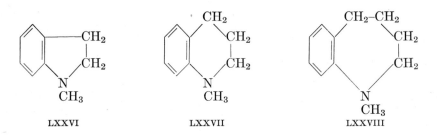

LXXVI   LXXVII   LXXVIII

THE POLARIZABILITY OF DOUBLE BONDS OR CONJUGATED SYSTEMS

The polarizability of a double bond is related to resonance in the same way that the polarizability of a single bond is related to permanent polarization. The carbonyl group, as we have seen, can be best repre-sented as a resonance hybrid of the structures LXXIX and LXXX in

$$\left[\begin{array}{ccc} | & & | \\ -C \!\!=\!\! \ddot{O}: & \leftrightarrow & -C \!\!-\!\! \ddot{O}: \\ & & \overset{\oplus}{} \quad \underset{\ominus}{} \end{array} \right]$$

LXXIX   LXXX

which each form contributes about equally. In the neighborhood of a proton it is reasonable to suppose that the normal electron distribution will be disturbed by the presence of the positive charge and the polariza-tion will be even greater than before. The additional electron displace-ment which may be superimposed upon a resonance hybrid by the ap-proach of a charged particle is known as the *electromeric displacement* (*E*). It refers to the ease with which the electronic system of an un-saturated molecule is deformed. Other systems in which electromeric displacements become important include a carbon-carbon double bond,

—C::C— [Approximate electron distribution in the resting state]

$\overset{\oplus}{H}$ + —$\overset{\ominus}{\underset{|}{C}}$:$\overset{\oplus}{\underset{|}{C}}$— [Form which becomes more important as a proton approaches]

a carbon-carbon conjugated system,

—C::C:C::C— [Approximate electron distribution in the resting state]

$\overset{\oplus}{H}$ + $\begin{bmatrix} —\overset{\ominus}{\underset{|}{C}}:\overset{\oplus}{\underset{|}{C}}:\underset{|}{C}::\underset{|}{C}— \\ \updownarrow \\ —\overset{\ominus}{\underset{|}{C}}:\underset{|}{C}::\underset{|}{C}:\overset{\oplus}{\underset{|}{C}}— \end{bmatrix}$ [Forms which become more important as a proton approaches]

and a carbon-halogen conjugated system,

$\begin{bmatrix} —\underset{|}{C}::\underset{|}{C}:\overset{..}{\underset{..}{Cl}}: & \leftrightarrow & —\overset{\ominus}{\underset{|}{C}}:\underset{|}{C}::\overset{\oplus}{\overset{..}{Cl}}: \end{bmatrix}$ [Resonance forms which are important in resting state]

$\overset{\oplus}{H}$ + —$\underset{|}{C}$:$\underset{|}{C}$::$\overset{\oplus}{\overset{..}{Cl}}$: [Form which becomes more important as a proton approaches]

As with resonance, we should expect that the ease with which electron release occurs from different atoms should parallel that of single-bond polarizability. As we move across a row in the periodic table this appears to be true. The ease with which partial double bonds are formed is shown by the sequence:

$$—\overset{\ominus}{\underset{|}{\overset{..}{C}}}— \; > \; —\overset{\ominus}{\underset{|}{N}}: \; > \; —\overset{\ominus}{\underset{..}{O}}:$$

The ease of partial double-bond polarization has the opposite order.

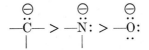

For comparing the ease of electromeric displacements within a group of the periodic table, there are apparently no data except for the halogen series, and these are very difficult to interpret. Baddeley, Bennett, Glasstone, and Jones [29] have concluded that electromeric displacements and resonance are intimately related and have a common origin. Consequently, these authors believe that an electromeric displacement is more easily induced with the halogens of low atomic weight:

$$F > Cl > Br > I$$

On the basis of aromatic substitution experiments, Ingold [30a] and Robertson [30b] conclude that the order should be reversed. The important point, however, is that a combination of resonance *and* electromeric displacements has the order shown above for those chemical reactions which call upon the halogen atoms for electron release [30c] (see Chapter 13).

HYPERCONJUGATION [31]

Hyperconjugation, or *no-bond resonance* as it is sometimes called, is a particular kind of resonance which involves hydrogen atoms alpha to a double-bond or an electronically deficient atom (p. 14). Actually it is an extension of the well-known principle that a hydrogen atom attached to a carbon atom adjacent to a carbonyl group is "activated" and has somewhat acidic properties. Sometimes this acidity is quite pronounced. Acetoacetic ester, for example, is about as strong an acid as phenol.[32] Accordingly the equilibrium must be farther to the right than we should

$$
\begin{array}{ccc}
\overset{\displaystyle |}{\underset{\displaystyle |}{C}}=O & & \overset{\displaystyle |}{\underset{\displaystyle |}{C}}=O \\
-\overset{\displaystyle |}{\underset{\displaystyle |}{C}}-H & \rightleftharpoons & -\overset{\displaystyle |}{\underset{\displaystyle |}{C}}:\ominus + \overset{\oplus}{H}
\end{array}
$$

normally expect for a carbon-hydrogen bond. An explanation for this phenomenon is again to be found in resonance theory. The negative ion is stabilized by the resonance forms LXXXI and LXXXII, and the

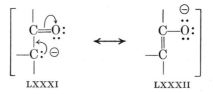

LXXXI   LXXXII

[29] Baddeley, Bennett, Glasstone, and Jones, *J. Chem. Soc.*, **1935**, 1830.

[30] (*a*) Bird and Ingold, *J. Chem. Soc.*, **1938**, 928. (*b*) De la Mare and Robertson, *ibid.*, **1948**, 105. (*c*) Baker and Hopkins, *ibid.*, **1949**, 1089.

[31] For a review of hyperconjugation, see Deasy, *Chem. Revs.*, **36**, 145 (1945).

[32] Goldschmidt and Oslan, *Ber.*, **33**, 1146 (1900).

equilibrium is correspondingly displaced to the right. Hyperconjugation is a term employed to describe this phenomenon even when a carbonyl group is replaced by an ordinary carbon-carbon double bond. Thus in a comparable manner we can write the equilibrium,

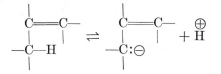

and here again the position of equilibrium lies farther to the right than might be expected because the negative ion is stabilized by the resonance forms LXXXIII and LXXXIV.

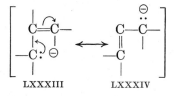

LXXXIII   LXXXIV

It is important to notice that the effect of hyperconjugation is that of electron release from the α-carbon atom involved, together with an accompanying polarization of the double bond. Furthermore *there is no reason to suppose that this electronic shift will take place only after the proton migrates away.* Although the drift will not be nearly as pronounced in the unionized form as in the ion (since there is an opposing positive pole created on the hydrogen atom), there is considerable evidence which points towards a small, *but sometimes noticeable,* contribution of forms such as LXXXV, LXXXVI, and LXXXVII to the resting state of the molecule.

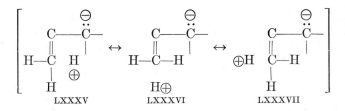

LXXXV   LXXXVI   LXXXVII

A similar situation exists in the ionization of phenol which has been discussed earlier (p. 24). Resonance becomes more important in the phenolate ion (LXXXVIII to XC) since there is no restoring positive

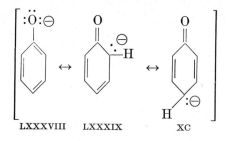

LXXXVIII   LXXXIX   XC

charge developed; nevertheless such forms as XCII and XCIII contribute significantly to the structure of the undissociated molecule.

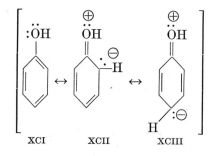

XCI   XCII   XCIII

With olefins, hyperconjugation gives new meaning to Markownikoff's rule. The resonance form of propylene (XCV) clearly indicates that the

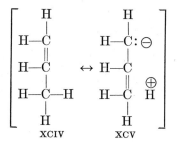

XCIV   XCV

normal addition of hydrogen bromide will occur so that the hydrogen atom will become attached to the terminal carbon atom. Also if we assume that the contribution of hyperconjugation diminishes with a decrease in the number of hydrogen atoms bonded to the α-carbon atom, the order of electron release *when a group is attached to an unsaturated system becomes*

$$CH_3— > CH_3CH_2— > (CH_3)_2CH— > (CH_3)_3C—$$

We might, therefore, have made the prediction that the addition of hy-

drogen chloride to 2-pentene would give predominantly 2-chloro-
pentane: [33]

$$CH_3CH_2\overset{-\delta}{CH}\!\!=\!\!\overset{+\delta}{CH}CH_3 \quad + \ HCl \ \longrightarrow \ CH_3CH_2CH_2CHClCH_3$$

In this particular case Markownikoff's rule would have been of no help.

There are many other examples of the agreement of such a principle
with fact, as we shall see in later chapters. Hyperconjugation plays an
important part in the theory of elimination reactions (Chapter 5); in the
position of equilibrium in carbonium ion rearrangements (Chapter 3);
and in the discussion of the migration of double bonds in unsaturated
carbonyl compounds (Chapter 15). Aromatic substitution reactions
(Chapter 13) and displacement reactions (Chapter 4) also appear to
involve hyperconjugation. In fact, the generalization seems to be
developing that in those reactions of *unsaturated* compounds in which
differences of reactivity are caused by different alkyl groups, hyperconjugation is one of the most important factors to be considered.

[33] Norris and Reuter, *J. Am. Chem. Soc.*, **49**, 2631 (1927).

CHAPTER 3

CARBONIUM IONS

In an ionic (heterolytic) cleavage of a covalent bond between two atoms X and Y (p. 1), one of them (X) loses the electron which it

$$:\ddot{X}:\ddot{Y}: \rightarrow \left[:\ddot{X}:\right]^{\oplus} + \left[:\ddot{Y}:\right]^{\ominus}$$

furnished in establishing the covalent bond with Y and thereby acquires a unit positive charge. Correspondingly, the other atom, Y, becomes negatively charged. When X is a carbon atom, the ion [—C$\oplus$], which has only six electrons in its valence shell, is called a *carbonium ion*. If Y is a carbon atom, the ion [—C:$\ominus$], which has an unshared electron pair, is called a *carbanion*. Carbanions appear to be capable of separate existence, but it is extremely improbable that an unsolvated open sextet of electrons ever exists on a carbon atom other than momentarily. The concept of a carbonium ion as a *transitory reaction intermediate*, however, is extremely useful in the theory of chemical transformations.

In general the stage is set for carbonium ion formation whenever an acid is brought into the vicinity of a molecule which can furnish a pair of electrons. The electrons may be those present as such in an unshared electron pair (I) or those participating in the formation of a multiple bond which can be mobilized into an unshared electron pair at the demand of a reagent (II and III):

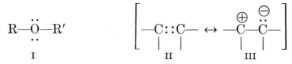

I   II   III

By acids are meant electron acceptors, and they include not only protons but also those substances such as the halides of aluminum, boron, and iron which have only six electrons in their outermost valence shell.[1]

---

[1] G. N. Lewis, *Valence and the Structure of Molecules*, p. 141, The Chemical Catalog Co., New York, 1923.

Specifically there are several different starting points for the formation of carbonium ions.

THE FORMATION OF CARBONIUM IONS [2]

(1) **By the addition of acids to unsaturated compounds.** As it was pointed out in the discussion of the polarizability of double bonds (p. 28), the presence of a proton displaces the normal position of the shared electrons comprising a multiple bond in the resting state so that the bond assumes a more polarized form. Whenever an unsaturated compound, then, is dissolved in a proton donating solvent, equilibria like 1, 2, or 3 are established:

$$-\overset{|}{C}::\overset{..}{\underset{..}{O}}: \ + \ H^{\oplus} \ \rightleftharpoons \ -\overset{|}{C}\overset{\oplus}{-}\overset{..}{\underset{..}{O}}H \qquad (1)$$

$$-\overset{|}{C}:::\overset{..}{N} \ + \ H^{\oplus} \ \rightleftharpoons \ -\overset{|}{C}\overset{\oplus}{=}\underset{..}{N}-H \qquad (2)$$

$$-\overset{|}{C}::\overset{|}{C}- \ + \ H^{\oplus} \ \rightleftharpoons \ -\overset{\oplus}{\underset{|}{C}}-\overset{\overset{H}{|}}{\underset{|}{C}}- \qquad (3)$$

Similarly, for an electronically deficient molecule such as aluminum chloride we have the equilibria 4, 5, or 6:

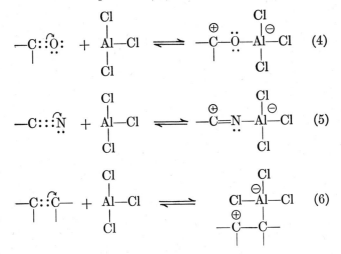

In each case the species formed contains a carbon atom with only six

[2] Whitmore, *Ind. Eng. Chem., News Ed.*, **26**, 669 (1948).

valence electrons. These are carbonium ions, and there can be no doubt of their existence (at least in solvated form) in special instances. Most esters, ketones, aldehydes, acids, and nitriles each give a molar freezing point depression twice that produced by a nonelectrolyte when they are dissolved in 100 per cent sulfuric acid.[3] The reaction can be only:

$$-\overset{|}{\underset{|}{C}}::\overset{..}{\underset{..}{O}}:\ +\ H_2SO_4\ \rightleftharpoons\ -\overset{\oplus}{\underset{|}{C}}-\overset{..}{\underset{..}{O}}H\ +\ HSO_4^{\ominus}$$

$$-\overset{|}{C}:::\overset{..}{N}\ +\ H_2SO_4\ \rightleftharpoons\ -\overset{\oplus}{C}=\overset{..}{\underset{..}{N}}H\ +\ HSO_4^{\ominus}$$

The starting materials can be recovered unchanged by the addition of water to the sulfuric acid solution. With olefins the situation is complicated by accompanying chemical reactions, but it is significant that aromatic hydrocarbons are soluble in liquid hydrogen fluoride while saturated hydrocarbons are not.[4] This fact suggests the electron donor capacity which equations 3 and 6 attribute to an unsaturated linkage.

Additions to olefins (p. 135), acid-catalyzed olefin self-condensation reactions (p. 141), and addition to carbonyl groups (p. 156), appear to involve carbonium ions formed by this process.

(2) **By the addition of acids to compounds containing an oxygen atom of the type** $-\overset{..}{\underset{..}{O}}-$. Alcohols, ethers, esters, acids, and acid anhydrides provide a source of carbonium ions when they are dissolved in acid solution (equations 7 to 11).

$$R-\overset{..}{\underset{..}{O}}H\ +\ \overset{\oplus}{H}\ \rightleftharpoons\ R-\overset{H}{\underset{\underset{\oplus}{|}}{O}}-H\ \rightleftharpoons\ \overset{\oplus}{R}\ +\ :\overset{H}{\underset{..}{O}}-H \qquad (7)$$

$$R-\overset{..}{\underset{..}{O}}-R'\ +\ \overset{\oplus}{H}\ \rightleftharpoons\ \underset{IV}{R-\overset{H}{\underset{\underset{\oplus}{|}}{O}}-R'}\ \rightleftharpoons\ \overset{\oplus}{R}\ +\ :\overset{H}{\underset{..}{O}}-R' \qquad (8)$$

$$\Updownarrow$$

$$\underset{V}{R-\overset{H}{\underset{..}{O}}:\ +\ \oplus R'}$$

---

[3] For an excellent discussion of solutions in sulfuric acid see Hammett, *Physical Organic Chemistry*, McGraw-Hill Book Co., New York, 1943. See also pp. 39, 225 in this book and Newman, Craig, and Garrett, *J. Am. Chem. Soc.*, **71**, 869 (1949).

[4] Klatt, *Z. anorg. Chem.*, **234**, 189 (1937). See also Brown and Brady, *J. Am. Chem. Soc.*, **71**, 3573 (1949).

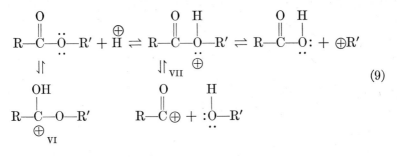

$$R\overset{\overset{O}{\|}}{-}\overset{..}{\underset{..}{C}}\overset{..}{-}\overset{..}{\underset{..}{O}}-R' + \overset{\oplus}{H} \rightleftharpoons R-\overset{\overset{O}{\|}}{\underset{}{C}}-\overset{\overset{H}{|}}{\underset{..}{O}}-R' \rightleftharpoons R-\overset{\overset{O}{\|}}{\underset{}{C}}-\overset{\overset{H}{|}}{\underset{..}{O}}: + \oplus R' \qquad (9)$$

$$\underset{\underset{\oplus}{VI}}{R-\overset{\overset{OH}{|}}{\underset{}{C}}-O-R'} \qquad R-\overset{\overset{O}{\|}}{\underset{}{C}}\oplus + \overset{\overset{H}{|}}{\underset{..}{:O}}-R'$$

$$R-\overset{\overset{O}{\|}}{\underset{}{C}}-\overset{..}{\underset{..}{O}H} + H\oplus \rightleftharpoons R-\overset{\overset{O}{\|}}{\underset{\oplus}{C}}-\overset{\overset{H}{|}}{\underset{}{O}}-H \rightleftharpoons R-\overset{\overset{O}{\|}}{\underset{}{C}}\oplus + \overset{\overset{H}{|}}{\underset{..}{:O}}-H \qquad (10)$$

$$R-\overset{\overset{OH}{|}}{\underset{\oplus}{C}}-O-H$$

$$R-\overset{\overset{O}{\|}}{\underset{}{C}}-\overset{..}{\underset{..}{O}}-\overset{\overset{O}{\|}}{\underset{}{C}}-R \rightleftharpoons R-\overset{\overset{O}{\|}}{\underset{}{C}}-\overset{\overset{H}{|}}{\underset{\oplus}{O}}-\overset{\overset{O}{\|}}{\underset{}{C}}-R \rightleftharpoons R-\overset{\overset{O}{\|}}{\underset{}{C}}\oplus + \overset{\overset{H}{|}}{\underset{..}{:O}}-\overset{\overset{O}{\|}}{\underset{}{C}}-R \qquad (11)$$

$$R-\overset{\overset{OH}{|}}{\underset{\oplus}{C}}-O-\overset{\overset{O}{\|}}{\underset{}{C}}-R$$

In all cases the step in which a proton adds to the oxygen atom is followed by dissociation into a carbonium ion and a simple molecule such as a carboxylic acid, an alcohol, or water. Similar equilibria may be written for other Lewis acids, such as boron trifluoride (equations 12 to 16).

$$R-\overset{..}{\underset{..}{O}}-H + BF_3 \rightleftharpoons R-\overset{\overset{\overset{\ominus}{BF_3}}{|}}{\underset{\oplus}{O}}-H \rightleftharpoons R\oplus + \overset{\overset{\overset{\ominus}{BF_3}}{|}}{\underset{..}{:O}}-H \qquad (12)$$

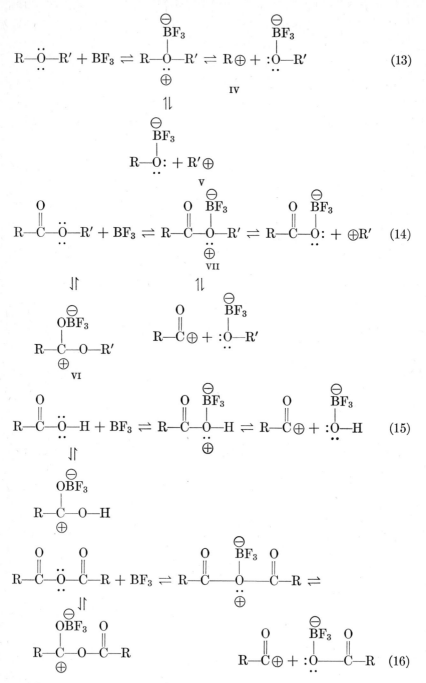

$$R—\overset{..}{\underset{..}{O}}—R' + BF_3 \rightleftharpoons R—\overset{\overset{\ominus}{BF_3}}{\underset{\underset{\oplus}{..}}{O}}—R' \rightleftharpoons R\oplus + :\overset{\overset{\ominus}{BF_3}}{\underset{..}{O}}—R' \qquad (13)$$

$$\text{IV}$$

$$\Updownarrow$$

$$R—\overset{\overset{\ominus}{BF_3}}{\underset{..}{O}}: + R'\oplus$$

$$\text{V}$$

$$R—\overset{O}{\overset{\|}{C}}—\overset{..}{\underset{..}{O}}—R' + BF_3 \rightleftharpoons R—\overset{O}{\overset{\|}{C}}—\overset{\overset{\ominus}{BF_3}}{\underset{\underset{\oplus}{..}}{O}}—R' \rightleftharpoons R—\overset{O}{\overset{\|}{C}}—\overset{\overset{\ominus}{BF_3}}{\underset{..}{O}}: + \oplus R' \qquad (14)$$

$$\text{VII}$$

$$\Updownarrow \qquad\qquad\qquad \Updownarrow$$

$$R—\overset{\overset{\ominus}{OBF_3}}{\underset{\oplus}{C}}—O—R' \qquad R—\overset{O}{\overset{\|}{C}}\oplus + :\overset{\overset{\ominus}{BF_3}}{O}—R'$$

$$\text{VI}$$

$$R—\overset{O}{\overset{\|}{C}}—\overset{..}{\underset{..}{O}}—H + BF_3 \rightleftharpoons R—\overset{O}{\overset{\|}{C}}—\overset{\overset{\ominus}{BF_3}}{\underset{\underset{\oplus}{..}}{O}}—H \rightleftharpoons R—\overset{O}{\overset{\|}{C}}\oplus + :\overset{\overset{\ominus}{BF_3}}{\underset{..}{O}}—H \qquad (15)$$

$$\Updownarrow$$

$$R—\overset{\overset{\ominus}{OBF_3}}{\underset{\oplus}{C}}—O—H$$

$$R—\overset{O}{\overset{\|}{C}}—\overset{..}{\underset{..}{O}}—\overset{O}{\overset{\|}{C}}—R + BF_3 \rightleftharpoons R—\overset{O}{\overset{\|}{C}}—\overset{\overset{\ominus}{BF_3}}{\underset{\underset{\oplus}{..}}{O}}—\overset{O}{\overset{\|}{C}}—R \rightleftharpoons$$

$$\Updownarrow$$

$$R—\overset{\overset{\ominus}{OBF_3}}{\underset{\oplus}{C}}—\overset{O}{\overset{\|}{}}{O}—\overset{O}{\overset{\|}{C}}—R \qquad\qquad R—\overset{O}{\overset{\|}{C}}\oplus + :\overset{\overset{\ominus}{BF_3}}{\underset{..}{O}}—\overset{O}{\overset{\|}{C}}—R \qquad (16)$$

Even with these simple molecules we see that the equilibria are exceedingly complex. Ethers can dissociate into either of two carbonium ions (IV and V), and esters are susceptible to attack at either the acyl oxygen (VI) or the ethereal oxygen atoms (VII). Furthermore, when attack occurs at the ethereal oxygen atom, dissociation produces either

$$\overset{\displaystyle O}{\overset{\displaystyle \|}{}}$$

an alkyl carbonium ion (R⊕) or an acyl carbonium ion (R—C⊕) (equations 9 and 14). Reactions involving each of these processes are known (p. 226).

There is good evidence for equations 7 and 10. Both triphenylcarbinol and 2,4,6-trimethylbenzoic acid show a fourfold freezing-point depression in sulfuric acid solution.[3] Again the most plausible explanation is that carbonium ions are formed.

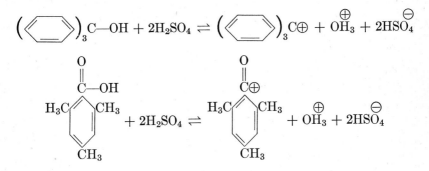

Some of the reactions which proceed through carbonium ions generated by the attack of acids on oxygen atoms of the type —Ö— include the pinacol rearrangement (p. 45), the Wagner-Meerwein rearrangement (p. 56), the acid-catalyzed dehydration of alcohols (p. 105), the Friedel-Crafts ketone synthesis (p. 259), acylation reactions (p. 260), and etherification reactions (p. 214).

(3) By the addition of acids to organic halides. By a process similar to the one just described, organic halides can combine with acids to give carbonium ions:

$$R—\overset{..}{\underset{..}{X}}: + \overset{\oplus}{H} \rightleftharpoons R—\overset{\oplus}{\underset{..}{X}}:H \rightleftharpoons R\oplus + :\overset{..}{\underset{..}{X}}—H \qquad (17)$$

$$R—\overset{..}{\underset{..}{X}}: + \overset{\oplus}{Ag} \rightleftharpoons R—\overset{\oplus}{\underset{..}{X}}:Ag \rightleftharpoons R\oplus + :\overset{..}{\underset{..}{X}}—Ag \qquad (18)$$

$$R\!-\!\overset{..}{\underset{..}{X}}\!: \; + \; AlCl_3 \; \rightleftharpoons \; R\!-\!\overset{\oplus}{\underset{..}{X}}\!:\!\overset{\ominus}{AlCl_3} \; \rightleftharpoons \; R\!\oplus \; + \; :\!\overset{..}{\underset{..}{X}}\!-\!\overset{\ominus}{AlCl_3} \qquad (19)$$

$$R\!-\!\overset{\displaystyle O}{\overset{\|}{C}}\!-\!\overset{..}{\underset{..}{X}}\!: \; + \; AlCl_3 \; \rightleftharpoons \; R\!-\!\overset{\displaystyle O}{\overset{\|}{C}}\!-\!\overset{\oplus}{\underset{..}{X}}\!:\!\overset{\ominus}{AlCl_3} \; \rightleftharpoons \; R\!-\!\overset{\displaystyle O}{\overset{\|}{C}}\!\oplus \; + \; :\!\overset{..}{\underset{..}{X}}\!-\!\overset{\ominus}{AlCl_3} \quad (20)$$

Transference experiments furnish evidence for equation 19. Ethyl chloride and ethyl bromide are nonconductors, but when the corresponding aluminum halide is introduced, the solutions can be electrolyzed and aluminum becomes concentrated in the anode compartment.[5]

The Friedel-Crafts reaction with alkyl halides (p. 260) or acid chlorides (p. 260) is a well-known example of a reaction which proceeds through carbonium ions formed by this mechanism.

(4) By the decomposition of diazonium salts. If we examine the structure of an aromatic or aliphatic diazonium salt, we see that the loss of a nitrogen molecule from the cation should give rise to a carbonium ion:

$$\left[\begin{array}{c} R\!:\!\overset{..}{N}\!:\!:\!\overset{\oplus}{N}\!: \\ \updownarrow \\ \overset{\oplus}{R}\!:\!N\!:\!:\!:\!N\!: \end{array}\right]\overset{\ominus}{Cl} \; \rightarrow \; R\!\oplus \; + \; :\!N\!:\!:\!:\!N\!: \; + \; \overset{\ominus}{Cl}$$

Indeed the properties of some diazonium reactions do suggest the intermediate formation of carbonium ions (the Demjanow rearrangement, p. 49; and the semipinacol rearrangement, p. 47). It is important, however, to consider the mechanism of diazonium reactions very carefully because these processes also show many of the characteristics of free radical reactions,[6] and the mechanism may change almost imperceptibly in some cases. For example, the reaction of an aliphatic amine with nitrous acid to give an alcohol appears to proceed through a carbonium ion (p. 43), yet 1-apocamphylamine also reacts with nitrous acid to form the corresponding alcohol.[7] In this case a carbonium ion intermediate does not seem probable because the cagelike structure of the bicyclic system would prevent its becoming planar (see p. 42).

(5) By the attack of another carbonium ion upon a saturated hydrocarbon. If the structure of a saturated hydrocarbon and the conditions for reaction are suitable, an equilibrium can exist:

[5] Wertyporoch, *Ber.*, **64B**, 1378 (1931).

[6] Hodgson, "The Sandmeyer Reaction," *Chem. Revs.*, **40**, 251 (1947); p. 2; Kornblum and Cooper, *Abstracts of Papers*, 116th Meeting of the American Chemical Society, p. 50M, Atlantic City, New Jersey, September 1949.

[7] Bartlett and Knox, *J. Am. Chem. Soc.*, **61**, 3184 (1939).

$$R\!-\!H + R'\!\oplus \ \rightleftharpoons \ R\!\oplus + H\!-\!R'$$

For most organic syntheses the reaction does not need to be considered since the structures and conditions must be such as to prevent other transformations and to favor this interchange. It is, however, one of the essential steps in the alkylation of olefins (p. 143) and the isomerization of alkanes (p. 59).

REQUIREMENTS FOR CARBONIUM ION STABILITY

From the preceding section it is evident that at some point in the formation of a carbonium ion there is a decomposition of the type:

$$-\overset{|}{\underset{|}{C}}\!:\!Z \ \rightleftharpoons \ -\overset{|}{\underset{|}{C}}\!\oplus + \ :\!\overset{\ominus}{Z}$$

caused by heat or collision with a solvent molecule. Thus any structural feature which can supply additional electrons to the carbon atoms from which the electrons are to be lost by the separation of $:Z\ominus$ should facilitate carbonium ion formation. Such an agency will not only aid bond breaking, but will also stabilize the carbonium ion once it is formed by distributing the localized charge throughout the structure of the ion, thereby lowering its tendency towards recombination. The following points might be considered.

(1) **The order of the ease of formation of alkyl carbonium ions is tertiary > secondary > primary.** This sequence follows as a consequence of the hyperconjugation resonance structures which can be written. In tertiary butyl carbonium ions, for example, there are nine hyperconjugation forms which contribute to the stability of the ion. With the isopropyl carbonium ion there are six such structures and with ethyl there are only three.

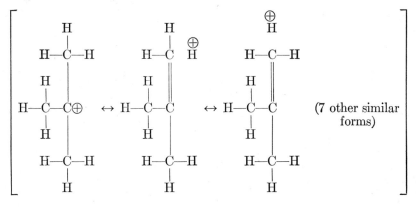

Conversely, however, it is important to notice that the order of *reactivity* of carbonium ions once they are formed is just reversed. We find, for example, in the isomerization of alkanes (p. 59) and in the alkylation of olefins (p. 143) that a primary or secondary carbonium ion extracts a hydrogen atom with a pair of electrons from an alkane so as to form a secondary or tertiary carbonium ion. For many carbonium ion transformations formation of the ion seems to be the rate-controlling step of the process. The Wagner-Meerwein rearrangement (p. 56) appears to be an exception to this rule.

(2) **A benzyl or allyl carbonium ion is formed with particular ease, provided that an electron withdrawing group is not conjugated with the system.** These carbonium ions are stabilized by the resonance forms VIII, IX, and X:

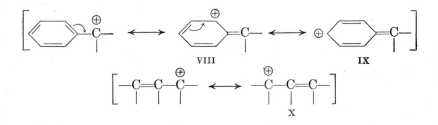

When carbonyl, carbethoxyl, nitro, or cyano groups are conjugated with the system, resonance operates to oppose the separation of $:Z^{\ominus}$. Under these conditions carbonium ion formation is unlikely.

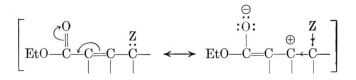

(3) **The carbonium ion must be able to pass through a planar configuration. If this is prevented no carbonium ion will form.** Thus 1-chloroapocamphane (XI) is inert to alcoholic silver nitrate,[7] and a solution of 1-bromotriptycene (XII) in liquid sulfur dioxide is a nonconductor.[8] Similarly, 1-apocamphanol does not undergo a Wagner-Meerwein rearrangement in sulfuric acid solution.[7]

[8] Bartlett, *Abstracts* of the Tenth National Organic Chemistry Symposium, p. 27, Boston, Mass., June 1947.

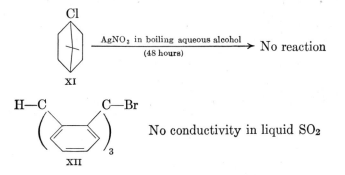

No reaction

No conductivity in liquid SO_2

(4) A tertiary carbonium ion with three large groups attached to it is formed with unexpected ease. This principle was originally called "B" or "Back" strain by H. C. Brown in connection with the anomalous base strengths of primary, secondary, and tertiary amines.[9] It is assumed to arise as a result of the fact that large groups have a "pressure" on each other when the valence bonds of carbon have a tetrahedral configuration. This strain can be relieved when the carbonium ion is formed, and consequently the equilibrium shown below is forced to the right.

$$R \overset{109°}{\underset{R}{\overset{|}{-}C}} :Z \ \rightleftharpoons \ R \overset{120°}{-}C \overset{R}{\underset{R}{\oplus}} \ + \ :Z^{\ominus}$$

Triisopropylcarbinyl chloride, for example, is hydrolyzed in acetone-water solution seven times as fast as t-butyl chloride. (See p. 88.)

REACTIONS OF CARBONIUM IONS

After a carbonium ion has been formed, its reactions depend largely upon the structure of the ion, the nature of the groups attached to it, and the medium in which the reaction is being carried out. Four courses of reaction are open.[2]

(1) It can recombine with a free electron pair of an ion or molecule other than :$Z^{\ominus}$ present in the reaction mixture. Thus in the diazotization of n-butylamine, the butyl carbonium ion can react with water, chloride ion, or nitrite ion, and the corresponding products, butanol, butyl chloride, and butyl nitrite, have been isolated.[10]

[9] Brown, Bartholomay, and Taylor, *J. Am. Chem. Soc.*, **66**, 441 (1944); Brown and Fletcher, *ibid.*, **71**, 1845 (1949).

[10] Whitmore and Langlois, *J. Am. Chem. Soc.*, **54**, 3442 (1932).

$$n\text{-Bu}-\text{NH}_2 \xrightarrow{\text{HONO}} n\text{-Bu}-\overset{\oplus}{\text{N}}\equiv\text{N}: \rightarrow n\text{-Bu}\oplus + :\text{N}\equiv\text{N}:$$

$$
n\text{-Bu}\oplus +
\left\{
\begin{array}{c}
\overset{\displaystyle H}{\underset{}{|}} \\
:\text{O}-\text{H} \\
\cdot\cdot \\
\ominus \\
:\overset{\cdot\cdot}{\text{Cl}}: \\
\overset{\cdot\cdot}{\underset{\cdot\cdot}{}}\ominus \\
:\text{ONO}
\end{array}
\right.
\rightarrow
\left\{
\begin{array}{l}
n\text{-Bu}-\overset{\displaystyle H}{\underset{\overset{\cdot\cdot}{\oplus}}{\text{O}}}-\text{H} \rightleftharpoons n\text{-Bu}-\overset{\displaystyle H}{\underset{\cdot\cdot}{\text{O}}}: + \text{H}\oplus \quad (25\%) \\[12pt]
n\text{-Bu}-\text{Cl} \quad (5.2\%) \\[8pt]
n\text{-Bu}-\text{ONO} \quad (\text{trace})
\end{array}
\right.
$$

This mode of reaction is also characteristic of solvolytic and first-order nucleophilic substitution reactions (S_N1). They will be discussed in Chapter 4.

(2) Elimination of a proton or an alkyl group from an adjacent carbon atom to form an olefin. This reaction differs from the first in that the carbonium ion reacts intramolecularly by attracting the electron pair connecting an α-carbon atom with a hydrogen atom or even another group.

This type of reaction, called an *elimination reaction*, will be discussed in Chapter 5.

(3) Abstraction of a hydrogen atom together with a pair of electrons from a saturated hydrocarbon. This reaction has already been mentioned (p. 40) and will be discussed again under the "Alkylation of Olefins" (p. 143) and the "Isomerization of Alkanes" (p. 59).

(4) Rearrangement. The last possibility for carbonium ion reaction is rearrangement. Carbonium ion rearrangements are characterized by the shift of an alkyl group or a hydrogen atom, together with an electron pair, from an adjacent carbon atom. A new carbonium ion is thus formed with the charge on the atom which was once the adjacent carbon atom. Subsequent reaction may then proceed by (1) (2) or (3). This general principle, first recognized by Whitmore,[11] can be illustrated as follows:

[11] Whitmore, *J. Am. Chem. Soc.*, **54**, 3274 (1932).

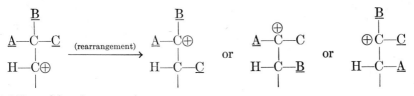

followed by, for example,

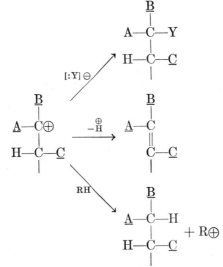

A number of such molecular rearrangements involving carbonium ions are known. They will be discussed in the next section.

MOLECULAR REARRANGEMENTS INVOLVING CARBONIUM IONS

Pinacol Rearrangement.[12]   Certainly one of the best-known examples of a carbonium ion rearrangement is the pinacol transformation in which polysubstituted ethylene glycols are converted into substituted ketones by the action of acidic reagents such as mineral acid, acetyl chloride, or acetic acid and iodine.   In accordance with Whitmore's theory of carbonium ion rearrangements,[11] the mechanism of the reaction can be outlined as follows, with pinacol itself as an example:

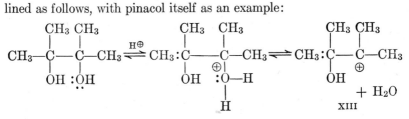

[12] For reviews of the reaction and a list of the leading references, see *Ann. Repts. Chem. Soc.* (London), **27**, 114 (1930); **30**, 181 (1933); and **36**, 195 (1939).

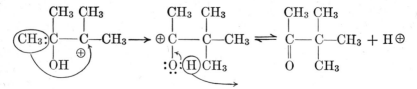

It is evident that the crucial step for the reaction is the generation of the transitory carbonium ion (XIII). Further support of this general scheme for the reaction is that other processes which would be expected to produce the same carbonium ion give exactly the same reaction. Thus pinacol bromohydrin (XIV) leads to pinacolone when it is treated with silver nitrate or silver oxide,[13] and the same product is obtained by the action of nitrous acid on 2,3-dimethyl-3-amino-2-butanol (XV).[14]

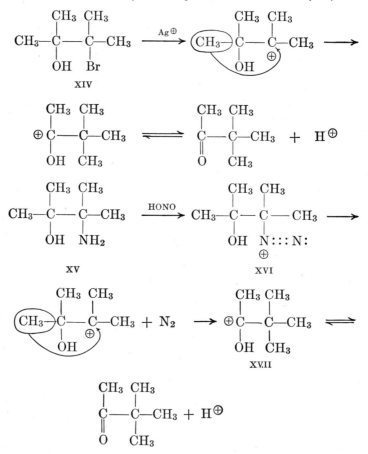

[13] Ayers, *J. Am. Chem. Soc.*, **60**, 2957 (1938).
[14] Krassusky and Duda, *J. prakt. Chem.* [2], **77**, 96 (1908).

Actually the reaction does not appear to proceed by the discrete steps: coordination, carbonium ion formation, and rearrangement. Rather, the transformation involves the *simultaneous* separation of the hydroxyl group (or nitrogen molecule or halogen atom), together with a shift of one of the groups to the *backside* of the carbon atom from which the separation occurred. Thus the semipinacolic deamination of (+)-1,1-diphenyl-2-amino-1-propanol (XVIII) takes place with a Walden inversion of the carbon atom to which the amino group was attached.[15]

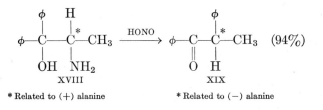

* Related to (+) alanine   * Related to (−) alanine

The tendency of various groups to migrate in the pinacol reaction has received considerable attention. It has been found with the symmetrical pinacols (XX) that this tendency, or *migrational aptitude*, may be expressed by a numerical value which will enable us to predict with remarkable accuracy the proportions of the two products, XXI and XXII, which might be obtained.[16, 17, 18]

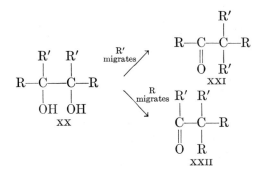

If this carbonium ion mechanism for the reaction is correct, these values should represent the ability that a group has for supplying electrons and should provide a means for comparing the relative importance

[15] Bernstein and Whitmore, *J. Am. Chem. Soc.*, **61**, 1324 (1939).
[16] Bailar, *J. Am. Chem. Soc.*, **52**, 3596 (1930).
[17] Bachmann and Moser, *ibid.*, **54**, 1124 (1932).
[18] Bachmann and Ferguson, *ibid.*, **56**, 2081 (1934).

of the electrical effects which were described in Chapter 2. For the *para*-substituted phenyl derivatives the order is: ethoxyl, 500; methoxyl, 500; methyl, 15.7; phenyl, 11.5; isopropyl, 9; ethyl, 5; hydrogen, 1; iodine, 1; bromine 0.7.[16, 17, 18]

It is interesting that with the unsymmetrical pinacols (XXIII) these migrational aptitudes not only do not agree at all with experiment but also it is difficult even to predict the major product of the reaction.[19, 20]

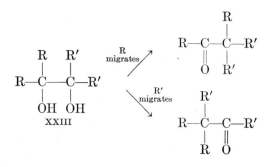

Furthermore, the position of substitution in symmetrical benzo-pinacols also plays an important part. It is characteristic of the trans-formation for a group in the *ortho* position of one of the benzene rings to hinder the migration of that phenyl group. Symmetrical di-*o*-methyl-benzopinacol,[16] di-*o*-methoxybenzopinacol (XXIV),[16] and di-*o*-phenyl-benzopinacol (XXV)[21] do not rearrange under normal conditions, and with the *o*-chloro and *o*-bromo analogs (XXVI), only migration of the phenyl group occurs.[22] The cause of the "ortho effect" in the pinacol re-arrangement is not well understood.

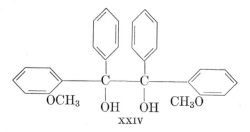

XXIV

[19] Bachmann, *ibid.*, **54**, 2112 (1934).

[20] Bachmann and Sternberger, *ibid.*, **56**, 170 (1934).

[21] Hatt, Pilgrim, and Stephenson, *J. Chem. Soc.*, **1941**, 478.

[22] Koopal, *Rec. trav. chim.*, **34**, 138 (1915).

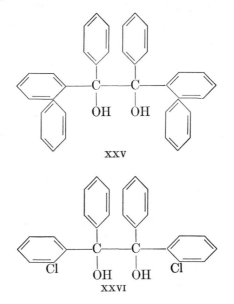

XXV

XXVI

The Demjanow Rearrangement. The action of nitrous acid on cycloalkylmethylamines is a general method for ring expansion, but the transformation is always accompanied by a number of side reactions.[23] Although it would be difficult to make predictions concerning the relative amounts formed, these products are readily understandable from Whitmore's general theory of carbonium ion rearrangements: Diazotization produces the unstable diazonium ion (XXVIII), which loses nitrogen to form a transitory carbonium ion (XXIX).

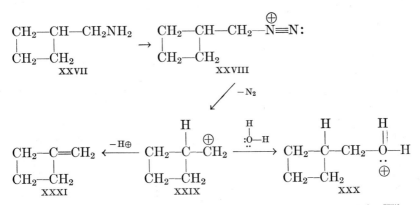

[23] Fuson, in Gilman, *Organic Chemistry, An Advanced Treatise*, p. 96, John Wiley and Sons, New York, 1943.

Without rearranging, the carbonium ion could react with water to form the protonated form of the corresponding alcohol (XXX), or a proton could be lost from the next carbon atom to form the olefin (XXXI). An alternative path of reaction would be the *interchange* of one of the groups on the adjacent carbon atom with the carbonium ion, followed by one of the reactions shown above. With the cyclobutyl-methyl carbonium ion, then, there are three possibilities: A hydrogen atom with its pair of electrons might move, producing the new carbonium ion (XXXII), which could then become stabilized by a reaction with water (XXXIII), or by the elimination of a proton from an adjacent carbon atom (XXXIV).

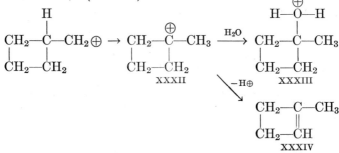

Alternatively, either one of the groups attached to the α-carbon atom of the cyclobutylmethyl carbonium ion might exchange with the carbonium ions (XXXV and XXXVI). In this particular case both groups (i.e., the methylene bridge) are equivalent, and both give a cyclopentyl carbonium ion (XXXVII), which can react as before to give the corresponding alcohol or olefin (XXXVIII):

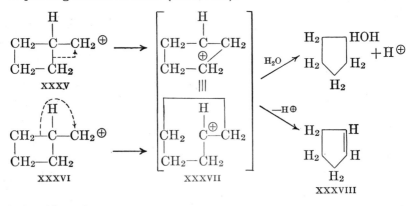

It is evident that if the carbonium ions formed from XXXV and XXXVI had not turned out to be identical, another alcohol and another olefin might have been formed. Of the products which *might* have been formed from this particular reaction, cyclopentanol, cyclopentene, cyclobutyl-carbinol (XXX), and methylenecyclobutane (XXXI) are obtained. Apparently the shift of the hydrogen atom with its pair of electrons did not occur.

Again it should be emphasized that this mechanism represents an oversimplification of the actual course of the reaction of nitrous acid with aliphatic amines (see p. 40). Hückel and Wilip [24] have found, for example, that in aqueous solution *l*-menthylamine (XXXIX) is transformed with no inversion or racemization into *l*-menthol (XL). When the reaction is carried out in aqueous alcohol, however, the ether which is formed is partially racemized (XLI and XLII). The formation of a

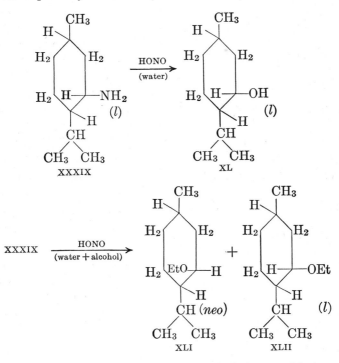

planar carbonium ion of separate existence probably would give a partially racemized product.

Reaction of Aliphatic Diazo Compounds with Carbonyl Groups. Aliphatic diazo compounds react readily with aldehydes and ketones to produce ketones of higher molecular weight.[25] With cyclic ketones the

[24] Hückel and Wilip, *J. prakt. Chem.*, **158**, 26 (1941).

[25] For a summary of the reaction, see Adamson and Kenner, *J. Chem. Soc.*, **1939**, 181, and Fuson, in Gilman, *Organic Chemistry, An Advanced Treatise*, p. 99, John Wiley and Sons, New York, 1943.

reaction is useful for the synthesis of higher homologs. For example, when cyclohexanone is treated with diazomethane, cycloheptanone and smaller amounts of methylenecyclohexane oxide (XLIII) and cyclo-octanone are obtained.[26] The reaction is a general one and has been

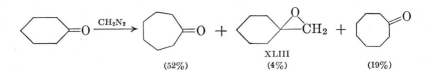

(52%)   XLIII   (19%)
                                   (4%)

widely used for the synthesis of cyclic ketones in the range of C_7 to C_{10}. This reaction also appears to proceed through a transitory carbonium ion intermediate.

The structure of diazomethane seems to be best represented as a hybrid of the resonance forms (XLIV) and (XLV):[27]

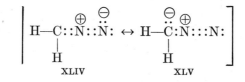

If reaction with a carbonyl compound occurs through XLV, the intermediate (XLVI) resembles an aliphatic diazonium ion ($RCH_2:\overset{\oplus}{N}\equiv N:$) and should undergo reactions similar to those described in the last section.

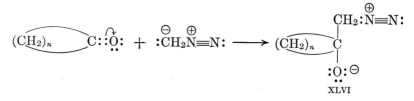

XLVI

Loss of nitrogen would produce the corresponding carbonium ion (XLVII), which could become stabilized by reaction with an atom having a completely filled valence shell (XLVIII) or by exchange of the methylene bridge with the carbonium ion (XLIX). In the first

[26] Mosettig and Burger, *J. Am. Chem. Soc.*, **52**, 3456 (1930). For the reaction of diazomethane with two unsymmetrical cyclic ketones, see Gutsche, *ibid.*, **71**, 3513 (1949).

[27] Taylor and Baker, *Sidgwick's Organic Chemistry of Nitrogen*, p. 362, Oxford University Press, London, England, 1942.

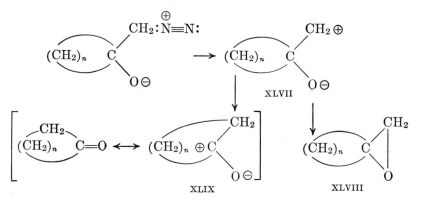

case the epoxide is formed; in the second, the completely polarized form of the next higher homolog of the cyclic ketone results. It is interesting that in most cases the yield of ketone is greater than that of the epoxide.

Wolff Rearrangement. One of the steps in the Arndt-Eistert synthesis for the preparation of an acid from its preceding homolog [28] involves the conversion of a diazo methyl ketone into an acid derivative. This transformation is usually called the Wolff rearrangement.

The mechanism of the reaction is complicated by the fact that a heterogeneous catalyst (silver oxide) is normally employed to give the acid derivatives (equation 21), and reactions of this kind frequently do not proceed through ionic intermediates (Chapter 1):

$$R-\overset{\overset{O}{\|}}{C}-CHN_2 + \begin{cases} H_2O \\ R'OH \\ NH_3 \\ R'NH_2 \end{cases} \xrightarrow{Ag_2O} \begin{cases} RCH_2COOH \\ RCH_2COOR' \\ RCH_2CONH_2 \\ RCH_2CONHR' \end{cases} \tag{21}$$

In the absence of catalyst and in the presence of water and formic acid, hydroxy methyl ketones are formed as by-products:

$$R-\overset{\overset{O}{\|}}{C}-CHN_2 + H_2O \xrightarrow{HCOOH} R-\overset{\overset{O}{\|}}{C}-CH_2OH$$

showing that the course of the reaction does indeed change under different conditions.

It is possible, however, to write a mechanism for the reaction based upon the principles of carbonium ion theory which will embrace many of the experimental facts concerning the reaction. The structure of the

[28] For a review of the Arndt-Eistert synthesis see Bachmann and Struve, in Adams, *Organic Reactions*, p. 38, Vol. I, John Wiley and Sons, New York, 1942.

diazomethyl ketone is probably the resonance hybrid L:

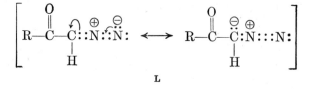

L

If nitrogen separates from the molecule under the influence of a catalyst or heat (e.g., boiling aniline), the intermediate (LI) is like a carbo-

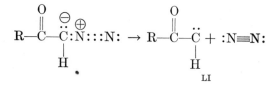

LI

nium ion in that it has only six electrons in its outer valence shell. If it behaves as a carbonium ion, we should expect that it would react by the exchange of the electron deficiency for a group attached to an adjacent carbon atom (LII), or by recombination with an atom having a completely filled valence shell (LIII):

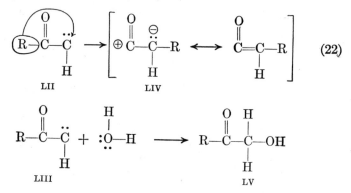

(22)

From the first course of reaction we obtain the completely polarized form of a ketene (LIV) and from the second a hydroxymethyl ketone (LV). Since ketenes are extremely reactive molecules they would be expected to combine at once with the solvent employed to give the products shown in equation 21.

The fact that in certain cases ketenes have been isolated supports this mechanism.[29]

There can be no doubt that the carbonyl group of the diazomethyl

[29] Schroeter, *Ber.*, **42**, 2346 (1909); **49**, 2704 (1916); Staudinger and Hirzel, *Ber.*, **49**, 2523 (1916).

ketone becomes the carboxyl group of the resulting acid as equation 22 indicates. Huggett, Arnold, and Taylor have shown this by the following series of transformations: [30]

$$\overset{*}{C}O_2 + C_6H_5MgBr \rightarrow C_6H_5\overset{*}{C}OOH \xrightarrow[(2)CH_2N_2]{(1)SOCl_2} C_6H_5\overset{*}{C}OCHN_2$$
(containing 2.51% C[13])

$$\xrightarrow[H_2O]{Ag_2O} C_6H_5\overset{?\ \ \ \ \ }{CH_2}COOH \xrightarrow[quinoline]{CuO\cdot Cr_2O_3} C_6H_5COOH + \overset{*}{C}O_2$$
(found to contain 2.53% C[13])

Since the carbon dioxide obtained by the decarboxylation of the phenylacetic acid was found to contain the same percentage of C^{13} as the carbon dioxide from which the benzoic acid was made, it is evident that a migration must have occurred during the Wolff rearrangement.

It is interesting that when R contains a tertiary asymmetric carbon atom bound to the carbonyl group of the diazomethyl ketone, the Wolff rearrangement takes place without racemization or inversion. This is also a characteristic of the Curtius (p. 63), the Hofmann (p. 76), and the Schmidt (p. 65) rearrangements. Thus when $(+)\alpha$-methyl-α-phenylcaproic acid (LVI) was taken through an Arndt-Eistert synthesis, followed by a Barbier-Wieland degradation, no loss in optical activity occurred.[31] The steps in the sequence may be outlined as follows:

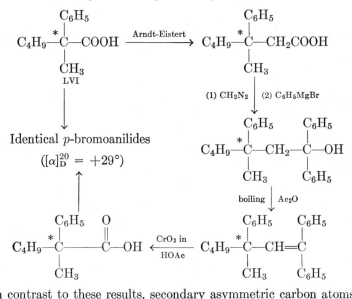

In contrast to these results, secondary asymmetric carbon atoms at-

[30] Huggett, Arnold, and Taylor, *J. Am. Chem. Soc.*, **64**, 3043 (1942).
[31] Lane and Wallis, *J. Am. Chem. Soc.*, **63**, 1674 (1941).

tached to the carbonyl group of a diazomethyl ketone are completely racemized [32] (equation 23):

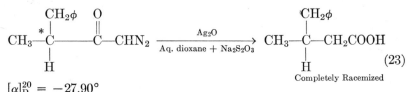

$$[\alpha]_D^{20} = -27.90°$$

This behavior is apparently due to a preliminary tautomerization of the diazomethyl ketone at the surface of the catalyst since it has been shown that these compounds do not racemize under the same conditions when the catalyst is absent.[32]

Wagner-Meerwein Rearrangement. When β-substituted alcohols are dehydrated (p. 105) or treated with such reagents as the halogen acids,[33] thionyl chloride,[34] or phosphorus pentachloride,[35] rearrangements of the carbon skeleton frequently occur. Similarly the addition of halogen acids to polycyclic olefins like dicyclopentadiene [36] gives rise to abnormal products. Such rearrangements are known as Wagner or Wagner-Meerwein rearrangements, and have in common a carbonium ion intermediate.

Probably the best-known examples of Wagner-Meerwein rearrangements are the conversions of camphene to isobornyl chloride and pinene to bornyl chloride by hydrochloric acid. In terms of carbonium ion theory these reactions may be interpreted as shown on pages 57 and 58.

The reversible equilibrium between the olefin and hydrogen chloride gives rise to a tertiary alkyl halide (LVII and LVIII). Ionization of the halide produces a carbonium ion (LIX and LX) that undergoes rearrangement with the characteristic inversion of the carbon atom to which the positive charge becomes attached (LXI and LXII). Subsequent recombination (or even more likely, simultaneous recombination) with the halogen ion produces isobornyl (LXIII) and bornyl chloride (LXIV) respectively.

As in other carbonium ion rearrangements, any groups attached to an α-carbon atom might have migrated as the carbonium ion was formed. With these compounds the two possibilities involving the ring systems

[32] Lane, Willenz, Weissberger, and Wallis, *J. Org. Chem.*, **5**, 276 (1940); Lane and Wallis, *ibid.*, **6**, 443 (1941).

[33] For example, see Whitmore and Rothrock, *J. Am. Chem. Soc.*, **54**, 3431 (1932).

[34] Wallis and Bowman, *ibid.*, **56**, 491 (1934).

[35] Hückel and Kümmerle, *Ber.*, **75B**, 115 (1942).

[36] Bruson and Reiner, *J. Am. Chem. Soc.*, **67**, 723 (1945); **67**, 1178 (1945); and Bartlett and Schneider, *ibid.*, **68**, 6 (1946).

are labeled *a* and *b* in each case. With camphene only one product is obtained (LXIII), since the migration of the other bond (*b*) would result in the formation of a very highly strained four-membered ring. With α-pinene, however, the migration of either bond *a* or bond *b* would give rise to a five-membered ring. It is interesting that this other possibility actually appears to have been realized (equation 24, page 59).

In the conversion of pinene to bornyl chloride liquid products are formed which have been shown to contain the fenchane carbon skeleton.[37]

A number of facts support an ionic intermediate for the reaction. The transformation is facilitated by solvents such as nitromethane [38] or liquid

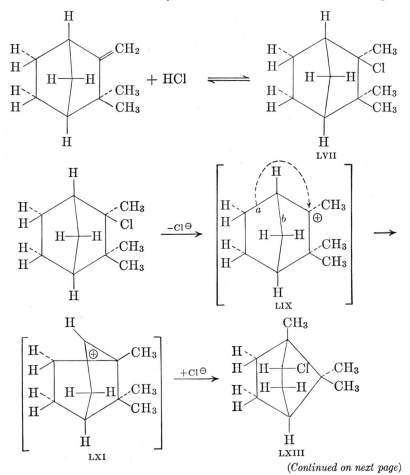

(*Continued on next page*)

[37] Barbier and Grignard, *Bull. soc. chim.*, [4] **7**, 342 (1910).
[38] Meerwein and van Emster, *Ber.*, **53**, 1815 (1920); **55**, 2500 (1922).

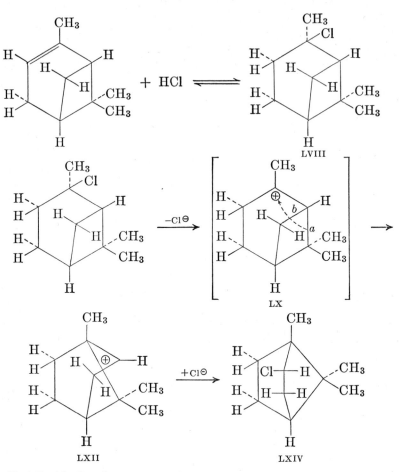

sulfur dioxide [38] and reagents such as hydrogen chloride,[38, 39] stannic chloride,[38] ferric chloride,[38] and phenols.[39]   All of these are known to promote the ionization of organic halides.   Kinetic experiments with hydrochloric acid,[38, 39] phenols,[39] deuterium chloride,[40] and hydrogen chloride containing radioactive chlorine [40] indicate that the reaction goes in two steps. The first involves the establishment of a rapid ionic equilibrium with chloride ion, and this step is followed by a slower reaction with the solvating molecule.

The exact nature of these steps is not clear.   Since cresol exhibits catalytic activity, it is evident that the catalyst does not function by a simultaneous donation and removal of a chloride ion.   This conclusion

[39] Bartlett and Pöckel, *J. Am. Chem. Soc.*, **60**, 1585 (1938); Bartlett and Gill, *ibid.*, **63**, 1273 (1941); Bartlett and Dauben, *ibid.*, **62**, 1339 (1940).
[40] Nevell, de Salas, and Wilson, *J. Chem. Soc.*, **1939**, 1188.

is further substantiated by the fact that the introduction of chloride ion (by means of lithium chloride) into the reaction mixture has no effect on the rate. Apparently in the actual rearrangement the halogen atom is loosened by solvation, but so far as the reaction is concerned, it never leaves the sphere of influence of the electronically deficient atoms which are involved in the transformation.

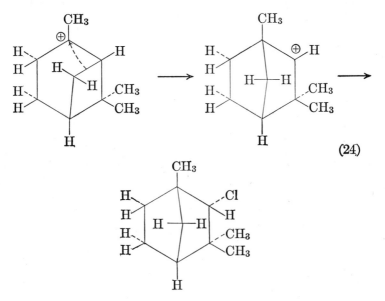

(24)

Isomerization of Alkanes. When alkanes are treated with acidic catalysts such as sulfuric acid or a mixture of an aluminum halide and the corresponding halogen acid, isomerization occurs with the formation of more highly branched products. Thus n-butane is isomerized to iso-butane. In recent years this reaction has become important because

$$CH_3CH_2CH_2CH_3 \xrightarrow{AlBr_3 + HBr} CH_3-\underset{\underset{CH_3}{|}}{CH}-CH_3$$

such branched chain paraffins combine with olefins to give products which are excellent motor fuels. (See "Alkylation of Olefins," p. 143.)

Actually this reaction does not occur at all unless a trace of olefin,[41] oxygen,[42] or water[43] is present, or unless the experimental conditions are conducive to the formation of decomposition products.[41] In AlBr$_3$-HBr catalysis, the initial step in the reaction is believed to be the formation

[41] Pines and Wackher, *J. Am. Chem. Soc.*, **68**, 595, 2518 (1946).
[42] Pines and Wackher, *ibid.*, 599.
[43] Wackher and Pines, *ibid.*, 1642.

of a trace of *sec*-butyl halide produced through the respective reactions:

$$CH_3CH_2CH{=}CH_2 + HBr \rightleftharpoons CH_3CH_2CHBrCH_3$$

and

$$AlBr_3 + O_2 \rightleftharpoons AlOBr + Br_2$$

$$CH_3CH_2CH_2CH_3 + Br_2 \rightarrow CH_3CH_2CHBrCH_3 + HBr$$

$$AlBr_3 + H_2O \rightleftharpoons HOAlBr_2 + HBr$$

$$HOAlBr_2 + CH_3CH_2CH_2CH_3 \rightleftharpoons$$

$$CH_3CH_2CHBrCH_3 + HOAlBrH[AlOBr + H_2]$$

In support of this hypothesis it has been observed that when aluminum bromide is treated with oxygen a reaction occurs which liberates bromine,[42] and further, the halogen atoms rather than the hydroxyl group are responsible for the catalytic activity of $HOAlBr_2$. Thus when the compound $DOAlBr_2$ is prepared, the hydrogen-deuterium exchange with *n*-butane is not at all proportional to isomerization.[43]

Accordingly the isomerization can be written as a combination carbonium ion rearrangement and exchange reaction:

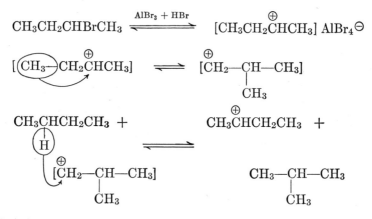

It is interesting that isomerization has been shown to occur even with propane. When this hydrocarbon, labeled with C^{13} in one end, is brought into contact with aluminum bromide, rearrangement occurs so as to move the heavy isotope into the central position:[44]

$$CH_3{-}CH_2{-}\overset{*}{C}H_3 \xrightarrow{\ AlBr_3\ } CH_3{-}\overset{*}{C}H_2{-}CH_3$$

[44] Beeck, Otvos, Stevenson, and Wagner, *J. Chem. Phys.*, **16**, 255 (1948).

The rate of isomerization is comparable to the rate of conversion of n-butane to isobutane under identical conditions; no molecules having more than one atom of C^{13} were found. Consequently, the reaction must be an intramolecular rearrangement. It is evident that, in the presence of an acid catalyst, the bonds in a saturated hydrocarbon are not as inert as we might suppose.

The Dienone-Phenol Rearrangement. There are a number of instances known in which cyclic dienones yield rearranged phenols under the influence of acids.[45] Wilds and Djerassi [46] have shown that the dienone (LXV) could be rearranged into LXVI by heating with sulfuric acid and acetic anhydride. The structure of (LXVI) was proved by an independent synthesis. Similarly,

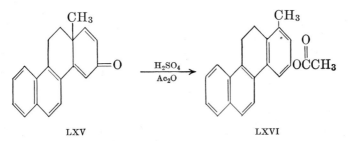

Arnold, Buckley, and Richter [47] were able to convert LXVII into the acetate of 3,4-dimethyl-1-naphthol (LXVIII):

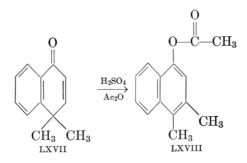

These reactions fit nicely into the theory of carbonium ion rearrangements. Attack of a proton on the carbonyl oxygen produces a carbonium ion which, by virtue of the conjugated system, is a hybrid of the forms (LXIX) and (LXX). In form (LXX) there is a positive charge on

[45] See Arnold and Buckley, *J. Am. Chem. Soc.*, **71**, 1781 (1949) and references 46 and 47 for several other examples which are not mentioned here.

[46] Wilds and Djerassi, *ibid.*, **68**, 1712, 1715 (1946).

[47] Arnold, Buckley, and Richter, *ibid.*, **69**, 2322 (1947).

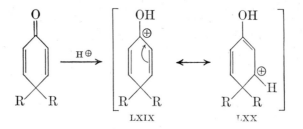

a carbon atom adjacent to one which is highly substituted, and we might expect a carbonium ion rearrangement (equation 24). The new carbonium ion could be stabilized by the loss of a proton to form the disub-

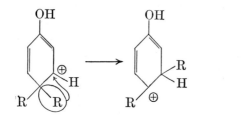

(24)

stituted phenol molecule (LXXI).

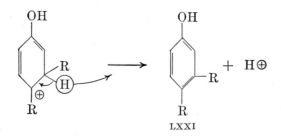

LXXI

The rearrangement of semibenzenes to trialkyl benzenes [48] can be written in a similar manner:

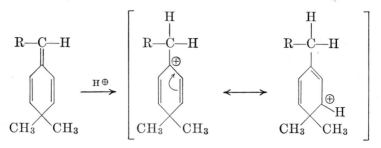

[48] v. Auwers and Ziegler, *Ann.*, **425**, 217 (1921).

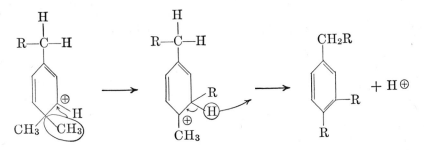

EXTENSION OF THE CARBONIUM ION PRINCIPLE TO THE NITROGEN ATOM

An examination of the driving force of the rearrangements which have been discussed reveals that it is an incomplete valence shell of only six electrons which is responsible for reaction. There are a number of similar rearrangements which occur when a pair of electrons is removed from the valence shell of the nitrogen atom. As before, the essential step in the transformations appears to be the migration of an alkyl group from an adjacent carbon atom with the formation of a carbonium ion.

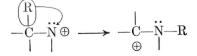

MOLECULAR REARRANGEMENTS INVOLVING ELECTRONICALLY DEFICIENT NITROGEN ATOMS

Curtius Reaction.[49] When acid azides are allowed to decompose, the first product which can be isolated is an isocyanate. It is evident that

$$R\overset{\overset{\displaystyle O}{\|}}{-}C-N_3 \rightarrow R-N=C=O + N_2$$

in the reaction there is a migration of the alkyl group from a carbon atom to a nitrogen atom. This rearrangement has been called the Curtius reaction. Frequently other products derivable from isocyanates (amines, urethans, amides, and ureas) are obtained by a secondary reaction of the isocyanate with the solvent or another component in the reaction mixture.

[49] For a review of the Curtius reaction, see Smith, in Adams, *Organic Reactions*, Vol. III, p. 337, John Wiley and Sons, New York, 1946.

A mechanism may be written for the reaction similar to the ones just described if we suppose that the driving force for the rearrangement is indeed a nitrogen atom with only six electrons in its valence shell. Separation of a nitrogen molecule from the azide (LXXII) leaves the electronically deficient nitrogen atom shown in (LXXIII). Interchange of the alkyl group and the electron deficiency leaves the completely polarized form of an isocyanate (LXXIV).

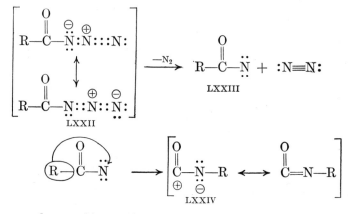

In several ways this reaction resembles the molecular rearrangements involving transitory carbonium ions. The reaction is acid-catalyzed [50] (see the Schmidt reaction). In the presence of triphenylmethyl free radicals no mixed products are formed.[51] The migrating group never leaves the field of the electronically deficient atoms concerned since the Curtius reaction with (−)o-(2-methyl-6-nitrophenyl)-benzoic acid (LXXV) produces an optically active amine [52] (LXXVI).

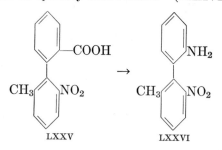

Optical activity in this case is a result of restricted rotation caused by the interference of the carboxyl group with the nitro and the methyl

[50] Newman and Gildenhorn, *J. Am. Chem. Soc.*, **70**, 317 (1948).

[51] Powell, *J. Am. Chem. Soc.*, **51**, 2436 (1929); Wallis, *ibid.*, 2982.

[52] Bell, *J. Chem. Soc.*, **1934**, 835.

group. If at any time during the rearrangement this restriction had been removed, racemization would have occurred.

The rearrangement indicated in the transformation of LXXIII to LXXIV calls for the migration of the group R with a pair of electrons. It now seems well established that intramolecular rearrangements of this kind proceed with retention of optical configuration and no racemization when there is an asymmetric carbon atom attached to the carbonyl group. In the conversion of $(+)\alpha$-methyl-α-phenylacetazide (LXXVII) to α-phenylethylamine (LXXVIII), the product was found to be 99.3 per cent optically pure and to have the same optical configuration as the starting material.[53]

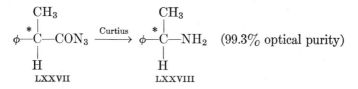

Schmidt Reaction.[54] Closely related to the Curtius reaction in its mechanism is the Schmidt reaction, whereby carbonyl compounds react with hydrazoic acid in acid solution to give rearranged products. Amines, amides, nitriles, and tetrazoles are the most common substances obtained from the reaction.

$$RCO_2H + HN_3 \xrightarrow{H_2SO_4} RNH_2 + CO_2 + N_2$$

$$RCHO + HN_3 \xrightarrow{H_2SO_4} RC\equiv N \quad \text{and} \quad RNHCHO + N_2 + H_2O$$

$$R_2CO + HN_3 \xrightarrow{H_2SO_4} RCONHR \quad \text{and} \quad R—C{=\!=\!=}N + N_2 + H_2O$$

Insight has been gained into the mechanism of the Schmidt reaction with acids by the observation that the transformation proceeds most easily with those hindered acids which, in sulfuric acid solution, give rise to acyl carbonium ions, $R—\overset{\overset{O}{\|}}{C}\oplus$.[50] For example, 2,4.6-trimethylbenzoic

[53] Kenyon and Young, *J. Chem. Soc.*, **1941**, 263.
[54] For a review of the Schmidt reaction, see Wolff, in Adams, *Organic Reactions*, Vol. III, p. 307, John Wiley and Sons, New York, 1946.

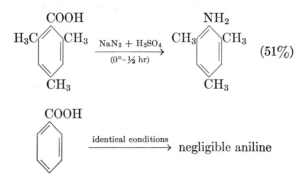

(51%)

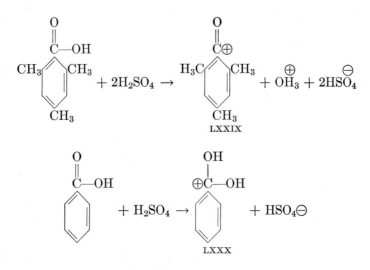

acid undergoes the reaction at 0° while benzoic acid requires a temperature of 35 to 50°C. Cryoscopic evidence indicates that 2,4,6-trimethylbenzoic acid is completely dissociated in sulfuric acid solution into the acyl carbonium ion (LXXIX), but that benzoic acid gives rise to a dihydroxycarbonium ion (LXXX).

Accordingly it has been suggested [50] that the initial step of the Schmidt reaction involves combination of a hydrazoic acid molecule (LXXXI) with the acyl carbonium ion (LXXXII). Scission of a nitrogen molecule from this intermediate (LXXXIII) leaves a nitrogen atom with only six outer electrons (LXXXIV) which can rearrange as described previously to give the protonated form of an isocyanate (LXXXV). This species is assumed to be hydrolyzed in the sulfuric acid reaction mixture to give the amine salt and carbon dioxide.

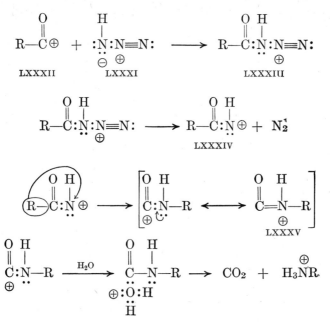

For those acids, such as benzoic, which do not give rise to acyl carbonium ions at low temperatures, it may be assumed either that a preliminary step involves the dissociation

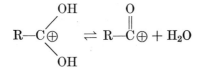

or, more probably, that rearrangement is preceded by dehydration of the complex formed between hydrazoic acid and the dihydroxycarbonium ion:

$$R—C(OH)_2^{\oplus} \quad + \quad :N:N≡N: \quad \rightleftarrows \quad R—C(OH)(NH): N:N≡N: \qquad (25)$$

$$R—C(OH)(NH):N:N≡N: \quad \rightleftarrows \quad R—C(OH)=N:N≡N: \quad + \quad H_2O \qquad (26)$$

LXXXVI

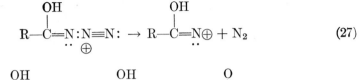

$$R-\overset{\overset{\displaystyle OH}{|}}{C}=N:N\equiv N: \rightarrow R-\overset{\overset{\displaystyle OH}{|}}{C}=N\oplus + N_2 \quad (27)$$

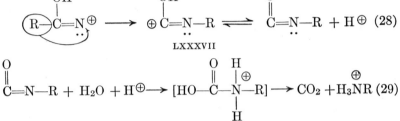

$$\overset{\overset{\displaystyle OH}{|}}{R-C}=N\oplus \longrightarrow \oplus\overset{\overset{\displaystyle OH}{|}}{C}=N-R \rightleftharpoons \overset{\overset{\displaystyle O}{\|}}{C}=N-R + H\oplus \quad (28)$$

LXXXVII

$$\overset{\overset{\displaystyle O}{\|}}{C}=N-R + H_2O + H\oplus \longrightarrow [HO-\overset{\overset{\displaystyle O}{\|}}{C}-\overset{\overset{\displaystyle H}{|}}{\underset{\underset{\displaystyle H}{|}}{N}}-R] \longrightarrow CO_2 + H_3NR \quad (29)$$

There are several pieces of evidence which substantiate the essential correctness of these individual steps. The intermediates LXXXIII and LXXXVI represent two possible species which might be obtained by dissolving acid azides in sulfuric acid solution. It has already been mentioned that the Curtius reaction is indeed acid-catalyzed (p. 64). Furthermore, LXXXV and LXXXVII are two possible cations which might be expected when an isocyanate is dissolved in sulfuric acid. In support of these intermediates, it has been found that phenylisocyanate decomposes immediately when dissolved in sulfuric acid and that aniline can be isolated from the reaction mixture.[50] As with all rearrangements of this type, optical configuration is retained without racemization if the carbon atom attached to the carbonyl group is asymmetric. The Schmidt reaction with act. α-phenylpropionic acid gives α-phenylethyl-amine of 99.6 per cent optical purity.[55] In a study of the rate of reaction of a number of substituted benzoic acids, the rate of nitrogen evolution increases as the electron releasing tendency of the group R becomes greater.[56] This implies that the decomposition of the azide is the slow step in the transformation. Electron-releasing groups have the same effect on the Hofmann (p. 76) and Lossen (p. 77) rearrangements.

The reaction of aldehydes and ketones with hydrazoic acid is more difficult to interpret. If we assume that the transformation proceeds through the intermediates LXXXVIII to XCIII and XCV (which are similar to those which were proposed for the reaction of 2,4,6-trimethyl-benzoic acid with hydrazoic acid), we see that the final product should be the amide XCIII or XCV, depending upon whether an alkyl group or a hydrogen atom with a pair of electrons migrates.

[55] Campbell and Kenyon, *J. Chem. Soc.*, **1946**, 26.
[56] Briggs and Lyttleton, *ibid.*, **1943**, 421.

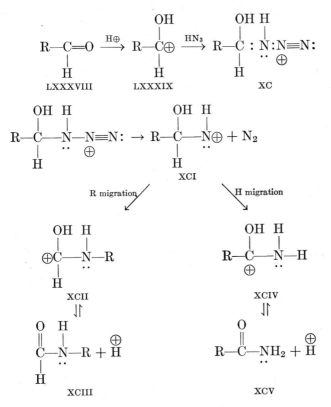

The products actually isolated, however, are the formamide (XCIII) and the nitrile RCN. Furthermore, the ratio of the two products does not depend upon a characteristic "migrational aptitude" but rather upon the experimental conditions of the reaction. Thus when benzaldehyde is treated with hydrazoic acid and small amounts of sulfuric acid, principally nitrile is formed. When larger amounts of sulfuric acid are employed, the anilide is the principal product.[57]

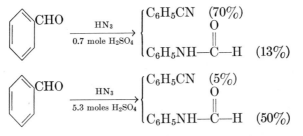

[57] Schmidt, Ger. Patent 427,858 [Frdl., **15**, 221 (1928)].

That the amide might be dehydrated by the sulfuric acid reaction mixture seems to be ruled out by the fact that benzamide shows a molar freezing point depression of two in sulfuric acid solution. Dehydration would cause a molar freezing point depression of four. Accordingly, it seems more likely [58] that dehydration of the intermediate XC occurs before rearrangement since a series of steps similar to those outlined in equations 25 to 29 would lead to the nitrile directly:

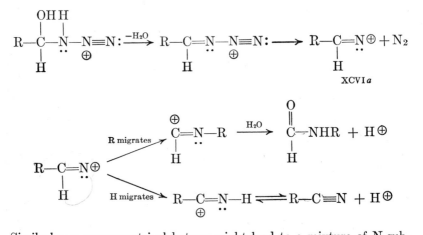

XCVI*a*

Similarly an unsymmetrical ketone might lead to a mixture of N-substituted amides:

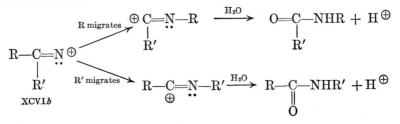

XCVI.*b*

We observe, however, that the intermediates XCVI (*a* and *b*) are identical to those obtained from the Beckmann rearrangement (p. 74). In this reaction the tendency to migrate is not dependent upon an inherent migrational aptitude but rather *upon the steric arrangement of the oxime*. The group which migrates is the one which is *trans* to the hydroxyl group (p. 72). Consequently, if the Schmidt reaction involves the same intermediate, attained by the loss of molecular nitrogen rather than the hydroxyl group, the group which would be expected to migrate would be the one *trans* to the azo group. Normally this should be the

[58] Smith, *J. Am. Chem. Soc.*, **70**, 320 (1948).

more bulky group, since the formation of the intermediate XCVII, in which the larger group and the diazo group are *anti* (*trans*) to each other, should be favored over the intermediate XCVIII in which they are *syn* (*cis*).[58]

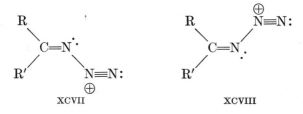

XCVII   XCVIII

(R is more bulky than R')

In Table 1 the data are summarized from a number of Schmidt reactions carried out with unsymmetrical ketones.

TABLE 1

MIGRATION OF GROUPS IN THE SCHMIDT REACTION WITH
UNSYMMETRICAL KETONES

Ketone, R—C(=O)—R'	% Migration of R	% Migration of R'
Methyl ethyl *	..	70 †
Methyl isobutyl *	..	71 †
Methyl p-tolyl *	..	90 †
Methyl p-anisyl *	..	50 †
Methyl β-naphthyl *	..	73 †
Ethyl phenyl ‡	15 §	85 §
Methyl phenyl ‡	5 §	94 §
Isopropyl phenyl ‡	50 §	50 §
Methyl benzyl ‡	50 §	50 §
Methyl β-phenylethyl ‡	5 §	95 §
Phenyl p-chlorophenyl ‡	59 §	41 §
Phenyl p-nitrophenyl ‡	49 §	51 §
Phenyl p-biphenyl ‡	48 §	52 §
Phenyl p-tolyl ‡	46 §	54 §
Phenyl p-anisyl ‡	32 §	68 §

* Sanford, Blair, Arroya, Sherk, *J. Am. Chem. Soc.*, **67**, 1942 (1945).

† This value represents the yield of rearrangement product isolated. The other isomer was not reported.

‡ Smith and Horwitz, *Abstracts of Papers*, 115th Meeting of the American Chemical Society, San Francisco, Calif., April 1949, p. 10L.

§ These values represent the percentage of migration in the *mixture* of products isolated.

It is evident that the larger group does migrate preferentially.   It is also significant that in the *p*-substituted benzophenone series, almost equal amounts of each rearrangement product are obtained.   This is not explicable in terms of purely electrical factors, but it is in agreement with the steric considerations which have been described.   Since the *para* substituents do not increase the bulk of a phenyl group as far as the azo group is concerned, an equal mixture of the isomers XCVII and XCVIII would be expected.   It is not clear why *p*-methoxybenzophenone is an exception.

Beckmann Rearrangement.[59]   For a very long time it has been known that the action of acids upon oximes produces amides.   More recently it has been found that oxime ethers and esters also undergo rearrangement to form amide derivatives:

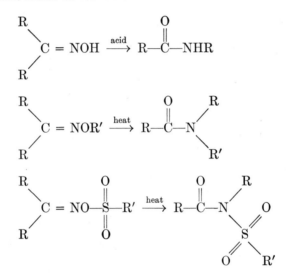

These reactions appear to follow a similar course and are usually called Beckmann rearrangements.   Again, they involve the migration of an alkyl group from carbon to nitrogen.

Probably the most interesting feature of the Beckmann rearrangement is the fact that when the reaction is carried out with an unsymmetrical ketoxime, migration is not governed by an intrinsic migrational aptitude but by the steric configuration of the oxime.   In every clear-cut case where the configuration of a ketoxime has been established, it is always the group *trans* to the hydroxyl group which migrates preferentially.   For example, the rearrangement of β-benzil monoxime (XCIX)

[59] For reviews of the Beckmann rearrangement, see Blatt, *Chem. Revs.*, **12**, 215 (1933), and Jones, *ibid.*, **35**, 335 (1944).

gives the amide (C).[60]   Since ozonolysis of 3,4-diphenylisoxazole-5-carboxylic acid (CI) gives the same oxime,[61] it is known that the benzoyl group and the hydroxyl group are *cis* to each other.

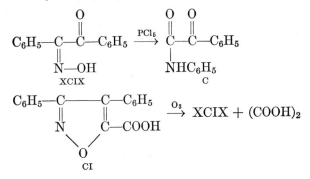

It has also been found that when the rearrangement involves the migration of an asymmetric carbon atom, the configuration is completely retained at that carbon atom.   When (+) α-phenylethyl methyl ketoxime (CII) is treated with sulfuric acid, N-α-phenylethyl acetamide (CIII) is formed in 99.6 per cent optical purity.[55]

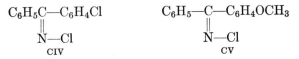

From the fact that such diverse reagents as phosphorus pentachloride, benzenesulfonyl chloride, sulfuric acid, and chloral have been employed as reagents for the reaction, it is evident that no single compound could be an intermediate in the reaction.   Chloroimido ketones such as CIV and CV do not appear to be necessary intermediates in the reaction

$$C_6H_5C—C_6H_4Cl \qquad\qquad C_6H_5—C—C_6H_4OCH_3$$
$$\underset{\text{CIV}}{N—Cl} \qquad\qquad\qquad \underset{\text{CV}}{N—Cl}$$

when hydrochloric acid or phosphorus pentachloride are the catalysts employed, since rearrangement of the oximes will take place under conditions that will not bring about the transformation of the chloro compounds.[62]   An acid is not a necessary requirement for rearrangement

[60] Beckmann and Köster, *Ann.*, **274**, 7 (1893).

[61] Kohler, *J. Am. Chem. Soc.*, **46**, 1733 (1924).

[62] Peterson, *Am. Chem. J.*, **46**, 325 (1911); Theilacker and Mohl, *Ann.*, **563**, 99 (1949).

since the reaction occurs when benzophenone oxime is treated with benzenesulfonyl chloride and alkali.[63] A catalyst is not always required. The picryl ethers of oximes rearrange readily on heating.[64]

A general mechanism can be written for the transformations which will include these facts if we assume that the first step of the process involves combination of the hydroxyl group of the oxime with a reagent or catalyst to form an intermediate of the general type:

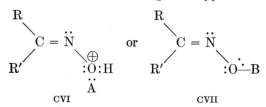

CVI   CVII

depending upon whether the reaction is carried out in the presence of an acid (CVI) or under conditions which would be expected to lead to esterification or etherification (CVII). Separation of :O:A or :O:B⊖ leaves a nitrogen atom with six valence electrons (CVIII), and this process is accompanied by a shift of the group nearest the backside of the nitrogen atom (CIX). Recombination of the fragment HOA with the carbonium ion which is formed, followed by the loss of a proton, produces an enol derivative of the amide concerned (CX).

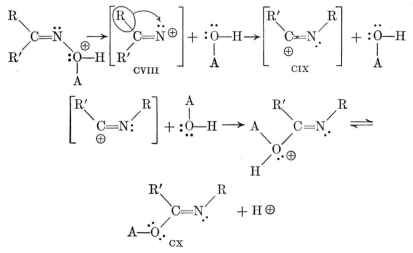

[63] Blatt, *Chem. Revs.*, **12**, 252 (1933).
[64] Chapman and Howis, *J. Chem. Soc.*, **1933**, 806.

Compounds of type CX are unstable when AOH is a strong acid, for attempts to prepare them by other routes result in spontaneous ketonization: [64]

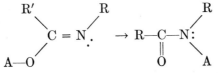

As with the carbonium ion rearrangements which have been discussed, the transformation probably proceeds by the simultaneous interchange of the groups concerned when the nitrogen-oxygen bond is weakened. It is interesting, however, that the entire process is not intramolecular. When benzophenone oxime is treated with phosphorus pentachloride and decomposed in water containing O^{18}, the resulting benzanilide is found to contain the heavy isotope in the same concentration as the water in which it was hydrolyzed.[65] Since benzanilide does not exchange with O^{18} under the same conditions [66] it is evident that at some stage in the transformation, HOA must have separated from the rest of the molecule.

This general mechanism is in agreement with most of the data known about the reaction. The processes are facilitated by heat,[64] polar solvents,[64,67] or an increase in the acid strength of the reaction medium.[68] Rearrangement is unaffected by light and follows first-order kinetics.[67] When electron-attracting groups are introduced into the benzophenone portion of the picryl ethers of benzophenone oxime, the reaction proceeds more slowly [69] (since the separation of the group initiating the reaction withdraws an electron pair from the nitrogen atom).

Conversely, the rearrangement of esters proceeds more and more rapidly in the series: benzophenone oxime acetate, chloroacetate, and benzenesulfonate.[70] Benzophenone oxime trinitro-m-cresylate rearranges more slowly than the picrate.[69] It is not clear, however, why unusually complex rate curves are obtained when the rearrangement is catalyzed by hydrochloric acid.[71]

[65] Brodskii and Miklukhin, *Compt. rend. acad. sci.* (U.R.S.S.), **32,** 558 (1941); *C.A.,* **37,** 1710 (1943).

[66] Miklukhin and Brodskii, *Acta Physicochim.* (U.R.S.S.), **16,** 63 (1942); *C.A.,* **37,** 2355 (1943).

[67] Sluiter, *Rec. trav. chim.,* **24,** 372 (1905); Pearson and Ball, *J. Org. Chem.,* **14,** 118 (1949).

[68] Jones, *Chem. Revs.,* **35,** 337 (1944).

[69] Chapman and Fidler, *J. Chem. Soc.,* **1936,** 448.

[70] Blatt, *Chem. Revs.,* **12,** 250 (1933).

[71] Chapman, *J. Chem. Soc.,* **1935** (1223).

Hofmann Reaction.[72] In contrast to the molecular rearrangements which have been discussed, the Hofmann reaction proceeds in an alkaline medium. In this reaction an amide is treated with a hypohalite solution, and, under the usual conditions of the reaction, an amine with one less carbon atom is obtained:

$$RCONH_2 + X_2 + 2NaOH \rightarrow RNH_2 + CO_2 + H_2O + 2NaX$$

As in the Curtius and Lossen reactions, when alcohol is employed as a solvent, a urethan is formed.

The mechanism of the reaction appears to involve the following steps. The reaction of hypohalite and the amide yields an N-haloamide (CXI). The N-haloamide reacts with alkali to give an unstable salt [73] (CXII), which, in some cases, has been shown to rearrange even in the dry state to give an isocyanate (CXIV). If we write this rearrangement as proceeding through the intermediate CXIII, it will be observed that the same species is common to the Curtius (p. 63) and Lossen (p. 77) reactions, the only difference being in the steps leading to this intermediate.

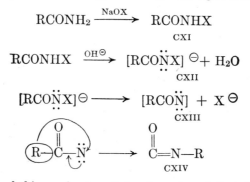

$$RCONH_2 \xrightarrow{\text{NaOX}} RCONHX$$
$$\text{CXI}$$

$$RCONHX \xrightarrow{OH^\ominus} [RCO\ddot{N}X]^\ominus + H_2O$$
$$\text{CXII}$$

$$[RCO\ddot{N}X]^\ominus \longrightarrow [RCO\ddot{N}] + X^\ominus$$
$$\text{CXIII}$$

$$\text{CXIV}$$

In support of this mechanism it has been found that the rate of decomposition of substituted benzamides (and presumably the ease of rearrangement) is more rapid when electron-releasing groups are introduced into the aromatic ring.[74] Thus the separation of the halide ion must be the controlling step for the reaction. When there is an asymmetric carbon atom attached to the carbonyl group, configuration is retained and virtually no racemization occurs.[75] (+)α-Methyl phenyl-

---

[72] For a review of the Hofmann reaction, see Wallis and Lane, in Adams, *Organic Reactions*, Vol. III, p. 267, John Wiley and Sons, New York, 1946.

[73] Mauguin, *Ann. Chim.* [8], **22**, 301 (1911).

[74] Hauser and Renfrow, *J. Am. Chem. Soc.*, **59**, 121 (1937).

[75] (a) Wallis and Nagel, *ibid.*, **53**, 2787 (1931). (b) Noyes, *Am. Chem. J.*, **16**, 500 (1894); Noyes and Potter, *J. Am. Chem. Soc.*, **37**, 189 (1915); *ibid.*, **34**, 1067 (1912); Noyes and Nickell, *ibid.*, **36**, 118 (1914). (c) Arcus and Kenyon, *J. Chem. Soc.*, **1939**, 916.

acetamide, for example, is converted into (+)α-phenylethylamine in a state of 95.5 per cent optical purity:[75c]

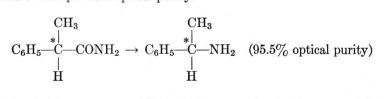

$$C_6H_5\overset{*}{\underset{H}{\overset{CH_3}{C}}}-CONH_2 \rightarrow C_6H_5\overset{*}{\underset{H}{\overset{CH_3}{C}}}-NH_2 \quad (95.5\% \text{ optical purity})$$

Similarly, the camphoramidic acids (CXV and CXVI), prepared from acids which readily form an anhydride lead to amino acids CXVII and

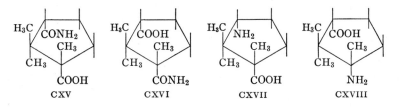

CXV   CXVI   CXVII   CXVIII

CXVIII, which will form lactams and are therefore *cis* to each other.[75b] As in the other molecular rearrangements, the migrating group never leaves the vicinity of the atoms which are concerned. Thus when a Hofmann reaction is carried out with (+) 3,5-dinitro-2-[α-naphthyl]-benzamide (CXIX) (which owes its optical activity to the restricted rotation of the bond connecting the benzene and naphthalene nuclei) an optically active amine (CXX) is formed [76] which has the same configuration as the starting material.[77]

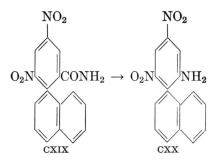

CXIX   CXX

Lossen Rearrangement.[78] The thermal decomposition of hydroxamic acid derivatives leads to isocyanates or, in aqueous solution, to amines. This reaction is usually called the Lossen rearrangement. Its mechanism

[76] Wallis and Moyer, *J. Am. Chem. Soc.*, **55**, 2598 (1933).

[77] Kenyon and Young, *J. Chem. Soc.*, **1941**, 265.

[78] For a review of the Lossen reaction, see Yale, *Chem. Revs.*, **33**, 242 (1943).

differs from the Hofmann reaction only in that the process is initiated

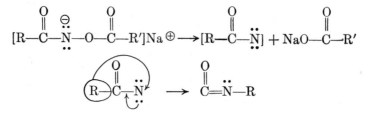

by the separation of a carboxylate ion rather than a halide ion.

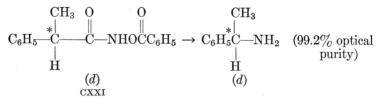

Like the other rearrangements which proceed through an electronically deficient nitrogen atom, the reaction is facilitated by electron-releasing groups in R.[79] Electron-withdrawing groups in R′ also increase the rate of reaction, and it is interesting that the effect is directly proportional to the strength of the acid R′COOH.[80] These data indicate that for the Lossen reaction, too, the separation of the anion is the most important step in the reaction. Like all the other similar rearrangements, the reaction proceeds with complete retention of configuration. Campbell and Kenyon have shown [55] that the benzoate of phenylmethylacetohydroxamic acid (CXXI) can be converted into α-phenylethylamine of 99.2 per cent optical purity by boiling the potassium salt in benzene and hydrolyzing the isocyanate which is formed.

$$\underset{\substack{(d)\\ \text{CXXI}}}{\text{C}_6\text{H}_5 \underset{\underset{\text{H}}{|}}{\overset{\overset{\text{CH}_3}{|}}{\underset{*}{\text{C}}}} \underset{}{\overset{\overset{\text{O}}{\parallel}}{\text{C}}} \text{—NHOCC}_6\text{H}_5} \rightarrow \underset{(d)}{\text{C}_6\text{H}_5 \underset{\underset{\text{H}}{|}}{\overset{\overset{\text{CH}_3}{|}}{\underset{*}{\text{C}}}} \text{—NH}_2} \quad (99.2\% \text{ optical purity})$$

[79] Renfrow and Hauser, *J. Am. Chem. Soc.*, **59**, 2308 (1937).
[80] Bright and Hauser, *ibid.*, **61**, 618 (1939).

CHAPTER 4

DISPLACEMENT REACTIONS [1]

Probably the most important type of reaction in organic chemistry is the displacement reaction. It has the general form:

$$A + BC \rightarrow AB + C$$

Depending upon the electronic structure of A and BC, there are two different ionic processes whereby this transformation may be effected. If A is a reagent which can accommodate two more electrons in its outermost valence shell, reaction with an unshared pair of electrons of B might liberate C as an electronically deficient species:

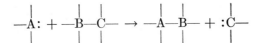

Since A is electron-seeking, this process is said to be an *electrophilic* substitution reaction and is given the symbol S_E. Many carbonium ion reactions (p. 45) and aromatic substitution reactions (p. 235) are initiated by electrophilic attack.

When A is a reagent having at least one unshared pair of electrons, collision with BC might result in the establishment of a bond A—B and the liberation of C with an unshared pair of electrons:

$$-\overset{|}{A}: + -\overset{|}{B}-\overset{|}{C}- \rightarrow -\overset{|}{A}-\overset{|}{B}- + :\overset{|}{C}-$$

In this reaction the attack of A is directed against the "nucleus" of B, and the process is said to be a *nucleophilic* displacement (S_N). Although

[1] For a more complete discussion see (a) Hammett, *Physical Organic Chemistry*, pp. 131–183, McGraw-Hill Book Co., New York, 1940; (b) Hughes, *Trans. Faraday Soc.*, **37**, 603 (1941); (c) Dostrovsky, Hughes, and Ingold, *J. Chem. Soc.*, **1946**, 173; (d) Hughes, *ibid.*, 968; (e) Evans, *Trans. Faraday Soc.*, **42**, 719 (1946).

the charge types are different, this is the fundamental process in the following reactions:

$$\overset{\ominus}{\text{H}\ddot{\text{O}}:} + \text{R}:\ddot{\text{X}}: \rightarrow \text{HOR} + :\overset{\ominus}{\ddot{\text{X}}}:$$

$$\text{R}_3\text{N}: + \text{R}:\ddot{\text{X}}: \rightarrow \text{R}_3\overset{\oplus}{\text{N}}{-}\text{R} + :\overset{\ominus}{\ddot{\text{X}}}:$$

$$\overset{\ominus}{\text{H}\ddot{\text{O}}:} + \text{R}{-}\overset{\oplus}{\text{N}}\text{R}_3 \rightarrow \text{HOR} + :\text{NR}_3$$

Routes Leading to Substitution at a Carbon Atom. In many instances of substitution at a carbon atom it is found that if a homologous series is arranged in the order of increasing chain branching at the seat of reaction, the total rate of reaction passes through a minimum. Thus, for the hydrolysis of alkyl bromides with hydroxide ion, we have the following relative rates of reaction:

CH_3Br	2140 [2]
CH_3CH_2Br	171
$(CH_3)_2CHBr$	5
$(CH_3)_3CBr$	1010

With methyl and ethyl bromide the rate of reaction is principally proportional to the concentration of hydroxide ion and of the halide. With isopropyl bromide no simple mathematical relationship exists, and with *tert*-butyl bromide rate of reaction is dependent only upon the concentration of the halide. At this point in the series, then, the rate of a substitution reaction at a saturated carbon atom is *completely independent of the concentration of the nucleophilic reagent* (hydroxide ion).

The most widely accepted explanation for this phenomenon is based upon the assumption that substitution at a carbon atom can occur in either of two ways and, sometimes, by the simultaneous operation of the two processes. Either $\overset{\ominus}{\text{A}:}$ can strike $-\overset{|}{\underset{|}{\text{C}}}:\text{X}$ producing $\text{A}-\overset{|}{\underset{|}{\text{C}}}-$ and $:\overset{\ominus}{\text{X}}$ (Scheme *A*) or $-\overset{|}{\underset{|}{\text{C}}}-\text{X}$ can undergo a preliminary slow dissociation into $-\overset{|}{\underset{|}{\text{C}}}\oplus$ and $:\text{X}\overset{\ominus}{}$, followed by a rapid reaction of $\text{A}:$ with the carbonium ion $-\overset{|}{\underset{|}{\text{C}}}\oplus$ (Scheme *B*).

---

[2] Hughes, *Trans. Faraday Soc.*, **37**, 612 (1941). These numbers are the sums of the first- and second-order rate constants.

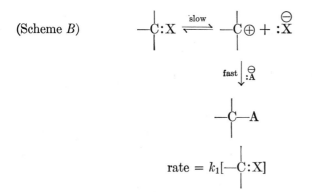

(Scheme A)

$$\text{rate} = k\,[\overset{\ominus}{A:}][-\overset{|}{\underset{|}{C}}:X]^-$$

Substitution at a carbon Nucleus, bimolecular, kinetically 2nd order; therefore, S_N2

(Scheme B)

$$\text{rate} = k_1[-\overset{|}{\underset{|}{C}}:X]$$

Substitution at a carbon Nucleus, kinetically 1st order; therefore, S_N1.

Since both paths lead to substitution at the nucleus of a carbon atom, they are called *nucleophilic substitutions*. They are differentiated by the symbols S_N1 and S_N2. This hypothesis at least correlates the facts of alkaline hydrolysis, since the increasing bulk of the alkyl groups would hinder approach of the hydroxide ion (S_N2) and stabilization of the carbonium ion (S_N1) would be favored by hyperconjugation.

Concerning the S_N2 reaction, there is now general agreement that the process proceeds by the attack of $A:\ominus$ at the backside of the carbon to which X is attached. The process is always accompanied by a Walden inversion,[3] and the behavior of the three other linkages has been described as like "the ribs of an umbrella in a gale." [4] The mechanism of the process may be diagrammed as follows:

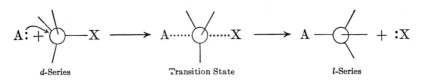

d-Series   Transition State   l-Series

[3] Hammett, *Physical Organic Chemistry*, p. 181, McGraw-Hill Book Co., New York, 1940.
[4] *Ibid.*, p. 159.

Concerning the actual process of the S_N1 reaction, our ideas are not nearly so precise. The process, however, is generally represented almost as shown in Scheme B. The driving force for the reaction is believed to be the tendency of the reaction medium to solvate or combine with the departing group so as to leave a solvated carbonium ion. The carbonium ion can then react with a solvent molecule or another anion. Thus we might have

$$(CH_3)_3C\text{---}Br + (n + m)H_2O \rightarrow$$

$$[(H_2O)_n\cdots\overset{+\delta}{(CH_3)_3C}\cdots\overset{-\delta}{Br}\cdots(H_2O)_m] \rightarrow$$

$$[(H_2O)_n(CH_3)_3\overset{\oplus}{C}] + [\overset{\ominus}{Br}(H_2O)_m]$$
$$\text{I}$$

or

$$(CH_3)_3C\text{---}Br + \overset{\oplus}{Ag} + \xrightarrow{nH_2O} [(H_2O)_n\cdots\overset{+\delta}{(CH_3)_3C}\cdots\overset{+\delta}{Br}\cdots Ag] \rightarrow$$

$$[(H_2O)_n(CH_3)_3\overset{\oplus}{C}] + AgBr$$
$$\text{I}$$

followed by

$$[(H_2O)_n(CH_3)_3\overset{\oplus}{C}] \rightarrow (CH_3)_3C\text{---}OH + \overset{\oplus}{H} + (n - 1)H_2O$$
$$\text{II}$$

This sequence of equations agrees with many of the data known about such reactions. Solvolyses with excess solvent are kinetically first order since the concentration of solvent does not change appreciably during the reaction. Certain mathematical consequences have been verified,[5] and a number of hydrolysis reactions are known in which the rates are independent of added base. The hydrolysis of α-phenylethyl chloride [6] and *tert*-butyl chloride [7] are examples:

$$\overset{Cl}{\underset{|}{\phi CHCH_3}} + H_2O \rightarrow \overset{OH}{\underset{|}{\phi CHCH_3}} \quad \text{(rate is independent of } \overset{\ominus}{OH})$$

$$(CH_3)_3C\text{---}Cl + H_2O \xrightarrow[5\% \text{ acetone}]{95\% \text{ H}_2\text{O}+} (CH_3)_3C\text{---}OH \quad \text{(rate is independent}$$

$$\text{of } \overset{\ominus}{OH} \text{ or } S_2O_3\overset{\ominus}{)}$$

There is, however, one principal objection to the concept of a free solvated carbonium ion; it is that a carbon atom attached to only three

[5] Hughes, *Trans. Faraday Soc.*, **37**, 611 (1941).

[6] Ward, *J. Chem. Soc.*, **1927**, 446.

[7] Swain and Ross, *J. Am. Chem. Soc.*, **68**, 658 (1946).

groups should assume a planar configuration and subsequent reaction of this species should lead to complete racemization. It is found, however, that although extensive racemization does indeed occur, the products obtained from solvolytic reactions are not always completely inactive but are often actually partially inverted. One possible explanation for this stereochemical result is that the carbonium ion may react rapidly with solvent while the departing group is still partially screening one side of the planar carbonium ion.[1]

Under the conditions normally employed for carrying out displacement reactions, namely, in the presence of a large excess of solvating molecules, it is not possible to determine the kinetic order of the process with respect to the solvent. Consequently there has been a tendency to minimize the importance of considering the solvation of *all* the species in both S_N1 and S_N2 reactions. By working in a nonpolar solvent (benzene) Swain [8] has been able to show that solvation forces are indeed extremely important, not only for providing the driving force in S_N1 reactions, but also for removing the departing ion from the transition state of S_N2 reactions. He has found, in fact, that several transformations which exhibit first- or second-order kinetics in a polar solvent are actually precisely *third-order* in benzene solution. Thus the solvolysis of triphenylmethyl chloride with small amounts of methanol is first-order in halide and second-order in methanol: [8a]

$$\phi_3CCl + CH_3OH + \text{pyridine} \xrightarrow{\text{benzene}}$$

$$\phi_3COCH_3 + \text{pyridine hydrochloride}$$

$$\text{rate} = k_1[\phi_3CCl][CH_3OH]^2$$

(*See footnote* 9)

Similarly, the reaction of methyl bromide with pyridine in the presence of methanol is first-order with respect to bromide, pyridine, *and methanol*, although no methanol is consumed in the process.[8b]

$$\text{rate} = k_2[CH_3Br][CH_3OH][\text{pyridine}]$$

From these data it appears that solvent molecules must participate to a considerable extent in these displacement processes, probably by solvating the ions which are formed. Thus, in the reaction of methyl

[8] Swain, (a) *ibid.*, **70**, 1119 (1948); (b) Swain and Eddy, *ibid.*, 2989.

[9] Pyridine has no effect upon the reaction other than to take up the hydrogen chloride formed.

bromide with pyridine, methanol aids the removal of bromide ion from the transition state by hydrogen bonding:

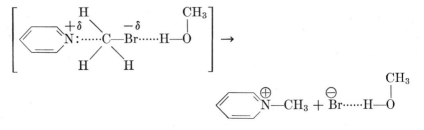

In the solvolysis of triphenylmethyl chloride, methanol solvates both the carbonium ion and the halide ion: [8a]

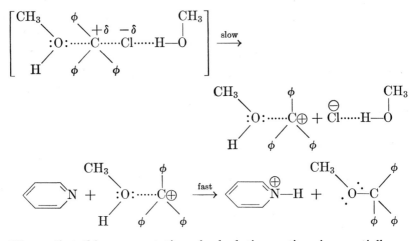

We see that this representation of solvolytic reactions is essentially no different from that on p. 82. We now know, however, that the numerical value of the subscripts m and n can be as low as one.

Clearly, if the order of a reaction is dependent upon the experimental conditions, the terms $S_N 1$ and $S_N 2$ lose some of their original connotation. The terms, however, persist and will be used throughout this book since they provide a convenient and reasonably descriptive means for classifying reactions having characteristics in common. It is evident that the important point to recognize in considering displacement reactions is not that they follow first-, second-, or third-order kinetics, but that such reactions may be broadly divided into two classes: one in which the rate of reaction is proportional to the concentration of an added reagent that ultimately becomes attached to carbon, and another in which the rate is independent of the concentration of such a reagent. Structural and environmental factors affect each in a characteristic, usually different, way, and useful generalizations can be made for both.

FACTORS INFLUENCING THE COURSE OF SUBSTITUTION REACTIONS

From the foregoing discussion it is clear that electron release or withdrawal will affect a substitution reaction differently, depending upon whether it is proceeding by preliminary dissociation or by the direct attack of an added reagent. For example, electron release from R would hinder the approach of a negatively charged hydroxide ion (S_N2) while it would facilitate dissociation of the halide ion:

$$
\overset{+\delta}{R} \rightarrow \overset{-\delta}{\underset{|}{C}} - X \quad \text{(repelled slightly)}
$$
$$
\underset{OH}{\overset{\ominus}{}} \nearrow
$$

$$
R \rightarrow \underset{|}{\overset{|}{C}} - X \rightleftharpoons R \rightarrow \underset{|}{\overset{|}{C}} \oplus + \overset{\ominus}{X}
$$

Thus in order to predict the effect of structure on reactivity, *the process by which substitution occurs must be known.* Often a careful study of reaction kinetics is the only way this question can be settled definitely.

Unfortunately, however, for many organic reactions, such studies have not yet been carried out. Furthermore, while structural modifications usually do favor one process at the expense of the other, it is not always possible to classify a given substance as belonging unequivocally to the S_N1 or to the S_N2 type. For a number of reactions it has been found that the substitution process may change from predominantly direct attack to predominantly preliminary ionization if the experimental conditions particularly favor this kind of reaction. The following factors of structure and environment might be considered.

Solvents. The influence of a solvent upon the two substitution processes can be deduced by considering the effect of that solvent upon the transition state of each. In Table 1 are summarized the results to be expected when substitution reactions of different charge types (mentioned on p. 80) are carried out in a more polar solvent. We observe that in both processes the one proceeding through dissociation is favored. Each of the expected results has been verified experimentally.[1b]

Table 1 is based upon the assumption that polar solvents facilitate the development of electrical charge and hinder its neutralization or dis-

TABLE 1

SOLVENT EFFECTS IN NUCLEOPHILIC SUBSTITUTION

(Data from Hughes, *Trans. Faraday Soc.*, **37**, 609 [1941])

Type and Mechanism	Charges Concerned in Rate-Determining Stage of Reaction			Effect on Charges of Forming Transition State		Expected Effect of Polar Media on Rate
	Reactants	Transition State	Products	Magnitude	Distribution	
$a\begin{cases}S_N1\\S_N2\end{cases}$	RX $Y\ominus$ + RX	$R^{+\delta}\cdots\cdots X^{-\delta}$ $Y^{-\delta}\cdots\cdots R\cdots\cdots X^{-\delta}$	$R\oplus$ + $X\ominus$ YR + $X\ominus$	Increase No change	.... Dispersed	Strong acceleration Weak retardation
$b\begin{cases}S_N1\\S_N2\end{cases}$	RX Y + RX	$R^{+\delta}\cdots\cdots X^{-\delta}$ $Y^{+\delta}\cdots\cdots R\cdots\cdots X^{-\delta}$	$R\oplus$ + $X\ominus$ $YR\oplus$ + $X\ominus$	Increase Increase	....	Strong acceleration Strong acceleration
$c\begin{cases}S_N1\\S_N2\end{cases}$	$RX\oplus$ $Y\ominus$ + $RX\oplus$	$R^{+\delta}\cdots\cdots X^{+\delta}$ $Y^{-\delta}\cdots\cdots R\cdots\cdots X^{+\delta}$	$R\oplus$ + X YR + X	No change Decrease	Dispersed	Weak retardation Strong retardation

tribution over a larger surface area.[10]   This assumption seems quite reasonable, for it is probable that charges are developed and maintained in solution only by the aid of solvating polar molecules.   Once developed, the neutralization or distribution of such a charge would require breaking all or some of the solvation bonds.

Steric Factors.   In the hydrolysis of alkyl halides by hydroxide ion, the rate of the S_N2 reaction decreases in the series $CH_3CH_2CH_2$—X > $(CH_3)_2CHCH_2$—X > $(CH_3)_3CCH_2$—X until it is almost negligible. Since the alkyl groups are removed by one carbon atom from the seat of reaction, it does not seem probable that this order should be ascribed to an inherent electron-releasing tendency of the methyl groups (see p. 8). This view is supported by the fact that 4,4-dimethyl-1-bromo-2-pentyne (III) reacts with potassium iodide in acetone at a rate comparable to that of 1-bromo-2-heptyne (IV).[11]   If electrical factors were re-

$$(CH_3)_3C—C\equiv C—CH_2Br \qquad CH_3CH_2CH_2CH_2—C\equiv C—CH_2Br$$
$$\text{III} \qquad\qquad\qquad\qquad\qquad \text{IV}$$

sponsible for the sequence shown above, the effects would be transmitted, partially at least, through the unsaturated linkage, and a corresponding decrease in the rate of reaction of III would be expected.

Examination of models, however, reveals that in neopentyl chloride the *tert*-butyl group protects the methylene carbon atom from a backside attack by the approaching reagent.   It is presumably this fact that is responsible for the abnormally low reactivity of a neopentyl system to S_N2 reactions.

In this connection it is interesting to note that 1-chloroapocamphane [12] (V) and 1-bromotriptycene [13] (VI) are completely inert both to S_N1 and S_N2 reactions.   Carbonium ions cannot be formed because a planar intermediate is prohibited (p. 42), and S_N2 reactions do not occur because the backside of the carbon atom to which the halogen is attached is com-

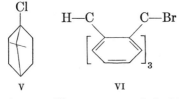

pletely screened by the cage-like structure of the bicyclic molecule.

[10] Hughes and Ingold, *J. Chem. Soc.*, **1935**, 252.

[11] Bartlett and Rosen, *J. Am. Chem. Soc.*, **64**, 543 (1942).

[12] Bartlett and Knox, *ibid.*, **61**, 3184 (1939).

[13] Bartlett, *Abstracts of Papers*, p. 28, Tenth National Organic Chemistry Symposium, Boston, Mass., June 1947.

S_N1 reactions are facilitated by the introduction of a number of bulky groups at the seat of reaction ("B strain," p. 43). Thus, in the series shown below, there is a continuous increase in the rate of solvolysis as we pass to the halides having larger and larger groups attached to the central carbon atom. It is important to notice that the factor under consideration here cannot be hyperconjugation since the number of hyperconjugation forms which might stabilize the carbonium ion decreases in descending the table.

TABLE 2

RELATIVE RATES OF IONIZATION OF TERTIARY CHLORIDES IN 1 TO 3 ACETONE-WATER SOLUTION AT 25°

(Data from Bartlett, *Abstracts of Papers*, Tenth National Organic Chemistry Symposium, p. 30, Boston, Mass., 1947)

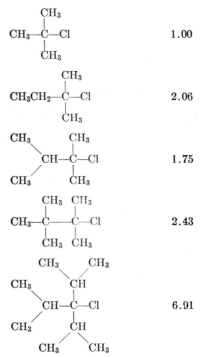

$$
\begin{array}{ll}
CH_3-\overset{\overset{\displaystyle CH_3}{|}}{\underset{\underset{\displaystyle CH_3}{|}}{C}}-Cl & 1.00 \\
\end{array}
$$

CH₃	1.00
CH₃CH₂	2.06
(CH₃)₂CH	1.75
	2.43
	6.91

Effect of Introducing a Second Halogen Atom. When a molecule contains two or more halogen atoms, two different cases must be considered: one in which the halogen atoms are attached to the same carbon atom and another in which the halogens are attached to different carbon atoms. In order to consider substitution reactions of those compounds in which two halogen atoms are attached to the same carbon atom, let

us suppose that we have the dihalide $X'—\overset{\overset{\displaystyle R}{|}}{\underset{\underset{\displaystyle R}{|}}{C}}—X$ and focus attention

upon the effect X' would be expected to have upon the ease of hydrolysis of the C—X bond. In S_N2 reactions, X' will withdraw electrons from the central carbon atom by permanent polarization and thus facilitate the approach of a negative ion. At the same time, however, the size of the halogen atom itself would tend to shield the carbon atom from rearward attack. Apparently the second of these two factors is more important for we find that methylene dichloride is more stable towards basic hydrolysis than methyl chloride.[14]

With S_N1 reactions there are also opposing factors to be considered. Permanent polarization operates to oppose the ionization of X (VII),

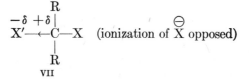

yet, after ionization is complete, the resonance form IX becomes important in stabilizing the carbonium ion (VIII). As is frequently the

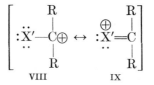

case (p. 238), resonance appears to outweigh permanent polarization, and with compounds like benzyl chloride, which are already predisposed to react by S_N1, the addition of a second halogen atom enhances the reactivity to the extent that the operative mechanism of benzal chloride becomes S_N1.[15]

When the halogen atoms are separated by two carbon atoms, the resonance factor cannot operate and the bulk of the halogen atom is removed from the site of reaction. Consequently, permanent polarization controls the situation. S_N2 is facilitated and S_N1 is retarded. Thus 1,2-diiodoethane undergoes S_N2 reactions more rapidly than ethyl io-

[14] Hughes, *Trans. Faraday Soc.*, **37**, 625 (1941).
[15] Olivier and Weber, *Rec. trav. chim.*, **53**, 869 (1934).

dide,[16] and when the tertiary halogen atoms of X and XI are hydrolyzed under conditions favoring S_N1, the rate of hydrolysis of XI is about 4000 times that of X.[17]

Effect of Introducing a Carbonyl Group. When a halogen atom is directly connected to a carbonyl group as in acyl halides, the effect of the polarization,

$$\left[\begin{matrix} O \\ \| \\ R-C-X \end{matrix} \leftrightarrow \begin{matrix} \overset{\ominus}{\overset{..}{:}\overset{..}{O}:} \\ | \\ R-C-X \\ \oplus \end{matrix} \right]$$

is to hinder the separation of $X^{\ominus}$ (S_N1) and to facilitate the approach of a negatively charged ion. With such a system, however, it is difficult to be sure whether direct replacement (S_N2) occurs or whether the reaction is preceded in some way by a preliminary addition to the carbonyl linkage. For example, the reaction of acid halides with Grignard reagents leads to ketones, and this may be regarded as a carbanion displacement reaction (Chapter 10).

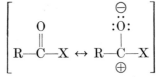

The fact that acid fluorides are more reactive than acid chlorides and these compounds more reactive than acid bromides,[18] however, leads us to suspect that the reaction is more complex than a simple displacement.

It is also interesting that in the Schotten-Baumann reaction (in which alcohols or amines are acylated in aqueous alkali) there is apparently a selectivity of the aromatic acyl halide for alcohol and amine molecules over water or hydroxide ions. The reason for this selectivity is not clear, but it is an example of the fact that the ease with which a reagent attacks a molecule does not always parallel its basicity (see also p. 112).

[16] Hammett, *Physical Organic Chemistry*, pp. 154 and 208, McGraw-Hill Book Co., New York, 1940.

[17] Brown, Kharasch, and Chao, *J. Am. Chem. Soc.*, **62**, 3438 (1940).

[18] Entemann and Johnson, *ibid.*, **55**, 2900 (1933).

Carbonyl compounds which are halogenated in the α-position are known to be extremely reactive halogen compounds. The mechanism is probably S_N2, since again the carbonyl polarization should favor S_N2 and hinder S_N1.

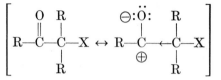

The first-order hydrolysis of α-halogenated acids appears to be an example of the participation of neighboring groups in substitution reactions (p. 96).

Effect of Introducing a Double Bond. In our discussion of resonance (p. 15) it was pointed out that with vinyl and aryl halides such a form as XIII contributes importantly to the resting state of the compound:

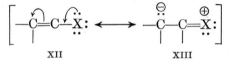

An electron drift in the direction of XIII clearly opposes the displacement of $X\ominus$ by either S_N2 or S_N1. It is surprising, perhaps, that this resonance renders vinyl and aryl halides so inert, but certainly some decrease in reactivity would be expected.

The reactivity of benzyl and allyl halides in organic reactions is well known to all chemists. It is interesting that the allyl or benzyl systems uniquely facilitate both S_N1 and S_N2 displacements. At the attack of a negatively charged ion, a polarization of the double bond is produced (polarizability) which will facilitate the approach of the ion.

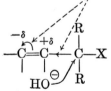

as the negative ion approaches

With S_N1 reactions, the carbonium ion XIV is stabilized by resonance with form XV. It will be observed also that subsequent recombination

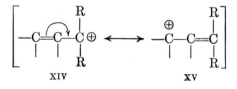

of a negative ion with this species through form XV would give rise to an *allylic shift* characteristic of this system (p. 277).

Another type of reaction which has been realized with the allyl system is the so-called S_N2' displacement. Here the attacking reagent strikes an atom different from the one to which the halogen atom is attached. An allylic shift occurs, and the halogen atom is displaced. Thus, when 3-chloro-1-pentene (XVI) is allowed to react with sodiomalonic ester, 2-pentenyl malonic ester is obtained (XVII).[19] Second-order kinetics

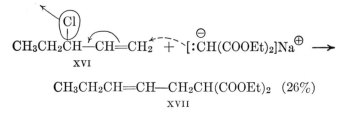

$$CH_3CH_2CH-CH=CH_2 \ + \ [:CH(COOEt)_2]Na^{\oplus} \ \longrightarrow$$
$$\text{XVI}$$

$$CH_3CH_2CH=CH-CH_2CH(COOEt)_2 \quad (26\%)$$
$$\text{XVII}$$

and the fact that the reaction was carried out in anhydrous alcohol make a preliminary rearrangement of the halide seem unlikely.

REPLACEMENT OF A HYDROXYL GROUP BY A HALOGEN ATOM

The replacement of an alcoholic hydroxyl group by a halogen atom is one of the most common reactions carried out in organic chemistry. The usual reagents for effecting the transformation include halogen acids, thionyl chloride, and phosphorus halides. The reaction is of particular theoretical interest since experiments with optically active alcohols suggest still another substitution process. It has been called an *internal* nucleophilic substitution reaction (S_Ni).[20]

The experimental facts of the displacement of a hydroxyl group by a halogen atom indicate that the process does not always take place by the same route. The rate of reaction of ethanol with dry hydrogen bromide has been shown to be predominantly first order in ethanol and first order in hydrogen bromide.[21] At room temperature or slightly above, the reaction of secondary alcohols with phosphorus halides, halogen acids, or thionyl chloride usually proceeds with optical inversion.[19] When the backside approach of these reagents is prohibited, as in 1-apocamphanol [12] or neopentyl alcohol,[22] no reaction occurs or the process stops at the formation of an ester halide.[23] *l*-Menthol appears to be an ex-

[19] Kepner, Winstein, and Young, *ibid.*, **71**, 115 (1949).
[20] Cowdrey, Hughes, Ingold, Masterman, and Scott, *J. Chem. Soc.*, **1937**, 1267.
[21] Grunwald and Winstein, *J. Am. Chem. Soc.*, **69**, 2051 (1947).
[22] Whitmore and Rothrock, *J. Am. Chem. Soc.*, **54**, 3431 (1932).
[23] Gerrard and Nechvatal, *Nature*, **159**, 812 (1947).

ception to the rule of inversion, since both phosphorus pentachloride and hydrogen chloride in the presence of metal salts give *l*-menthyl chloride with retention of configuration.[24]   Phenylalkylcarbinols are unique in that the reaction with thionyl chloride and hydrogen bromide under certain conditions produces *almost complete retention of configuration* (no inversion).   To obtain this result, the reaction with thionyl chloride is conducted in the absence of pyridine.   When hydrogen bromide is used, the reaction must be carried out at low temperatures, preferably about −40 to −80°.[25]   If these precautions are not observed, partial inversion occurs in both instances.

With all these reagents it can be assumed that the first step in the process involves the formation of an ester-halide (XVIII and XIX) or the hydrogen bonded addition complex (XX).   Many compounds such

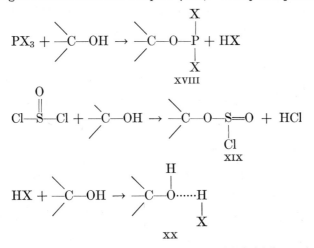

as XVIII and XIX have been isolated.[23]   After this initial step is taken, there are three paths open for further reaction.   They may be illustrated with the reaction employing thionyl chloride.   Collision of the ester-halide with a halide ion (S_N2) might produce an alkyl halide with an accompanying Walden inversion:

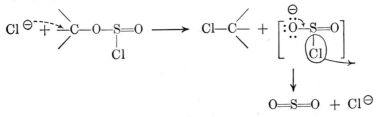

[24] Hückel and Pietrzok, *Ann.*, **540**, 250 (1939).
[25] Levene and Rothen, *J. Biol. Chem.*, **127**, 237 (1939).

Dissociation (S_N1) would give rise to much racemization but some inversion, since one side of the reactive carbonium ion would be shielded temporarily by the departing group:

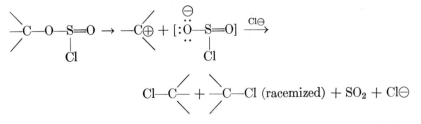

For the third route (in which optical configuration is retained) an internal displacement reaction ($S_N i$) has been postulated.[20, 26] Thus it is suggested that the ester halides (or the hydrogen bonded addition complex) undergo intramolecular rearrangement with elimination of the corresponding oxide in such a way that configuration is retained.

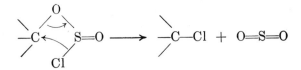

Although the evidence for such a mechanism is largely the fact that configuration *is* retained during the replacement, it is interesting that when hydrogen bromide is added to ethylphenylcarbinol at −30° a white, crystalline addition complex is formed together with a liquid bromide.[25] Since the lower the temperature, the smaller the amount of liquid halide formed and the greater the percentage of retention of configuration, it seems plausible that the mechanism leading to retention does indeed proceed by an intramolecular path.

NUCLEOPHILIC DISPLACEMENTS ON ATOMS OTHER THAN CARBON

Although all the nucleophilic substitution reactions discussed so far have been at carbon atoms, it is nevertheless important to realize that displacement reactions also occur on hydrogen or halogen atoms. Several specific examples include alkoxide-hydroxide ion equilibria (p. 208),

$$ \text{ROH} + \text{OH}^{\ominus} \rightleftharpoons \text{RO}^{\ominus} + \text{HOH} $$

base-catalyzed carbanion formation (p. 123),

[26] Hughes, Ingold, and Whitfield, *Nature*, **147**, 206 (1941).

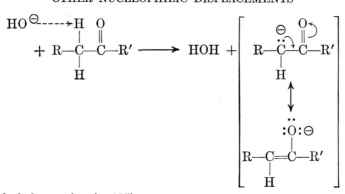

dehydrohalogenation (p. 105),

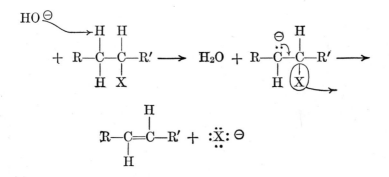

and the addition of halogens to olefins (p. 135).

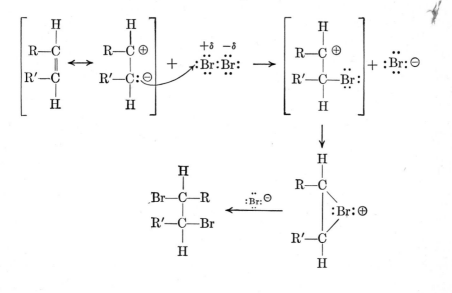

NEIGHBORING GROUP DISPLACEMENT REACTIONS

There are a number of displacement reactions which appear to contradict the generalization that S_N2 reactions always proceed with inversion of configuration whereas S_N1 reactions lead to extensive racemization. It is characteristic of those systems in which such anomalous stereochemical results are obtained that there is always a neighboring group in the molecule with an unshared pair of electrons. It now seems fairly certain that such anomalous results arise from the fact that the displacement process actually proceeds in two steps. The first step consists of an intramolecular S_N2 reaction effected by the unshared electron pair of the neighboring group. The second one is the opening of the ring thus formed by the attacking reagent. The two inversions result in no apparent Walden inversion.

Similarly, certain rearranged products result from displacement reactions carried out with compounds containing amino nitrogen or thiosulfur atoms. Again these atoms appear to be involved in the actual intermediates.

The Hydrolysis of *cis* and *trans* Cyclohexene Chlorohydrin. When *trans* cyclohexene chlorohydrin is treated with strong alkali, *trans* cyclohexene glycol is obtained. Thus inversion does not appear to have occurred during the displacement. When the reaction is carried out with the *cis* isomer, cyclohexanone is formed.[27] These facts can be explained if it is assumed that the first step in the reaction is the removal of a proton from the hydroxyl group (XXI to XXIII and XXII to XXIV), followed by the displacement of chloride ion by the *alkoxide* ion of the *trans* form (XXIII to XXV) and by a *hydride ion* in the *cis* form (XXIV to XXVII). Displacement by alkoxide leads to cyclohexene oxide (XXV), and this intermediate can be further attacked by hydroxide ion to give the *dl trans* glycol (XXVI). Cyclohexanone is produced by the hydride displacement (XXIV to XXVII):

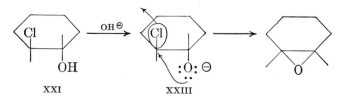

[27] Bartlett, *J. Am. Chem. Soc.*, **57**, 224 (1935).

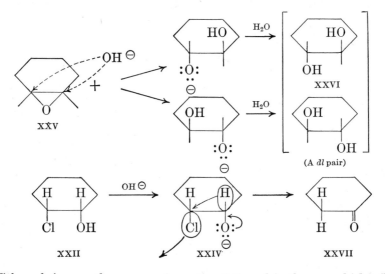

With each isomer the course of reaction followed is the *one which will permit a backside displacement of the chloride ion.*

Since the action of dilute alkali on *trans* cyclohexene chlorohydrin constitutes a synthetic preparation for cyclohexene oxide,[28] there seems to be little doubt that the epoxide is an intermediate in the reaction of the *trans* chlorohydrin. There appears to be no evidence for the hydride ion displacement shown for the *cis* isomer.

Rearrangements in the Displacement Reactions of β-Hydroxy and β-Haloamines or Sulfides. When displacement reactions are carried out with β-hydroxy and β-haloamines or sulfides, the product formed often is found to have the nitrogen or sulfur atom attached to the carbon atom where substitution would have been expected. The new substituent becomes affixed to the carbon atom which originally held the nitrogen or sulfur atom.* Thus when the glycol XXVIII was treated with hydrochloric acid, the dichloride XXIX was obtained.[29] It is

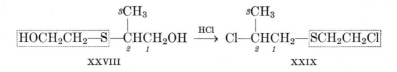

evident that the group —CH_2CH_2S— migrated from carbon 2 to 1.

---

* For a summary of these reactions, see footnote 31.

[28] Osterberg, in Gilman-Blatt, *Organic Syntheses*, Collective Vol. I, p. 185, John Wiley and Sons, New York, 1941.

[29] Fuson, Price, Burness, *J. Org. Chem.*, **11**, 476 (1946).

Similarly, basic hydrolysis of the hydrochloride of 1-diethylamino-2-chloropropane (XXX) gave 2-diethylamino-1-propanol (XXXI).[30]

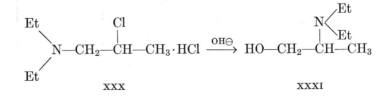

| XXX | XXXI |

These reactions can be readily correlated by the assumption of a preliminary intramolecular displacement reaction effected by the nitrogen or sulfur atom to form a cyclic onium salt. The complete sequence may be outlined as follows:

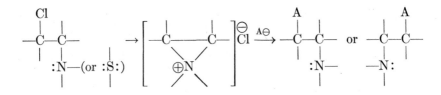

Thus, for the reaction of 1-diethylamino-2-chloropropane with alkali, we would expect the "ethylenimmonium" ion XXXII.

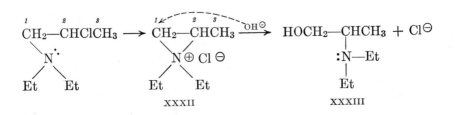

Attack by hydroxide ion should occur at the less substituted carbon atom (1) giving rise to the product XXXIII which is actually obtained. It is important to notice, however, that if a preliminary ring opening occurred (S_N1), the carbonium ion XXXIV would be more stable than XXXV:

---

[30] Ross, *J. Am. Chem. Soc.*, **69**, 2982 (1947). For another example, see Reitsema, *ibid.*, **71**, 2041 (1949).

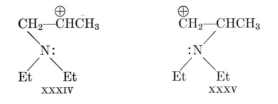

XXXIV · · · · · XXXV

We should then expect to find the negative substituent on the secondary carbon atom. As Fuson and Zirkle have pointed out,[31] regardless of which 1,2-aminochloroalkane hydrochloride we start with (XXXVI or XXXVII), the chloroamine usually isolated by treatment with dilute alkali is the one to be expected from the carbonium ion corresponding to XXXIV. Apparently under these conditions, ring opening occurs[32] in effect by a preliminary ionization.

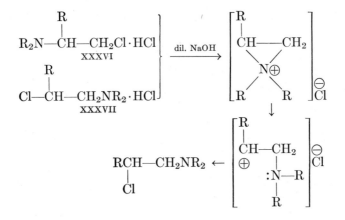

Reactions of 1,2-Glycol Derivatives. One of the most interesting examples of the participation of neighboring groups in displacement reactions is the conversion of the 3-bromo-2-butanols to the corresponding dihalides by the action of concentrated hydrogen bromide. The *erythro* and the *threo* bromohydrins are converted into the *meso* and the *dl* isomers, respectively. Thus no apparent loss of the stereochemical configuration occurs in either reaction.[33]

[31] Fuson and Zirkle, *J. Am. Chem. Soc.*, **70**, 2760 (1948).

[32] For a discussion of the kinetics and reactions of β-chloroamines, see Bartlett, Ross, and Swain, *J. Am. Chem. Soc.*, **69**, 2971 (1947); Bartlett, Davis, Ross, and Swain, *ibid.*, **70**, 2977 (1947).

[33] Winstein and Lucas, *J. Am. Chem. Soc.*, **61**, 1576 (1939).

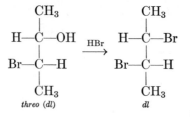

[No loss of stereo-
chemical config-
uration in either
case]

The probable course of reaction for the *threo* isomer is outlined in formulas XXXVIII to XLI.

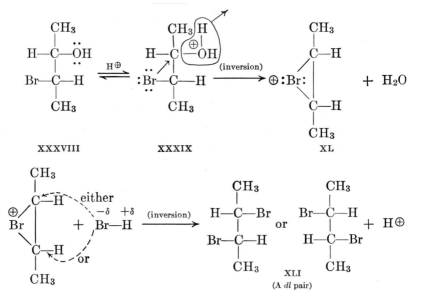

The first step consists in the addition of a proton to the hydroxyl group (XXXVIII to XXXIX) followed by the displacement (with inversion) of a water molecule by an unshared electron pair of the bromine atom (XXXIX to XL). The cyclic *bromonium ion,* as it is called, is then attacked by another hydrogen bromide molecule to form the dibromides (XLI) and a proton. The result of this second displacement gives rise to the overall effect of retention of stereochemical configuration.

The steric course in the reaction of the *erythro* isomer is more difficult to show on paper. Since displacement reactions occur from the backside of the carbon atom holding a substituent, it is necessary to twist one of the carbon atoms about the carbon-carbon bond from its more familiar formula, XLII to LXIII. This, of course, does not change the configuration of the molecule but only brings the groups into reaction position. The displacement of the water molecule can then occur as before (XLIII to XLV), giving rise to the bromonium ion (XLV). Attack of this three-membered ring at either carbon atom gives rise to the same product; in this case, the *meso* dibromide (XLVI).

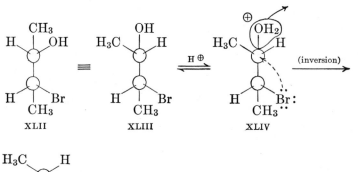

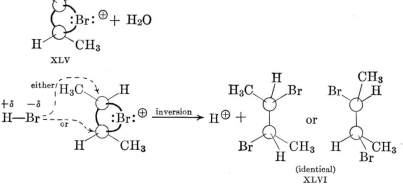

There can be little doubt that these steps represent the true course of the reaction. At the stage of the second inversion in each process, attack of the hydrogen bromide molecule could occur at either carbon atom, but the same *stereoisomeric* product would result. This very fact, however, requires that if the *threo* bromohydrin were *optically active* the dibromide formed from it should be completely *inactive* since equal amounts of the d and l isomers would be formed. This consequence has been investigated and verified.[34] Other mechanisms which might seem plausible for the transformation would result in at least partial retention of optical activity.

The participation of neighboring groups in systems of this kind is a very general phenomenon. It has been observed in the formation of 2,3-dichlorobutane from the corresponding chlorohydrin and thionyl chloride;[35] in the reaction of vicinal dihalides,[36] acetoxy halides,[37] or methoxy halides[37] with silver acetate in dry acetic acid; in the reaction of phosphorus tribromide with 3-bromo-2-butanols;[38] and in the acetolysis of the *trans*-acetoxy-*p*-toluene sulfonate of cyclohexene glycol[39a] and 2-aminocyclohexanol.[39b] In all cases, retention of the stereochemical configuration is the observed result. The rate studies which have been carried out,[40] together with the isolation of certain intermediates,[41] put these reactions on an unusually sound theoretical basis.[42]

Reactions of the α-Halogen Acids. It is interesting that the displacement of halogen from an α-halogen acid appears to involve participation of the neighboring carboxyl group while the reaction of α-halogen esters does not. Thus, with α-bromopropionic acid in strong base (where the kinetics is second order), inversion of configuration is observed.[43] In dilute base or water, where the kinetics is first order, almost complete optical retention occurs.

The most likely explanation of retention of configuration is that the first step involves a displacement by the carboxylate ion to form the α-lactone (XLVII), which is then opened with a second inversion by water to restore the original configuration (XLVIII).[44] Although the question

---

[34] Winstein and Lucas, *J. Am. Chem. Soc.*, **61**, 2845 (1939).

[35] Lucas and Gould, *ibid.*, **63**, 2541 (1941).

[36] Winstein and Buckles, *ibid.*, **64**, 2780 (1942); Winstein and Seymour, *ibid.*, **68**, 119 (1946).

[37] Winstein and Henderson, *ibid.*, **65**, 2196 (1943).

[38] Winstein, *ibid.*, **64**, 2791 (1942).

[39] (a) Winstein, Hess, and Buckles, *ibid.*, **64**, 2796 (1942); (b) McCasland, Clark, and Carter, *ibid.*, **71**, 638 (1949).

[40] Winstein, Hanson, and Grunwald, *ibid.*, **70**, 812 (1948); Winstein, Grunwald, Buckles, and Hanson, *ibid.*, 816; Winstein, Grunwald, and Ingraham, *ibid.*, 821.

[41] Winstein and Buckles, *ibid.*, **65**, 613 (1943).

[42] Winstein and Grunwald, *ibid.*, **70**, 828 (1948).

[43] Cowdrey, Hughes, and Ingold, *J. Chem. Soc.*, **1937**, 1208.

[44] Hammett, *Physical Organic Chemistry*, p. 175, McGraw-Hill Book Co., New York, 1940.

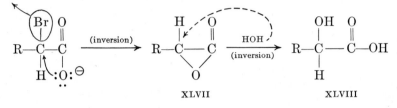

XLVII   XLVIII

of the formation of such an intermediate is not yet settled,[45] it is interesting that β-propiolactone (XLIX) reacts with alcohol in basic solution to give esters of β-hydroxypropionic acid (L), but in neutral or acid solution to give β-alkoxypropionic acids (LI).[46] These facts are in the right

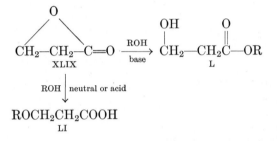

direction for the abnormal lactone hydrolysis shown in the step XLVII to XLVIII (see p. 227).

[45] Grunwald and Winstein, *J. Am. Chem. Soc.*, **70**, 841 (1948).
[46] Gresham, Jansen, Shaver, Gregory, and Beears, *ibid.*, **70**, 1004 (1948).

CHAPTER 5

ELIMINATION REACTIONS [1]

Whenever a substitution reaction is carried out, one of the side reactions which may be expected is an *elimination reaction*. An unsaturated linkage is formed, and a simple molecule such as water, an acid, or an amine is lost. Examples include the treatment of alkyl halides with alkali,

$$HO^{\ominus} + RCH_2CH_2X \xrightarrow{\text{\textit{substitution}}} RCH_2CH_2OH + X^{\ominus}$$
$$\xrightarrow{\text{\textit{elimination}}} RCH{=}CH_2 + X^{\ominus} + H_2O$$

the reaction of alcohols with mineral acid,

$$RCH_2CH_2OH + HX \xrightarrow{\text{\textit{substitution}}} RCH_2CH_2X + H_2O$$
$$\xrightarrow{\text{\textit{elimination}}} RCH{=}CH_2 + H_2O + HX$$

and the decomposition of quaternary ammonium hydroxides:

$$RCH_2CH_2\overset{\oplus}{N}(CH_3)_3 + OH^{\ominus} \xrightarrow{\text{\textit{substitution}}} RCH_2CH_2OH + {:}N(CH_3)_3$$
$$\xrightarrow{\text{\textit{elimination}}} RCH{=}CH_2 + H_2O + {:}N(CH_3)_3$$

In many instances (notably the last of those mentioned above), elimination is the predominating reaction. It should always be kept in mind, however, that elimination and substitution processes compete with each other and usually occur simultaneously. The one which predominates depends upon environmental as well as structural factors. It is the purpose of this chapter to discuss the mechanisms of elimination, and to

[1] For excellent references from which much of this material was adapted, see Hughes and Ingold, *Trans. Faraday Soc.*, **37**, 657 (1941), and Dhar, Hughes, Ingold, Mandour, Maw, and Woolf, *J. Chem. Soc.*, **1948**, 2093.

consider the factors which influence elimination and substitution reactions.

MECHANISMS OF ELIMINATION REACTIONS

Acid-Catalyzed Elimination Reactions. The simplest kind of elimination reaction is catalyzed by acids and proceeds through a transitory
carbonium ion (p. 44). Consider *tert*-butyl alcohol. In the presence
of acid, an oxonium ion is formed (I) which can dissociate into water and
a carbonium ion (II). As with all carbonium ions, there are then four
courses of reaction open. (1) It can react with another water molecule
or anion. (2) It can rearrange. (3) It can abstract a hydrogen atom with
a pair of electrons from another molecule. (4) It can attract an electron
pair from the carbon-hydrogen bond of an adjacent carbon atom so as
to liberate a proton and to form an olefin (III to IV). The fourth possibility is the process by which many acid-catalyzed elimination reactions occur.

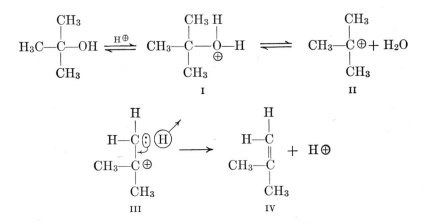

It should be repeated that in such processes the carbonium ion itself
has only a very transitory existence. The loss of the β-proton probably
occurs at the instant the water molecule separates from the oxonium
ion.

Base-Catalyzed Elimination Reactions. Base-catalyzed elimination
reactions are more complex. In the type of reaction which appears to
be the most common, the process is initiated by the attack of base at a
β-hydrogen atom (i.e., a hydrogen atom attached to a carbon atom which
is adjacent to the one holding the functional group). A transitory carbanion (pp. 34 and 123) is thus formed (V), and displacement of the ion

or molecule :Z by the free electron pair results in the formation of an olefin (VI to VII).

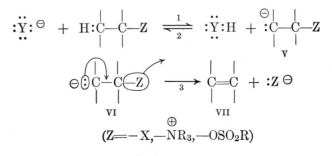

$$(Z = -X, -\overset{\oplus}{N}R_3, -OSO_2R)$$

Here the process is truly a simultaneous one and does not proceed in the stepwise manner which is indicated. This has been shown by an experiment carried out with β-phenylethyl bromide in a solution of C_2H_5OD containing sodium ethylate. After the elimination of hydrogen bromide was about half completed, the still unreacted organic bromide was found to contain no deuterium.[2] If reactions 1 and 2 proceeded faster than 3, the starting material would have been equilibrated with deuterium at this point by the reactions:

$$C_2H_5\overset{..}{\underset{..}{O}}{:}^{\ominus} + \phi CH_2CH_2Br \rightarrow C_2H_5OH + \phi \overset{\ominus}{\underset{..}{C}}HCH_2Br$$

$$\Big\Updownarrow C_2H_5OD$$

$$\phi \overset{D}{\overset{|}{C}}HCH_2Br + C_2H_5\overset{..}{\underset{..}{O}}{:}^{\ominus}$$

This mechanism for β-elimination is supported by the fact that other processes which would be expected to produce carbanions *beta* to groups easily displaced also cause elimination to occur. It is well known that Grignard and Wurtz reactions of β-haloethers lead to olefins. Tetrahydrofurfuryl chloride, for example, gives 4-pentene-1-ol on treatment with sodium,[3] and β-bromoethyl phenyl ether yields phenol and ethylene[4] when it is allowed to react with magnesium in dry ether. Presumably the mechanisms are:

[2] Skell and Hauser, *J. Am. Chem. Soc.*, **67**, 1661 (1945).

[3] Brooks and Snyder, in Bachmann, *Organic Syntheses*, Vol. 25, p. 84, John Wiley and Sons, New York, 1945.

[4] Grignard, *Compt. rend.*, **138**, 1048 (1904).

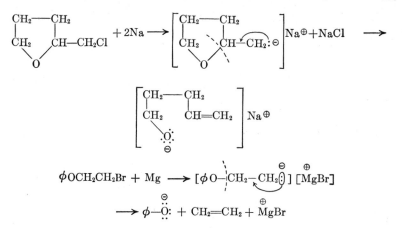

$$\phi OCH_2CH_2Br + Mg \longrightarrow [\phi O\!-\!\overset{\ominus}{C}H_2\!-\!CH_2\overset{\oplus}{(\cdot)}]\,[MgBr]$$

$$\longrightarrow \phi\!-\!\overset{\ominus}{\underset{\cdot\cdot}{O}}\colon + CH_2\!=\!CH_2 + \overset{\oplus}{MgBr}$$

Although base-catalyzed elimination reactions usually appear to involve attack by the base on a β-hydrogen atom, there are examples known in which both the hydrogen and the halogen atoms are removed from the same carbon atom. 1,1-Diaryl-2-chloroethenes (VIII), for example, are converted in good yield to diarylacetylenes (IX) by the action

$$\underset{\substack{|\\ Ar\\ \text{VIII}}}{\overset{\substack{Ar\quad H\\|\qquad|}}{C}}\!\!=\!\!C\!-\!Cl \xrightarrow[\text{liq. NH}_3]{\text{KNH}_2\text{ in}} Ar\!-\!C\!\equiv\!C\!-\!Ar$$

VIII   IX

of potassium amide in liquid ammonia.[5] For such *α-elimination reactions*, which are frequently accompanied by rearrangements, Hauser has pointed out [6] that an intermediate may be postulated comparable to that suggested for the Wolff rearrangement (p. 53) and similar to that for the Lossen (p. 77) and Hofmann (p. 76) reactions. Thus if attack of base occurred at an α-hydrogen atom (X to XI) and from this carbanion a halide ion was lost (XI to XII), the intermediate XII would be an electronically deficient species and should react by one of the paths open to carbonium ion-like intermediates. Migration of one of the groups

[5] Coleman and Maxwell, *J. Am. Chem. Soc.*, **56,** 132 (1934); Coleman, Holst, and Maxwell, *ibid.*, **58,** 2312 (1936).

[6] (*a*) Hauser, *ibid.*, **62,** 933 (1940); (*b*) Hauser, Skell, Bright, and Renfrow, *ibid.*, **69,** 589 (1947).

from an adjacent carbon atom would lead to the rearranged unsaturated compound (XII to XIII).

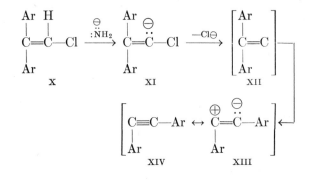

It now appears that olefins prepared from simple alkyl halides are formed with practically no rearrangement of the carbon skeleton. Even with β-phenylpropyl or β-phenylbutyl bromides (XV), systems unusually susceptible to arrangement, the olefins (XVI) were almost entirely of

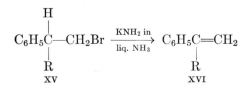

the same carbon skeleton as the starting material.[6b] Consequently β-elimination appears to be the preferred mechanism of dehydrohalogenation whenever it is operable.

Elimination Reactions of Halides or Onium Salts Not Catalyzed by Acids or Bases. As with substitution, elimination from halides or onium salts occurs in two kinetically distinguishable paths. The ones which have been mentioned are bimolecular (E_2) in which the rate of reaction is dependent upon the concentration of both base and the organic molecule. There are elimination reactions, however, in which the rate of reaction is independent of the concentration of hydroxide ion. The dehydrohalogenation of tertiary butyl bromide, for example, exhibits first-order kinetics in aqueous solvents.[7] Such reactions are called E_1 reactions. As in S_N1 processes, the driving force is presumably solvation of the departing group.

[7] Hughes and Ingold, *Trans. Faraday Soc.*, **37**, 660 (1941).

$$(CH_3)_3C—Br + (n + m)H_2O \longrightarrow [(CH_3)_3\overset{\oplus}{C}]·(H_2O)_n + \overset{\ominus}{Br}·(H_2O)_m$$

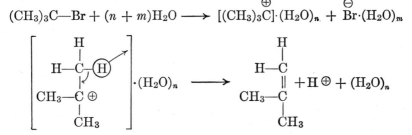

Tetraälkylammonium salts and primary or secondary alkyl halides usually react by E_2, while tertiary alkyl halides and sulfonium salts react by E_1.[8]

First-order kinetics does not necessarily indicate an E_1 mechanism. For example, the decomposition of the quaternary salt of dimethyl-β-(p-nitrophenyl)-ethylamine is first order in aqueous solution. Nevertheless, the transformation undoubtedly occurs by an E_2 process, since a large increase in the rate of reaction is observed when a base stronger than water is present. When the hydrogen atoms in the β-position are particularly sensitive to attack as they are here, even the weak base, water, must be able to initiate the reaction:[9]

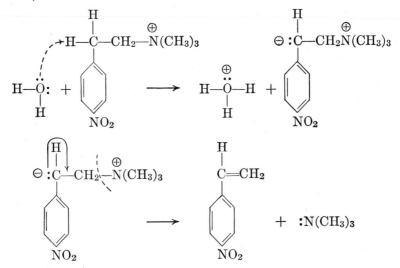

Examination of E_1 and E_2 mechanisms reveals that they are closely related to S_N1 and S_N2. In fact, E_1 and S_N1 *involve the same species as an intermediate*, whereas S_N2 and E_2 differ in that displacement occurs at

[8] *Ibid.*, 658 and 660.
[9] *Ibid.*, 659.

a carbon atom in one case (S_N2) and at a hydrogen atom in the other (E_2). Consequently, there will be a competition among E_1, E_2, S_N1, and S_N2. The following discussion will consider some of the factors which influence the course of a reaction when both substitution and elimination can occur.

FACTORS INFLUENCING THE COURSE OF E AND S REACTIONS OF HALIDES AND ONIUM SALTS

Concentration of Base. Since the rates of the E_1 and S_N1 type reactions are independent of base, lowering the concentration of base increases the importance of these reactions by reducing the rate of the second-order processes. In the first-order reactions, if we assume that the carbonium ion partially decomposes before collision with an anion, the ratio of elimination to total reaction $\left(\dfrac{E_1}{E_1 + S_1} \right)$ should depend principally upon the structure of the carbonium ion. For a number of compounds of the general structure R—Z this has been found to be true regardless of whether Z is Cl, Br, I, or $\overset{\oplus}{S}R_2$.[10]

When the concentration of base is higher, the second-order reactions become important. The proportion of olefin formed will again be almost constant since the ratio of products will depend upon the ratio of the respective rates of formation. As the equations below show, this ratio remains constant for second-order reactions:

$$\frac{\text{Amount of olefin}}{\left\{\begin{array}{c}\text{Amount of olefin and}\\ \text{amount of substitution}\end{array}\right\}} = \frac{\text{Rate of olefin formation}}{\left\{\begin{array}{c}\text{Rate of olefin formation and}\\ \text{rate of substitution}\end{array}\right\}}$$

$$= \frac{k_E[\text{RX}][\text{OH}]}{k_E[\text{RX}][\text{OH}] + k_S[\text{RX}][\text{OH}]} = \frac{k_E}{k_E + k_S} = K$$

k_E = specific rate constant for elimination
k_S = specific rate constant for substitution

It is clear, therefore, that changes in the concentration of the attacking reagent can shift the operative mechanism either towards $E_1 - S_N1$ or $E_2 - S_N2$, but that within the same kinetic order of reaction the ratio of products will be independent of the concentration of reagent.

Ionizing Power of the Medium. The effect of an ionizing solvent upon the course of elimination reactions can be deduced by considering the distribution of electrical charge in the transition state of the different reactions (see p. 85). In Table 1 are summarized the conclusions

[10] *Ibid.*, 661.

TABLE 1

Effect of Ionizing Media on Substitution and Elimination Reactions

(Data from Hughes and Ingold, *Trans. Faraday Soc.*, **37**, 666 [1941])

Process	Initial State	Transition State	Effect on Charges (from Initial to Transition State)	Effect of Ionizing Media on Reaction Rate
S_N2	$Y^{\ominus} + $	$-\delta \quad -\delta$ $Y\cdots C\cdots X$	Dispersed	Small decrease
E_2	$Y^{\ominus} + $	$-\delta \quad\quad -\delta$ $Y\cdots H\cdots C\cdots X$	Dispersion greater	Larger decrease
S_N1 or E_1	RX	$+\delta \quad -\delta$ $R\cdots X$	Developed	Large increase
S_N2	$Y^{\ominus} + $	$-\delta \quad\quad +\delta$ $Y\cdots C\cdots Z$	Partial neutralization	Large decrease
E_2	$Y^{\ominus} + $	$-\delta \quad\quad +\delta$ $Y\cdots H\cdots C\cdots Z$	Partial neutralization	Large decrease
S_N1 or E_1	$R{-}\overset{\oplus}{Z}$	$+\delta \quad +\delta$ $R\cdots Z$	Dispersed	Small decrease

which may be reached concerning substitution and elimination reactions of different charge type. This table is again based upon the two assumptions which were made for substitution reactions in general, namely, that solvation facilitates the development of fractional charges and hinders their dispersion or neutralization. It can be seen again that polar solvents decrease the rate of the second-order reactions but that the effect on first-order reactions depends upon charge type. Alkyl halides, for example, react by E_1 more rapidly in polar solvents whereas onium salts proceed less rapidly in polar media. In comparing S_N2 with E_2 it is important to observe that the charge dispersion in E_2 is larger than in S_N2 since the transition state involves two more atoms over which the charge must be distributed: $[\text{Y}\cdots\text{C}\cdots\text{X}(\text{Z}\oplus)$ as compared to $\text{Y}\cdots\text{H}\cdots\text{C}—\text{C}\cdots\text{X}(\text{Z}\oplus)]$. Consequently *ionizing media suppress E_2 more than S_N2*. It is therefore clear why dry alcoholic potassium hydroxide is a better reagent than aqueous alkali for the preparation of olefins from alkyl halides.

Basicity of the Reagent. Experience has shown that the ease with which a reagent is able to effect a displacement reaction at a saturated carbon atom (i.e., its nucleophilic power) roughly parallels its basic strength. In fact, base strength as it is usually determined is a measure of the ease with which a reagent is able to effect a displacement reaction at a hydrogen atom:

$$\overset{\ominus}{\text{Y}}\text{: } + \text{H—Z} \rightleftharpoons \text{YH} + \overset{\ominus}{\text{:Z}} \quad \text{(measure of base strength)}$$

$$\overset{\ominus}{\text{Y}}\text{: } + \diagdown{\text{C—Z}}\diagup \rightleftharpoons \text{Y—C}\diagup\diagdown + \overset{\ominus}{\text{:Z}} \quad \text{(measure of nucleophilic power)}$$

Consequently as we proceed along the series (XVII) from acetate ion

$$\ominus\text{OAc}, \ominus\text{O}\phi, \ominus\text{OH}, \ominus\text{OR}$$

XVII

$---------\rightarrow$
(increasing base strength)

to alkoxide ion, the main effect is to increase the importance of the second-order reactions at the expense of the first-order reactions.

In comparing S_N2 with E_2, however, we have to evaluate the relative nucleophilic activity of the reagent towards a hydrogen or a carbon atom. In all cases the parallelism is not exact. The general direction of the deviation is that while strong bases are strong towards hydrogen atoms, weak bases undergo displacements on carbon atoms more readily than their basicity would indicate. We have already seen that the halogen atom of an acyl halide is displaced by an amine or phenol in preference to hydroxide ion in the Schotten-Baumann reaction (p. 90). Another example of abnormal nucleophilic power is the extreme ease with which alkyl halides undergo exchange or racemization reactions with the corresponding halide ion. As we pass from alkoxide to acetate ion in the above series, then, we observe a decrease in the relative importance of the E_2 reaction and substitution (S_N2) predominates. Such a decrease in the tendency of a given compound to form olefins when it is treated with a weaker base is well known. It is for this reason that alcohols are often prepared from alkyl halides which dehydrohalogenate readily by treating them with potassium acetate and then saponifying the ester rather than by allowing the halide to react directly with alkali.

Temperature. In general an increase in the temperature of reaction increases the proportion of olefin formed. The reason for this temperature effect is not well understood.[11]

Structural Effects. By far the most important question to be answered in considering an elimination reaction is this: "What will be the structure of the product which is obtained?" If, for example, we have a halide of the general type $R\!-\!CH_2\!-\!\overset{\displaystyle X}{\overset{\displaystyle |}{C}H}\!-\!CH_2R'$, elimination may produce $RCH\!=\!CHCH_2R'$ or $RCH_2CH\!=\!CHR'$.

Two important rules concerning elimination reactions have been developed empirically, and it should be interesting to see if they can be given a theoretical interpretation.

Hofmann Rule. In the decomposition of quaternary ammonium hydroxides, that olefin will be formed which will have the smallest number of alkyl groups attached to it.

Saytzeff Rule. When a halide is converted to an olefin, the most highly branched olefin will be formed.

It is evident, therefore, that if these rules are correct, different products will be obtained, depending upon whether we start with a quaternary salt or a halide.

In a careful study of elimination reactions designed to determine whether the differences between the Hofmann and the Saytzeff rules might be due to the nature of the alkyl compound (halide or onium), the

[11] *Ibid.*, 669–672.

type of alkyl group (primary, secondary, or tertiary), or the mechanism of the reaction (E_2 or E_1), the following results were obtained: [12]

RULE FOLLOWED (HOFMANN OR SAYTZEFF) IN ELIMINATION REACTIONS

Mechanism	Onium Ions			Halides		
	1°	2°	3°	1°	2°	3°
E_2	H	H	H	S	S	S
E_1		S	S		S	S

It is clear that in order to employ the Hofmann rule we must be sure that the reaction is following second-order kinetics. The Saytzeff rule, however, appears to be perfectly general.

From what we already know of carbonium reactions we see that E_1 reactions should indeed lead to the more highly branched olefin. If we have a system of the general type $RCH_2—\overset{\underset{|}{R}}{CH}—Z—\overset{\oplus}{CH_2}CH_2R$, the carbonium ion $RCH_2\overset{\underset{|}{R}}{CH}\oplus$ should be much more stable than $\oplus CH_2CH_2R$. Consequently, the expected olefin would be $RCH=CHR$. In the system $CH_3CH_2—\overset{\oplus}{Z}—\overset{\underset{|}{R}}{CH_2}CH_2$, neither the carbonium ion $CH_3CH_2\oplus$ nor $\oplus \overset{\underset{|}{R}}{CH_2}CH_2$ would be expected to be formed readily. In fact it seems unlikely that an E_1 reaction would ever occur with such a compound unless the formation of one of the carbonium ions were assisted or accompanied by immediate decomposition. Since the olefin $CH_2=\overset{\underset{|}{R}}{CH}$ would be stabilized by hyperconjugation of the hydrogen atoms in R (unless R were a tertiary group), the energy necessary for its formation would be lower than that of $CH_2=CH_2$, and the route leading to the more highly substituted olefin would again be favored. Similarly, when the alkyl halide $RCH_2—\overset{\underset{|}{Cl}}{CH}—CH_3$ undergoes an E_1 reaction, the olefin $RCH=CHCH_3$ would be expected to predominate, since there is always at least one more hydrogen atom *alpha* to the double bond in it than there is in the compound $RCH_2—CH=CH_2$.

With an E_2 reaction, the problem is complex. Different products are

[12] *Ibid.*, 680.

obtained, depending upon which starting material is employed, yet both reactions are presumed to proceed by the same mechanism.   In onium compounds where a strong electrostatic field is present, the *position* of attack by the base seems to be the controlling factor.   Thus, if our interpretation is correct in the system $RCH_2CH_2\overset{\oplus}{-Z}-CH_2CH_3$, the β-hydrogen atoms in the ethyl group are the more exposed to attack and ethylene results.   In general, then, attack of base at the less-hindered β-position will result in the formation of the olefin with the smallest number of groups attached to it.   This is of course the Hofmann rule.

It is interesting, however, that with dimethyl-ethyl-(β-phenylethyl)-ammonium hydroxide (XVIII), styrene is formed rather than ethylene.[13] This is an exception to the Hofmann rule.   A moment's reflection, however, reveals that while this result might not have been predicted, it is not surprising in view of the fact that the approach of a negative ion is always facilitated at a benzyl or an allyl position (p. 91).

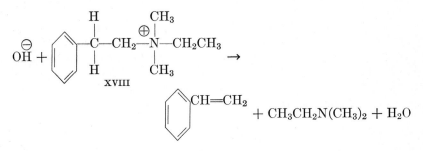

With the E_2 reaction of the halides, it appears that the *ease of decomposition of the transition state* is more important for control of an elimination reaction than the position at which attack of base would be expected to occur.   Again this result might not have been predicted.   Let us consider an alkyl halide of the general type $RCH_2\overset{Cl}{-}\overset{|}{CH}-CH_3$ and the transition states XIX and XX which lead to an E_2 elimination re-

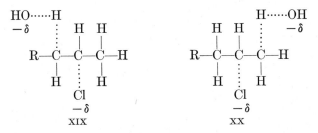

[13] Hanhart and Ingold, *J. Chem. Soc.*, **1927**, 1001.

action.   If we suppose that the concentration of these species is approximately the same and that the most probable course of the decomposition of such a complex is simply regeneration of the starting materials, the olefinic product which would be expected to predominate from a mixture of XIX and XX would be the one which could be formed more easily from its transition complex.   Here we see that the olefin XXI is more stabilized by hyperconjugation than XXII (at least three

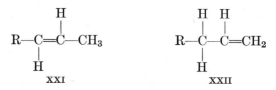

XXI   XXII

hyperconjugation forms as compared to a maximum of two).   Consequently the energy necessary for the formation of XXI would be lower than that for XXII, and this olefin would be expected to predominate from the mixture of transition complexes.

The application of the principle of hyperconjugation to the elimination reactions of saturated molecules, therefore, may be stated as follows:

Except for the second-order reaction of onium salts, the structure of the principal product obtained from an elimination reaction will be the one having the greater number of α-hydrogen atoms.

For example, dehydrohalogenation of the compound

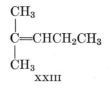

would be expected to produce

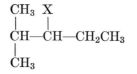

XXIII

rather than

CH$_3$
|
CHCH=CHCH$_3$
|
CH$_3$

XXIV

since in the first olefin there are eight α-hydrogen atoms and in the second there are only four. Many such compounds have been examined, and the principle appears to be quite general.[12]

Before leaving our discussion of elimination reactions, the distinction which has been drawn between E_2 reactions of alkyl halides and onium salts should be emphasized. When onium salts are decomposed it has been assumed that the most important step in the process is the formation of a reactive complex between the cation and a base. Once this transition state is attained, olefin formation occurs directly so that the process is effectively irreversible. Consequently, if there is more than one point within a molecule where such complexes can be formed, reaction will proceed predominantly through the one which can be attained most easily.

With the alkyl halides it has been assumed that while there may be small differences in the ease with which different possible transition states are attained, the important phase of these reactions is rather the ease with which the complexes break down into the olefin. Olefin formation, therefore, occurs principally through the form whose decomposition is most aided by the resonance stability of the olefin.

Qualitatively these assumptions are in the right direction, for we should expect the transition complex between the positively charged onium ion and hydroxide ion to be much more tightly bound together and much less susceptible to reversal than the one formed from the neutral halide molecule. Until conclusive experiments have been performed, however, we should accept the explanation of these rules with some reservation.

It is interesting that the Saytzeff rule may also be interpreted as a consequence of strain. Brown has pointed out [14] that since alkyl groups possess a certain bulk, two alkyl groups and a hydrogen atom attached to a single carbon atom may comprise a more strained system than two alkyl groups attached to a doubly bonded carbon atom. Consequently, in the example mentioned above, the olefin XXIV would be more probable than XXIII because the angle between the methyl groups of XXIV is 116° [15] as compared to 109° for XXIII.

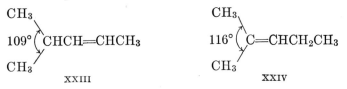

$$\text{CH}_3 \diagdown$$
$$109° \Big(\text{CHCH}=\text{CHCH}_3$$
$$\text{CH}_3 \diagup$$
XXIII

$$\text{CH}_3 \diagdown$$
$$116° \Big(\text{C}=\text{CHCH}_2\text{CH}_3$$
$$\text{CH}_3 \diagup$$
XXIV

[14] Brown, *Science*, **103**, 387 (1946); Brown and Fletcher, *J. Am. Chem. Soc.*, **71**, 1845 (1949).

[15] Branch and Calvin, *The Theory of Organic Chemistry*, p. 122, Prentice-Hall, New York, 1945.

STEREOCHEMISTRY OF ELIMINATION REACTIONS

Elimination reactions, like displacement reactions, usually involve elements which are *trans* to each other. Thus *cis* 2-phenyl-1-cyclo-hexanol (XXV) on dehydration with phosphoric acid gives principally 1-phenylcyclohexene (XXVI), but the corresponding *trans* alcohol (XXVII) gives mostly 3-phenylcyclohexene (XXVIII).[16] Similarly chlorofumaric acid (XXIX) is dehydrohalogenated to acetylenedicar-

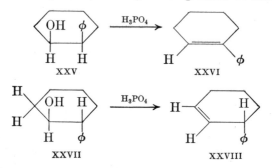

boxylic acid at a rate about forty-eight times as fast as that of chloro-maleic acid (XXX).[17]

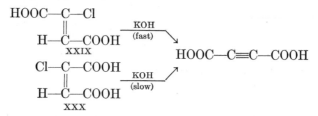

Another interesting example of the striking tendency towards *trans* elimination can be illustrated by the reaction of vincinal dibromides XXXI with iodide ion.[18] The reaction may be generalized:

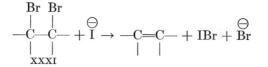

It was found that *meso*-2,3-dibromobutane gave a butene which was 96 per cent *trans* and *dl*-2,3-dibromobutane gave a butene which was 91 per cent *cis*. These facts, together with second-order kinetics,[19] suggest

[16] Price and Karabinos, *J. Am. Chem. Soc.*, **62**, 1159 (1940).
[17] Michael, *J. prakt. Chem.*, **52**, 308 (1895).
[18] Winstein, Pressman, and Young, *ibid.*, **61**, 1645 (1939).
[19] Young, Pressman, and Coryell, *ibid.*, 1640.

that the bromine atoms must be in a *trans* position to each other for reaction to occur and that the process is initiated by a displacement at one
of the bromine atoms.   Although the steps are again probably simultaneous, the reaction stages can be outlined as follows for the *meso* dibromide:

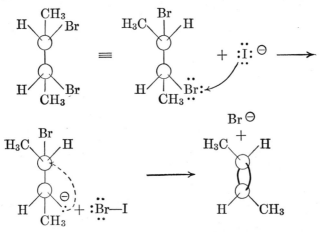

Actually these drawings do not give a complete picture of the reaction,
because the *meso* dibromides almost always react more rapidly than the
dl isomers.   Young has pointed out [20] that these results are in agreement
with the assumption that even when rotation is not restricted there is a
preferred orientation of the dihalide molecule such that the *smallest
group on one asymmetric carbon atom will lie between the two largest groups
on the other asymmetric carbon atom*.   If this is true for all dihalides, it can
be seen in the formulas XXXII and XXXIII that the two bromine atoms

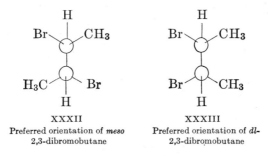

XXXII
Preferred orientation of *meso*
2,3-dibromobutane

XXXIII
Preferred orientation of *dl*-
2,3-dibromobutane

are more nearly trans to each other in the meso form than in the dl form.
Consequently, elimination would be expected to proceed more readily

[20] Young, *Abstracts of Papers*, Eighth National Organic Chemistry Symposium of
the American Chemical Society, St. Louis, Mo., Dec. 1939, pp. 92–95.

with the *meso* isomer. For the stilbene dibromides, at least, X-ray data and dipole moment studies show conclusively that the *meso* and *dl* isomers have preferred orientations corresponding to those shown above.[20, 21]

MISCELLANEOUS ELIMINATION REACTIONS

Acid-Induced Enolization. The acid-induced enolization of ketones may be considered an elimination reaction:

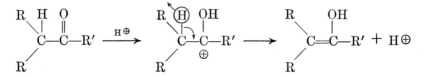

Chugaev Reaction. The conversion of an alcohol to an olefin by the thermal decomposition of its xanthate ester is called the Chugaev reaction. The unique feature of the reaction is that alcohols which frequently undergo rearrangements by usual dehydration methods can be dehydrated with no change in the carbon skeleton. Thus pinacolyl alcohol (**XXXIV**) leads to *tert*-butylethylene (**XXXV**),[22] and optically

$$
\underset{\textbf{XXXIV}}{(CH_3)_3C\!\!-\!\!\underset{\underset{OH}{|}}{C}HCH_3} \rightarrow (CH_3)_3C\!\!-\!\!\underset{\underset{\overset{|}{O}\!\!-\!\!\overset{\overset{S}{\|}}{C}\!\!-\!\!SCH_3}{}}{CH}\!\!-\!\!CH_3 \rightarrow
$$

$$
\underset{\textbf{XXXV}}{(CH_3)_3C\!\!-\!\!CH\!\!=\!\!CH_2 + COS + CH_3SH}
$$

active 2-methyl-3-ethoxy-2-butanol (**XXXVI**) produces optically active 2-methyl-3-ethoxy-1-butene (**XXXVII**).[23]

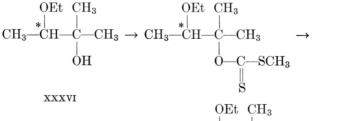

[21] McCullough, *J. Am. Chem. Soc.*, **62**, 480 (1940).
[22] Fomin and Sochanski, *Ber.*, **46**, 246 (1913).
[23] Stevens, *J. Am. Chem. Soc.*, **54**, 3736 (1932).

Little is known of the actual mechanism of the Chugaev reaction, and, since it is a thermal decomposition, the possibility of a free radical process must be considered. It has been suggested,[24, 25] however, that the transformation is initiated by intramolecular hydrogen bonding of a sulfur atom with a β-hydrogen atom:

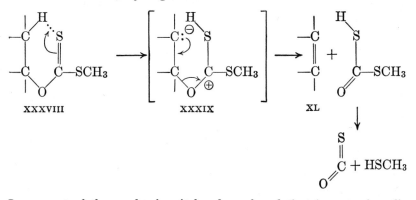

XXXVIII   XXXIX   XL

In support of the mechanism it has been found that in several cyclic systems which have been studied *xanthate decompositions led predominately to elimination of the cis hydrogen atom.* Thus methyl *l*-menthylxanthate (XLI) gives 70 per cent 3-menthene, whereas methyl *d*-neomenthylxanthate (XLII) gives 80 per cent 2-menthene.[25]

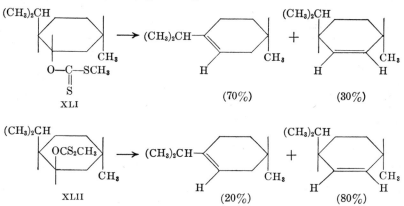

Similarly, methyl *cis*-2-phenylcyclohexylxanthate (XLIII) gives 93 per cent 3-phenylcyclohexene and 7 per cent 1-phenylcyclohexane, whereas methyl *trans*-2-phenylcyclohexylxanthate (XLIV) gives 14 per cent 3-phenylcyclohexene and 86 per cent 1-phenylcyclohexene:[26]

[24] Stevens and Richmond, *ibid.*, **63**, 3132 (1941).
[25] Hückel, Tapp, and Legutke, *Ann.*, **543**, 191 (1940).
[26] Alexander and Mudrak, unpublished experiments.

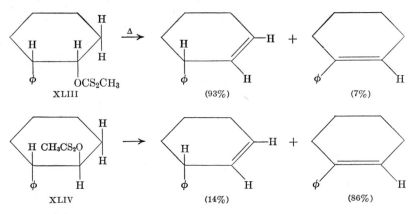

It will be observed that these results are just opposite to those obtained from the phosphoric acid dehydration of *cis* and *trans*-2-phenyl-cyclohexanol (p. 118). These reactions are of particular interest, for if the mechanism indicated is correct, the transformation of XXXIX to XL constitutes one instance in which the departing group is not displaced by the *rearward* attack of an unshared electron pair. A similar mechanism has been proposed for the pyrolysis of carboxylic esters: [27]

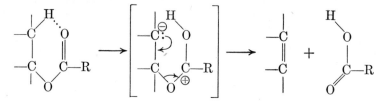

Again rearrangement does not seem to occur [28] and preferential *cis* elimination is observed with the *cis* and *trans* 2-phenylcyclohexyl [26] acetates.

[27] Hurd and Blunck, *J. Am. Chem. Soc.*, **60**, 2421 (1938).
[28] Marvel and Williams, *ibid.*, **70**, 3842 (1948).

CHAPTER 6

CARBANIONS

When an organic compound is treated with a strong base, it is some-times found that a hydrogen atom attached to a carbon atom is re-moved as a proton. The resulting ion, containing a carbon atom with an unshared electron pair, is called a *carbanion*:

$$[\text{Base:}]\ominus + \text{H:C}{\overset{\diagup}{\underset{\diagdown}{}}} \rightarrow [\text{base:H}] + \overset{\ominus}{:}\text{C}{\overset{\diagup}{\underset{\diagdown}{}}}$$

Many organometallic combinations, such as Grignard reagents or metal alkyls, undergo reactions which can be conveniently classed as car-banion reactions. Although there can be no doubt that in some in-stances the carbon-metal bond is principally covalent (p. 130), organo-metallic compounds react as if the equilibrium,

$$-\overset{|}{\underset{|}{\text{C}}}\cdot + \cdot\text{M} \rightleftharpoons -\overset{|}{\underset{|}{\text{C}}}:\text{M} \rightleftharpoons -\overset{|}{\underset{|}{\text{C}}}:\overset{\ominus}{} + \overset{\oplus}{\text{M}}$$

Free Radicals   Covalent Compound   A Carbanion

were involved. In the presence of polar groups and in the absence of free radical promoters, these reagents often appear to react through the ionized form.

In this chapter we shall discuss the conditions favoring carbanion formation, the relation of carbanion formation to enolization, and the reactions which carbanions undergo.

CARBANION FORMATION

In general, base-induced carbanion formation depends upon two fac-tors. They are the basic strength of the attacking reagent and the structure of the molecule which is to undergo reaction. As an example of the first factor, the experimentally determined order of base strength

123

decreases as follows:

$$\left[\begin{array}{c} \text{H}_3\text{C} \overset{\text{CH}_3}{\underset{\text{CH}_3}{\diagup\!\!\!\diagdown}} :\ominus \\ \phi_3\text{C}:\ominus \end{array} \right\} > (\text{CH}_3)_3\text{C}-\overset{\ominus}{\underset{..}{\text{O}}}: \; > (\text{CH}_3)_2\text{CH}-\overset{\ominus}{\underset{..}{\text{O}}}: \; >$$

$$\text{CH}_3\text{CH}_2\text{CH}_2-\overset{\ominus}{\underset{..}{\text{O}}}: \; > \text{CH}_3-\overset{\ominus}{\underset{..}{\text{O}}}: \; > \overset{\ominus}{\text{HO}} > \text{amines} > \text{CH}_3\text{CO}\overset{\ominus}{\text{O}}$$

Sodium triphenylmethyl or mesitylmagnesium bromide, for example, will bring about the self-condensation of ethyl isobutyrate (p. 186) while the weaker bases will not. As an example of the second factor, carbanions are formed only from those compounds containing a functional group capable of weakening a near-by carbon-hydrogen bond. Saturated hydrocarbons are known to be completely inert to strong bases. This weakening of the carbon-hydrogen bond may be due to a strong permanent polarization attracting electrons away from the carbon-hydrogen bond, an important stabilization of the carbanion by resonance, or, more frequently, a combination of both. It is interesting, for example, that the bicyclic sulfone (I) is soluble without decomposition in aqueous sodium bicarbonate, whereas the homolog (II) is not.[1] Clearly the acidity of I is due to the bridgehead hydrogen atom. Although the

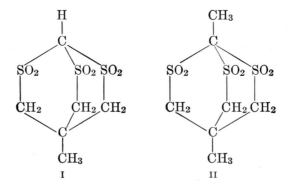

nature of the activating effect of a sulfone group has not been established,[1] it is sometimes considered that the sulfone group activates an

[1] Doering and Levy, *Abstracts of Papers*, p. 66L, 112th Meeting of the American Chemical Society, New York, September 1947.

α-hydrogen atom only by the strong permanent polarization (I_s) of the carbon-sulfur bond:[2]

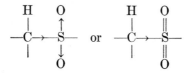

If such an interpretation is correct, this is an example of the facilitation of carbanion formation which does not involve resonance stabilization of the carbanion.

Molecules such as cyclopentadiene (III), indene (IV), and fluorene (V) are capable of forming sodium or potassium salts although permanent polarization must be small. Presumably with these compounds the abnormal acidity of the hydrocarbon is due to resonance stabilization of the carbanion.

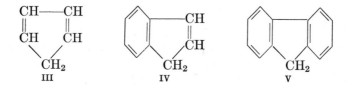

Consequently the equilibrium shown below is displaced abnormally to the right:

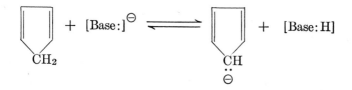

The anion of cyclopentadiene, for example, has five equivalent resonance structures (VI to X), and resonance stabilization would be expected to be very important.

[2] See Arndt, Loewe, and Ginkök, *Rev. faculte sci. univ. Istanbul*, Ser. A, **11**, No. 4, 147 (1946), (*C.A.*, **41**, 3760 [1947]); Shriner and Adams, in Gilman, *Organic Chemistry*, Vol. I, pp. 393–394, John Wiley and Sons, New York, 1943; Fehnel and Carmack, *J. Am. Chem. Soc.*, **71**, 231 (1949).

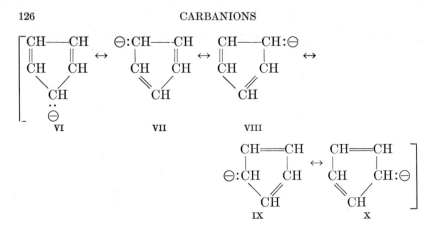

It is interesting that cyclopentadiene and indene are relatively strong acids,[3] but that fluorene is somewhat weaker than indene.[4] Apparently with fluorene the resonance energy is already so great in the undissociated molecule that it is increased only slightly by formation of the ion.[5]

In the formation of most carbanions by bases, the ready removal of a proton attached to a carbon atom is the result of a combination of permanent polarization and resonance stabilization of the carbanion. The α-hydrogen atoms of carbonyl compounds or nitriles are well known to be "active." Here not only does the functional group attract electrons by a permanent polarization of the bond to the α-carbon atom (XI), but also the carbanion which is formed is stabilized by resonance (XII and XIII).

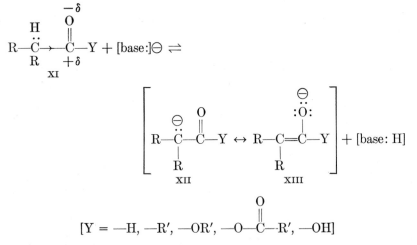

---

[3] Wheland, *J. Chem. Phys.*, **2**, 474 (1934).

[4] Conant and Wheland, *J. Am. Chem. Soc.*, **54**, 1214 (1932).

[5] Wheland, *The Theory of Resonance*, p. 174, John Wiley and Sons, New York, 1944.

The ease of carbanion formation from the various carbonyl compounds decreases in the order: aldehydes, ketones, esters, amides, and acids. This order is understandable if we consider the nature of Y. The more electron-releasing Y becomes, the less will the carbonyl group be able to withdraw electrons from the α-carbon atom (XI). Thus in comparing aldehydes and ketones, hyperconjugation in Y permits another resonance structure which does not place a positive charge on the carbonyl carbon atom (XIV). Consequently, both stabilization of the anion

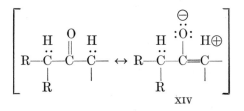

(XII and XIII) and permanent polarization (XI) are reduced. Similarly esters, amides, and carboxylate ions have the resonance structures XV, XVI, and XVII which tend to decrease the ease of carbanion formation:

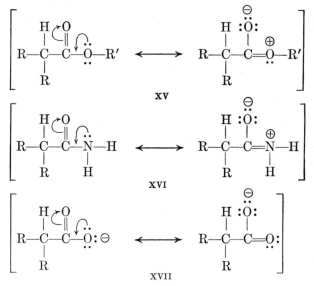

The negatively charged oxygen atom is the most electron-repelling group of all because of its negative charge (p. 29). The nitrogen atom in an amide is more electron repelling than the oxygen atom of an ester because it lies to the left of oxygen in the periodic table (p. 29).

An interesting question arises about the carbanion which will be formed when the carbonyl compound is an unsymmetrical ketone. The answer is by no means clear cut. The reaction of a ketone with an aldehyde in the presence of base is believed to proceed through the intermediate formation of a ketone carbanion (p. 176):

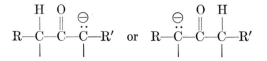

Consequently it might be expected that the structure of the crossed aldol product would show the carbanion through which reaction occurred, and this in turn might indicate which carbanion forms more readily. We find, however, that the structure of the product is dependent upon *both the ketone and the aldehyde.* Thus, formaldehyde and straight-chain aliphatic aldehydes condense with methyl ethyl ketone at the methylene group.[6] Similarly formaldehyde reacts at the methinyl group of methyl isopropyl ketone.[7] When the methyl ketone contains more than five carbon atoms, however, formaldehyde and other aliphatic aldehydes condense through the methyl group.[8] With benzaldehyde[9] or aldehydes branched at the α-carbon atom,[10] reaction also occurs preferentially at the methyl group of methyl ketones. It is clear, therefore, that *this reaction gives no information as to which carbanion per se is easier to form.* It emphasizes the fact that in reactions which proceed through several steps, such as carbanion formation, addition, and dehydration (p. 180), it is often impossible to pick out one of the steps and to fix upon it responsibility for the structure of the final product.

Finally it should be pointed out that carbanion formation is particularly easy when the carbon-hydrogen bond is weakened by two activating groups as it is in malonic ester, cyanoacetic ester, β-ketoesters, β-diketones, etc. In these compounds there is a doubled permanent polarization (XVIII), and the carbanion is a resonance hybrid of three forms:

[6] See Powell, Murray, and Baldwin, *J. Am. Chem. Soc.,* **55,** 1153 (1933).
[7] Decombe, *Compt. rend.,* **203,** 1078 (1936).
[8] Wickert and Freure, U. S. Patent 2,088,018 (1937).
[9] Gettler and Hammett, *J. Am. Chem. Soc.,* **65,** 1824 (1943).
[10] See Powell and Hagemann, *ibid.,* **66,** 372 (1944).

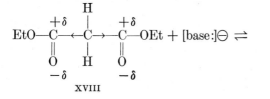

$$
\left[
\begin{array}{c}
\quad\quad\quad\quad O \\
\quad\quad\quad\quad \| \\
EtO—C{=}C—C—OEt \\
\quad\quad :\ddot{O}:\ H \\
\quad\quad \ominus \\
\quad\quad\quad\quad \updownarrow \\
\quad\quad\quad \ominus \quad O \\
\quad\quad\quad \ddot{} \quad \| \\
EtO—C—C—C—OEt \\
\quad\quad \| \ \ | \\
\quad\quad O \ H \\
\quad\quad\quad \updownarrow \\
EtO—C—C{=}C—OEt \\
\quad\quad \| \ H \ :\ddot{O}: \\
\quad\quad O \\
\quad\quad\quad\quad\quad \ominus
\end{array}
\right] + \text{[base: H]}
$$

Compounds containing active methylene groups undergo carbonyl addition reactions (p. 175) and substitution reactions (p. 201) with great ease.

Aliphatic nitro compounds and aromatic compounds containing methyl group *ortho* or *para* to a nitro group also undergo reactions which appear to involve carbanions stabilized by resonance (p. 23):

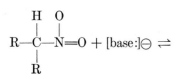

$$
\left[
\begin{array}{c}
\quad \ominus \quad O \\
\quad \ddot{} \quad | \\
R—\ddot{C}—N{=}O \ \leftrightarrow \ R—C{=}N—\ddot{O}: \\
\quad | \quad\quad\quad\quad | \\
\quad R \quad\quad\quad\quad R
\end{array}
\right] + \text{[base: H]}
$$

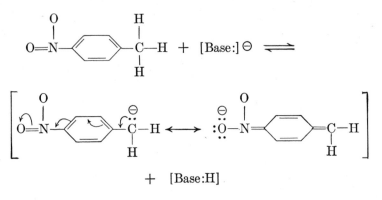

When resonance of the nitro group is inhibited, these reactions do not occur (p. 23).

Pyridine and quinoline derivatives substituted with methyl groups in the α or γ position also form carbanions readily. In the presence of a strong base, such as phenyl lithium, one of the aliphatic hydrogen atoms of α-picoline is replaced and the useful synthetic intermediate (XIX) is formed.[11] Although organo-lithium compounds show many of the prop-

erties of carbanions in their reactions, dipole moment data indicate that lithium alkyls should be regarded as covalent compounds with about 45 per cent ionic character.[12] The quaternary salts of these methylpyridines are even more active. Quinaldine, for example, will not condense with benzaldehyde in the presence of piperidine, whereas quinaldine meth-iodide reacts readily.[13] This is undoubtedly due to the powerful attraction of the unit positive charge and the resulting stabilization of the ion XX.

[11] Walter, *Organic Syntheses*, Vol. 23, p. 83, John Wiley and Sons, New York, 1943.
[12] Rogers and Young, *J. Am. Chem. Soc.*, **68**, 2748 (1946).
[13] Taylor and Baker, *Sidgwick's Organic Chemistry of Nitrogen*, p. 556, Oxford University Press, London, England, 1942.

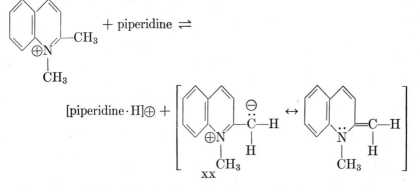

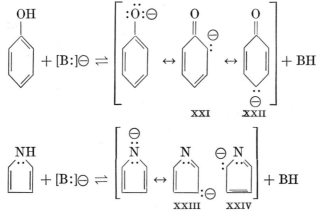

Pyrrole and phenol derivatives also form carbanions when they are treated with bases:

The contribution of the resonance forms **XXI, XXII, XXIII,** and **XXIV** to the structure of the anions is frequently overlooked, yet many base-catalyzed condensation reactions of phenol and pyrrole undoubtedly proceed through these resonance structures at the moment reaction occurs. The condensation of phenol with aqueous formaldehyde, the Kolbe synthesis (p. 197), and the Reimer-Tiemann reaction (p. 202) are striking examples of reactions which occur through the seemingly less important carbanion structure of the resonance hybrid. (See p. 133.)

REACTIONS OF CARBANIONS

Compounds which will form stable or transitory carbanions commonly undergo two different kinds of reactions. They are *displacement* reactions and *addition* reactions. A carbanion displacement reaction at a saturated carbon atom results in *alkylation*. Thus sodiomalonic ester is "alkylated" by methyl bromide:

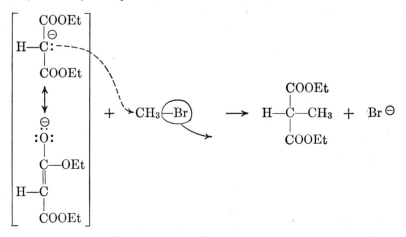

A number of carbanion displacement reactions are discussed in Chapter 10.

Carbanion additions occur frequently at carbonyl or nitrile groups and occasionally at carbon-carbon double bonds. The Grignard synthesis of alcohols is an example:

$$\overset{-\delta}{R}\!-\!\overset{+\delta}{MgX} + \overset{+\delta}{-C}\!\!=\!\!\overset{-\delta}{O} \rightarrow -\overset{R}{\underset{|}{C}}\!-\!OMgX$$

Carbanion addition reactions are discussed in Chapter 11.

THE RELATION BETWEEN REACTIONS REQUIRING CARBANIONS AND THE FORMATION OF AN ENOL

It will be observed that throughout this discussion of carbanions no mention has been made of the intermediate formation of an enol or of enolization. It now seems extremely probable that in reactions such as aldol formation (p. 176), the Claisen condensation (p. 185), acetoacetic or malonic ester reactions (pp. 182, 201), and the halogenation of ketones (pp. 206, 207) the carbanion is the actual reaction intermediate and that the formation of an enol simply represents an alternative nonessential course of reaction for the carbanion. In the alkylation of malonic ester, for example, a carbanion (XXV and XXVI) may be formed by reaction of the neutral ester with ethoxide ion.

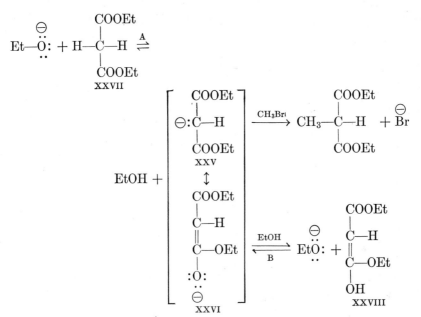

This carbanion certainly exists in a reversible equilibrium with both the neutral ester (XXVII) and the neutral enol (XXVIII), established by reaction of the carbanion with alcohol through the resonance forms XXV or XXVI.   It is evident, however, that if the equilibrium B is not established very rapidly with respect to A *the rate of enol formation will be slower than the rate of carbanion formation.*   According to this interpretation, it will not be correct to say that the rate of reaction is dependent upon the rate of "enolization" of the active methylene component.[14]

It is interesting and characteristic of ions which are resonance hybrids of structures such as XXV and XXVI that alkylation usually occurs almost exclusively through the carbanion (XXV) rather than the alcoholate form (XXVI).   This fact is somewhat surprising, since the structure XXVI (in which the negative charge resides on the more electronegative atom) would be expected to make the larger contribution to the structure of the ion.

Two pieces of evidence may be cited to support the theory that carbanions and not enols are involved in carbonyl condensation and alkylation reactions.   First, the ultraviolet absorption spectrum of sodio-acetoacetic ester is very different from that of the enol ethyl ether

---

[14] Carbonyl reactions which are effected by acids, however, do appear to involve the intermediate enol. See Hauser and Adams, *J. Am. Chem. Soc.*, **66**, 345 (1944).

(XXIX).[15] And second, the rates of enolization and racemization of an

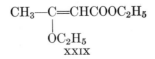

$$CH_3\!-\!C\!=\!CHCOOC_2H_5$$
$$\mid$$
$$OC_2H_5$$
$$\text{XXIX}$$

asymmetric α-carbon atom are not always the same.[16] This has been demonstrated with the menthyl ester of α-phenylacetoacetic ester (XXX). This material crystallizes from methanol solution in one of

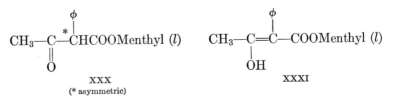

$$\overset{\phi}{\underset{\parallel}{\underset{O}{CH_3\!-\!C\!-\!\overset{*}{C}HCOOMenthyl\ (l)}}}$$ $$\overset{\phi}{CH_3\!-\!C\!=\!\underset{\underset{OH}{\mid}}{C}\!-\!COOMenthyl\ (l)}$$

XXX   XXXI
(* asymmetric)

the diastereoisomeric *keto* modifications. This is indicated by the fact that the freshly prepared material is dextrorotatory; it gives no color with ferric chloride, and it shows no enol content by the familiar Kurt Meyer method of bromine titration. On standing in hexane, however, the solution approaches an equilibrium. The optical rotation becomes strongly *levo*, and the product is 71 per cent in the enolic modification (XXXI). It is possible, therefore, to determine independently the rate of racemization and enolization. It was found that the rate of racemization was about twice that of enolization. Consequently, racemization cannot be due solely to the intermediate formation of the neutral enol.

The simplest interpretation in agreement with these facts is that racemization is due to the formation of a carbanion which is not able to retain asymmetry and that the enol is formed by a second slower reaction from this carbanion.

[15] Hantzsch, *Ber.*, **43**, 3049 (1910).
[16] Kimball, *J. Am. Chem. Soc.*, **58**, 1963 (1936).

CHAPTER 7

ADDITION REACTIONS OF CARBON-CARBON DOUBLE BONDS

NATURE OF THE CARBON-CARBON DOUBLE BOND

A double bond connecting two carbon atoms differs appreciably from a single bond. This difference is reflected in greater electron polarizability and in the high energy barrier against free rotation which gives rise to *cis-trans* isomerism. Such a bond is believed to consist of one ordinary type linkage of two electrons and, in addition, a bond of lower energy containing the so-called π-electrons. This pair of electrons is less firmly held between the two nuclei and is responsible for the high polarizability and chemical reactivity of unsaturated compounds.

Although some authors [1] prefer to discuss the various reactions of carbon-carbon double bonds in terms of π-electrons, it may be simpler for the present discussion to consider reactions of the double bond as proceeding through intermediates such as B or C.

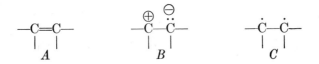

MECHANISMS OF ADDITION

Superficially at least, additions to carbon-carbon double bonds appear to be rather simple reactions. When they are investigated carefully, however, they are found to be extremely complex. The rate of addition of hydrogen chloride to isobutylene in heptane solution, for example, appears to be third order in hydrogen chloride and first order in isobutylene.[2] In fact the data which have been collected indicate that reaction rarely, if ever, proceeds by the direct addition of a molecule across a double bond. Instead, the reaction appears to occur by the stepwise ad-

---

[1] Price, *Reactions at Carbon-Carbon Double Bonds*, Interscience Publishers, New York, 1946; Dewar, *The Electronic Theory of Organic Chemistry*, Oxford University Press, London, 1949.

[2] Mayo and Katz, *J. Am. Chem. Soc.*, **69**, 1339 (1947).

dition of part of the addendum first to one side of the double bond and then the remainder to the other. In nonpolar solvents, particularly in the presence of ultraviolet light or peroxides, intermediates such as C are involved and the process proceeds by a *free radical* or *electron pairing* [3] mechanism:

$$:\ddot{B}r:\ddot{B}r: \xrightarrow[\text{or peroxides}]{\text{ultraviolet light}} :\ddot{B}r\cdot + \cdot\ddot{B}r:$$

$$:\ddot{B}r\cdot + CH_2::CH_2 \longrightarrow :\ddot{B}r-CH_2-CH_2\cdot$$

$$:\ddot{B}r-CH_2-CH_2\cdot + :\ddot{B}r:\ddot{B}r: \longrightarrow :\ddot{B}r-CH_2-CH_2-\ddot{B}r: + :\ddot{B}r\cdot \text{ etc.}$$

Under conditions more favorable to ionic reactions, the approach of a positively or negatively charged ion or pole induces a charge separation like the one shown in B, and the reaction then occurs through the attraction of unlike electrical charges for each other. For example:

$$\overset{-\delta}{X}:\overset{+\delta}{Y} + \overset{-\delta}{CH_2}=\overset{+\delta}{CH_2} \longrightarrow \overset{\ominus}{X}: + \overset{\oplus}{Y-CH_2-CH_2}$$

$$\overset{\ominus}{X}: + \overset{\oplus}{Y-CH_2-CH_2} \longrightarrow Y-CH_2-CH_2-X$$

Although it is frequently very difficult to decide whether a reaction is proceeding by a free radical or an ionic mechanism, an attempt will be made to limit this discussion to reactions which follow an ionic course. A classic example of the ease with which a mechanism can change is the now well-known *peroxide effect*, discovered by Kharasch in the addition of hydrogen bromide to olefins.[4] In the presence of air or a trace of peroxides the usual ionic reaction becomes a free radical process with the result that the normal (Markownikoff) direction of addition becomes almost completely reversed.

Since the double bond in an olefin connects two atoms almost identical in their affinity for electrons, we might expect that the normal electronic distribution of the double bond could be deformed almost equally well by the approach of a positive or a negative charge. It is now quite clear that addition reactions *can* be initiated both by electron-seeking (electrophilic) and by nucleus-seeking (nucleophilic) species, but the processes do not proceed with nearly the same facility. Most additions to carbon-

[3] Remick, *Electronic Interpretation of Organic Chemistry*, p. 484, John Wiley and Sons, New York, 1949.

[4] For a review of the *peroxide effect*, see Mayo and Walling, *Chem. Revs.*, **27**, 351 (1940).

carbon double bonds take place through a preliminary rate-controlling addition of an electron-seeking reagent such as $H \oplus$, $X \oplus$, or a carbonium ion. It is only with bidiphenyleneethylene (p. 148) or when the olefin bond is attached to a strongly electronegative group ($-SO_2R$, $-COOR$, $-CN$, $-F$, etc.) that reaction occurs as a result of the attack of $OR \ominus$, RNH_2, or a carbanion (p. 147).

In the following sections a number of addition reactions initiated by the attack of anions and cations will be discussed.

THE NATURE OF ADDITION REACTIONS INITIATED BY THE ATTACK OF CATIONS

Facts Pertinent to the Mechanism of Addition. A very large number of experimental facts have been collected from which we can draw certain conclusions concerning the mechanism of addition initiated by the attack of a cation. Some which appear to be particularly significant are the following.

(1) *Addition is usually facilitated by the presence of a negative charge in a molecule, but it is hindered by a positive charge.* Sodium maleate and sodium fumarate, for example, undergo halogenation at far greater speeds than the acids themselves:[5]

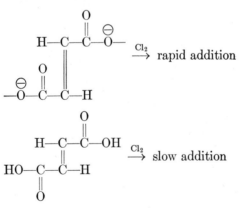

The allyl group in neutral molecules adds bromine rapidly, but in a positive ammonium ion it is unreactive.[6]

$$CH_2\!\!=\!\!CH-CH_2OH \xrightarrow{Br_2} \text{adds rapidly}$$

$$CH_2\!\!=\!\!CH-CH_2\overset{\oplus}{N}R_3 \xrightarrow{Br_2} \text{unreactive}$$

[5] Terry and Eichelberger, *J. Am. Chem. Soc.*, **47**, 1068 (1925).
[6] Robertson, Clare, McNaught, and Paul, *J. Chem. Soc.*, **1937**, 335.

(2) *When the addition of bromine is carried out in the presence of an anion other than the bromide ion, that anion may appear in the final product.* When ethylene is shaken with bromine and sodium chloride, α-chloro-β-bromoethane is produced: [7]

$$CH_2{=}CH_2 + Br_2 + \overset{\ominus}{Cl} \rightarrow \overset{\overset{\displaystyle Br}{|}}{CH_2}{-}\overset{\overset{\displaystyle Cl}{|}}{CH_2} + \overset{\ominus}{Br}$$

Similarly in the presence of sodium nitrate, β-bromoethyl nitrate is formed.

(3) *Many addition reactions are favored by electron-releasing groups.* Thus a progressive increase in the number of methyl groups attached to the ethylene link is accompanied by an increase in the rate of addition. In the following series the numerical values correspond to the rate of addition of hydrogen bromide relative to that of ethylene.[8]

$CH_2{=}CHBr$	$CH_2{=}CH_2$	$CH_3CH{=}CH_2$	$(CH_3)_2C{=}CH_2$
Small	1.0	2.0	5.5

$(CH_3)_2C{=}CHCH_3$	$(CH_3)_2C{=}C(CH_3)_2$
10.4	14.0

(4) *Unsymmetrical reagents add to olefins in such a way that the more negative fragment appears on the carbon atom carrying the smaller number of hydrogen atoms.* (*Markownikoff's rule.*) In terms of hyperconjugation theory, this is the more positive atom (see p. 32).

(5) *Solvents known to form oxonium salts with acids retard the addition of hydrogen halides.* Thus the addition of hydrogen chloride or hydrogen bromide to cyclohexene or 3-hexene proceeds more slowly in ether or dioxane than in heptane or benzene.[9]

(6) *Addition to a trans olefin usually gives a meso product. Addition to a cis olefin leads to a racemic modification.* Thus when bromine is added to maleic acid, racemic dibromosuccinic acid is formed. When the same reaction is carried out with fumaric acid, the product is mostly *meso*-dibromosuccinic acid.[10]

---

[7] Francis, *J. Am. Chem. Soc.*, **47**, 2347 (1925).

[8] Anantakrishman and Ingold, *J. Chem. Soc.*, **1935**, 1396.

[9] O'Connor, Baldinger, Vogt, and Hennion, *J. Am. Chem. Soc.*, **61**, 1454 (1939).

[10] For a discussion of this and other halogen addition reactions, see Hammett, *Physical Organic Chemistry*, pp. 147–149, McGraw-Hill Book Co., New York, 1940.

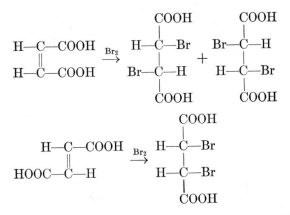

Deductions from the Experimental Data Concerning the Mechanism of Addition to an Olefin Not Attached to a Strongly Electronegative Group. Individually, none of the facts which have just been mentioned gives a very convincing picture of the mechanism of addition. Collectively, however, they provide a somewhat firmer foundation for our theory.

Because mixed products are obtained when olefins are treated with bromine in the presence of chloride ion (2), it is evident that addition must take place stepwise and not by the direct addition of a halogen molecule across the double bond. Points 1, 3, and 5 indicate that the attack is led by a positively charged species. For bromine this must be by Br⊕ or its equivalent. When the addition involves a hydrogen halide, the proton adds first. If it is coordinated with a solvent molecule the reaction proceeds slowly (5).

If it were not for the stereochemical results which have been obtained (6), we could consider that the addition of bromine, for example, proceeds essentially through the steps:

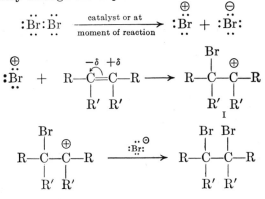

It is evident, however, that such intermediates cannot be wholly correct for free rotation would be expected about the carbon-carbon single bond in I, and this would lead to a mixture of *meso* and *racemic* products from either the *cis* or *trans* isomer.   Roberts and Kimball, however, have pointed out that when there is an atom, such as bromine, which has three pairs of unshared electrons near a carbonium ion, a covalent bond would almost surely be formed between the atom with unshared electrons and the carbon atom having an incomplete valence shell.[11]   Consequently, the true nature of the intermediate I is a three-membered *bromonium* ion (II) which would indeed prevent rotation about the carbon-carbon bond:

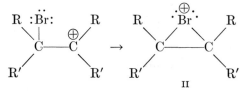

This intermediate, it will be observed, is the same one that was postulated to explain the abnormal course of the displacement reactions of the halohydrins (pp. 96, 99).

We can thus outline the complete formation of *meso*-dibromosuccinic acid from fumaric acid:

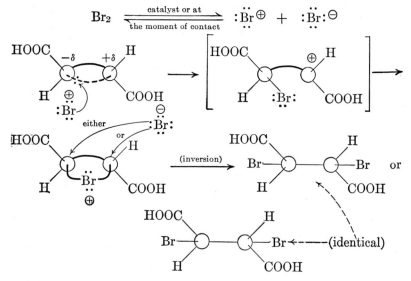

[11] Roberts and Kimball, *J. Am. Chem. Soc.*, **59**, 947 (1937).

In the addition of bromine to a conjugated system such as butadiene, both 1,2- and 1,4-addition products can occur, depending upon whether the reaction proceeds through form III or form IV:

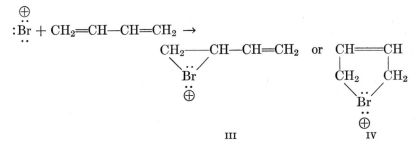

III   IV

Since form III is more highly strained, it is to be expected that 1,2-addition occurs at low temperatures in nonpolar media whereas higher temperatures and polar solvents favor addition to the ends of the conjugated system.[12] A conjugated acetylenic linkage, however, appears to be an exception. The addition of hydrogen chloride to vinylacetylene to give 2-chloro-1,3-butadiene has been shown to proceed by a preliminary 1,4-addition, followed by a rearrangement:[13]

$$H—C\equiv C—CH=CH_2 \xrightarrow{\text{conc. HCl}}$$

$$CH_2=C=CH—CH_2Cl \xrightarrow[\text{(Cu}_2\text{Cl}_2 + \text{HCl)}]{\text{rearrangement}} CH_2=\overset{\overset{\displaystyle Cl}{|}}{C}—CH=CH_2$$

REACTIONS INITIATED BY THE ATTACK OF CATIONS

Besides the addition of such reagents as halogens, hydrogen halides, or the hypohalous acids, there are other reactions which appear to proceed through addition mechanisms, but the exact course of the process is sometimes considerably obscured. The Friedel-Crafts addition of alkyl halides to olefins (p. 145), the self-condensation of olefins, and the alkylation of isoparaffins are examples in which attack at the double bond seems to be led by a carbonium ion.

The Self-Condensation of Olefins. In the search for hydrocarbon fuels having a high octane rating, considerable progress has been made by recombining the products of low molecular weight which are obtained

[12] For a discussion of addition to conjugated systems, see Allen in Gilman, *Organic Chemistry, An Advanced Treatise*, pp. 666–700, John Wiley and Sons, New York, 1943.

[13] For a leading reference, see Carothers and Berchet, *J. Am. Chem. Soc.*, **55**, 2807 (1933).

from cracking operations. Isobutylene, for example, will combine with itself in the presence of sulfuric acid to form a mixture of "diisobutylene," "trisobutylene," "tetraisobutylene," and products of even higher molecular weight. This process is usually called the self-condensation or polymerization of olefins.

The most generally satisfactory interpretation of this reaction [14] involves addition of the carbonium ion (V), formed by preliminary reaction of the olefin with sulfuric acid, to a molecule of unchanged olefin.

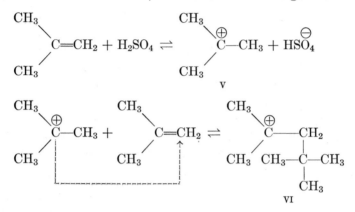

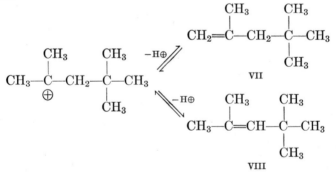

The new carbonium ion (VI) can then undergo elimination of the proton attached to the first or third carbon atom to form the olefins VII or VIII.

The establishment of similar equilibria between the newly formed olefins and V would of course lead to products of higher molecular weight.

It is interesting that "diisobutylene" actually contains a mixture of VII and VIII in the ratio 4 to 1.[15] This result would not have been pre-

[14] Whitmore, *Ind. Eng. Chem.*, **26**, 94 (1934).
[15] Whitmore and Church, *J. Am. Chem. Soc.*, **54**, 3711 (1932).

dicted from hyperconjugation (p. 116), but is in agreement with strain theory (p. 117).

The Alkylation of Isoparaffins. It has also been found that branched-chain paraffins will combine with olefins in the presence of an acid catalyst. Isobutylene and isobutane, for example, combine to form a mixture of hydrocarbons from which both *normal* products (those having a multiple of four carbon atoms) and *abnormal* products (those having a number of carbon atoms not a multiple of four) have been isolated. A flow sheet is outlined in Chart I (see p. 144) which will account for some of the products commonly obtained.

Although they follow each other in various combinations to obtain the products shown, the essential steps in the reaction are the following: [16]

(1) The formation of a carbonium ion by the addition of an acid to an olefin (pp. 35, 39):

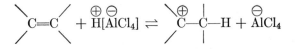

(2) The addition of this carbonium ion to another molecule of unreacted olefin:

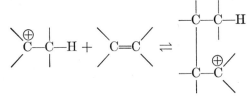

(3) The reaction of this or any other carbonium ion formed from it through:

   (a) The abstraction of a hydrogen atom together with its pair of electrons from an isobutane molecule (pp. 40, 60):

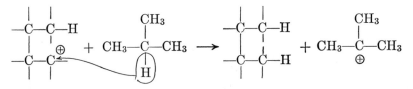

[16] (a) Bartlett, Condon, and Schneider, *J. Am. Chem. Soc.*, **66**, 1534 (1944); (b) Schmerling, *ibid.*, **67**, 1778 (1945).

CHART I

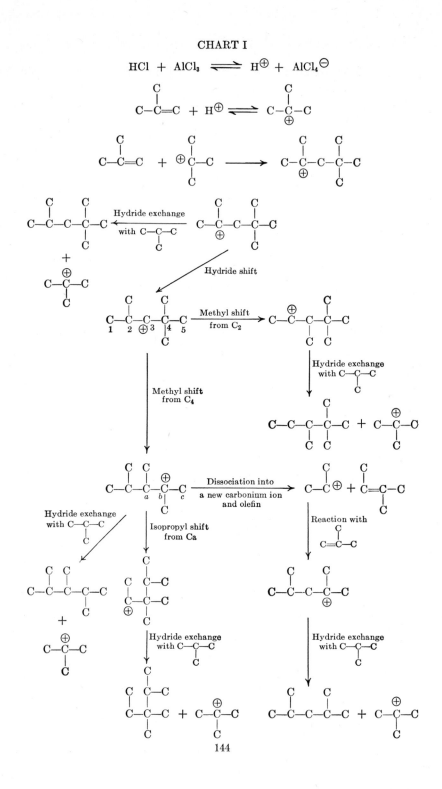

(*b*) The migration of a hydrogen atom with its pair of electrons from an α-carbon atom (p. 44):

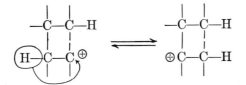

(*c*) The migration of an alkyl group with its pair of electrons from an α-carbon atom (p. 44):

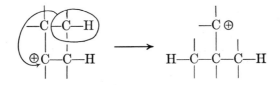

(*d*) The dissociation into a new carbonium ion and olefin:

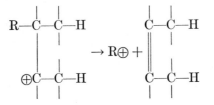

Actually there is indirect evidence for the individual steps of this rather complicated reaction series. Reaction 1 seems justified because isobutylene undergoes addition reactions readily (p. 138), and we have already seen that in the presence of aluminum chloride a hydrocarbon solution of an alkyl halide becomes a conductor (p. 40). Reaction 2 is an example of the well-known Friedel-Crafts addition of alkyl halides to olefins, but the product and one reactant are written in the carbonium ion forms which might be expected in the presence of aluminum chloride. The addition of *tert*-butyl chloride to ethylene, for example, gives 1-chloro-3,3-dimethylbutane in 75 per cent yield.[17]

$$CH_3-\underset{\underset{CH_3}{|}}{\overset{\overset{CH_3}{|}}{C}}-Cl + CH_2{=}CH_2 \xrightarrow[(-15 \text{ to } -10°)]{AlCl_3} CH_3-\underset{\underset{CH_3}{|}}{\overset{\overset{CH_3}{|}}{C}}-CH_2-CH_2Cl$$

[17] Schmerling, *ibid.*, **67**, 1152 (1945).

Undoubtedly it proceeds through the steps:

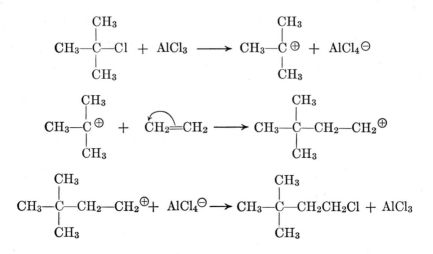

Reactions 3*b* and 3*c* illustrate principles of carbonium ion theory (Chapter 3). Reaction 3*a* has been beautifully demonstrated by Bartlett and his coworkers.[16a] When, for example, aluminum bromide in iso-pentane is treated with *tert*-butyl chloride at room temperature, after about 0.001 second the principal product is *tert*-amyl bromide:

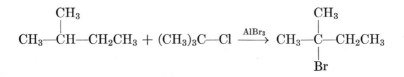

Clearly, the tertiary hydrogen atom is very rapidly equilibrated with bromide ion in such reaction mixtures. Although no isobutane was isolated from this particular combination, it has been shown that the reaction of isobutane with isopropyl chloride at 40 to 70° gave 60 to 90 per cent of the theoretical yield of propane.[16b]

THE NATURE OF ADDITION REACTIONS INITIATED BY THE ATTACK OF ANIONS

The addition reactions discussed thus far proceed by the preliminary attack of cations on the double bond. It was pointed out that most ionic addition reactions follow this course, and certain pieces of evidence were presented in its favor (pp. 137, 139). Some substituents, however, can so alter the normal availability of electrons in double bonds that attack may be initiated by nucleus-seeking (nucleophilic) reagents such as alkoxide ions, carbanions, or ammonia. This is particularly noticeable when such groups as cyano, nitro, or sulfonyl are present. Vinyl sulfones, for example, will add phenylmagnesium bromide, alcohol, or malonic ester.[18] These reagents usually do not react with isolated double bonds.

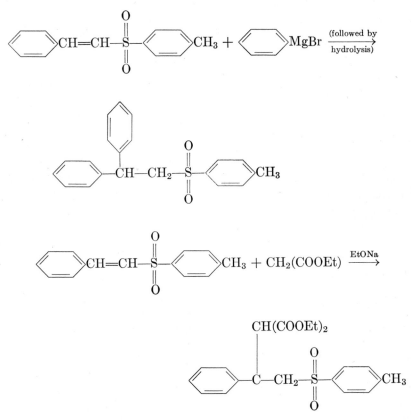

In many cases of addition to an α,β-unsaturated compound we cannot be sure whether addition takes place at the olefin double bond (i.e., 3,4-addition) or whether the preliminary step involves 1,4-addition followed by ketonization. Thus for the addition of a Grignard reagent to the

[18] Rothstein, *J. Chem. Soc.*, **1934**, 684; Kohler and Potter, *J. Am. Chem. Soc.*, **57**, 1316 (1935).

double bond of benzalacetophenone, we might write either

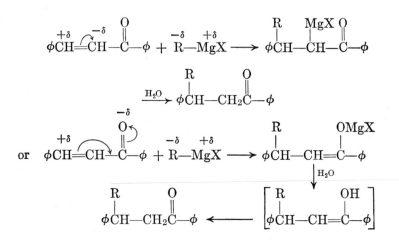

With certain reactions 1,4-addition seems to be clearly indicated. With benzaldesoxybenzoin, for example, it has been possible to isolate the pure crystalline enol (IX) from the hydrolysis of the Grignard addition product. The enol slowly rearranges irreversibly into the isomeric ketone (X), which is the product usually isolated from the reaction mixture.[19]

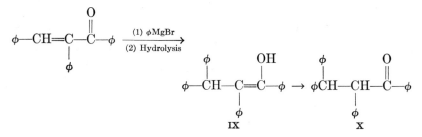

In at least two instances, however, anion-initiated addition to an olefinic linkage occurs when 1,4-addition is not possible: Fluoroethylenes will add alcohols in the presence of sodium alkoxide,[20] and bidiphenylene-ethylene (XI) will add Grignard reagents [21] as well as undergo the Michael condensation with fluorene.[22]

[19] Kohler, *Am. Chem. J.*, **36**, 181 (1906).

[20] Hanford and Rigby, U. S. Patent 2,409,274 (Oct. 15, 1946), (*C.A.*, **41**, 982 [1947]); Miller, Fager, and Griswold, *J. Am. Chem. Soc.*, **70**, 431 (1948). See also Coffman, Raasch, Rigby, Barrick, and Hanford, *J. Org. Chem.*, **14**, 747 (1949).

[21] Fuson and Porter, *ibid.*, 895.

[22] Pinck and Hilbert, *ibid.*, **68**, 2014 (1946).

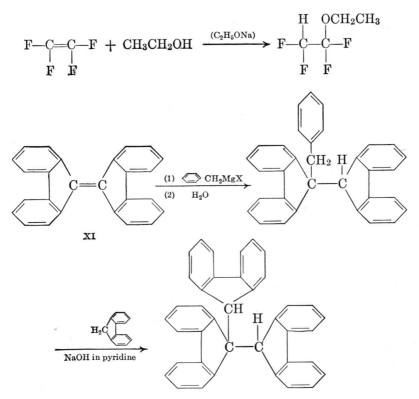

REACTIONS INITIATED BY THE ATTACK OF ANIONS

Michael Condensation.   One of the best-known examples of addition to a carbon-carbon double bond initiated by the attack of an anion is the Michael condensation in which compounds containing active methylene groups can be added to α,β-unsaturated molecules.   An example is the addition of malonic ester to benzalacetophenone: [23]

$$CH_2(COOEt)_2 + \phi CH{=}CH{-}\overset{O}{\overset{\|}{C}}{-}\phi \xrightarrow{NaOEt} \phi\overset{CH(COOEt)_2}{\overset{|}{C}H}{-}CH_2{-}\overset{O}{\overset{\|}{C}}{-}\phi$$

A very large number of active methylene components and acceptor components have been used successfully.[24]

It is interesting that from Michael condensations three different kinds of products have been obtained.[23]   (1) A *normal product* such as shown

[23] Connor and Andrews, *J. Am. Chem. Soc.*, **56**, 2714 (1934).

[24] Connor and McClellan, *J. Org. Chem.*, **3**, 570 (1939); Doering and Weil, *J. Am. Chem. Soc.*, **69**, 2461 (1947); Kloetzel, *ibid.*, **70**, 3571 (1948); Weiss and Hauser, *ibid.*, **71**, 2026 (1949).

above in which the fragments of the addendum appear to add to the α,β-unsaturated system as H $\oplus$ and an unrearranged carbanion [for example, :CH(COOEt)$_2$]. (2) A *rearrangement addition product* in which neither the carbon skeleton of the addendum nor the acceptor molecule remains intact. (3) New α,β-unsaturated carbonyl compounds and active methylene components which appear to be derived from a reversal of a Michael condensation, the *normal* product of which would have led to the intermediates described in (2). These products are called *rearrangement-retrogression products*.

The three possible products may be illustrated by the condensation of benzalacetophenone and ethyl methylmalonate.[25]

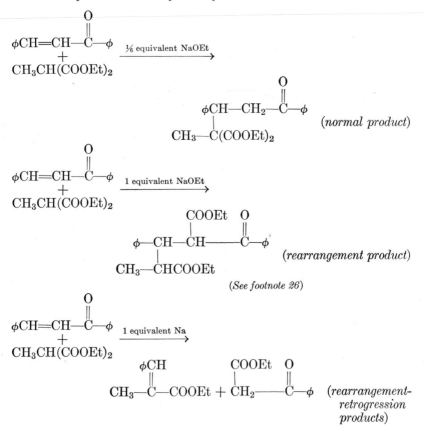

[25] (a) Holden and Lapworth, *J. Chem. Soc.*, **1931**, 2368; (b) Michael and Ross, *J. Am. Chem. Soc.*, **52**, 4598 (1930).

[26] In the reaction between benzalacetophenone and ethyl methylmalonate, this particular product has not been isolated. It is, however, illustrative of the structure which would be expected of a rearrangement product. See footnote 25a.

The normal addition reaction appears to be an example of addition to a double bond initiated by the attack of a carbanion:

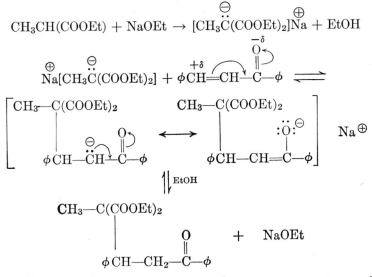

About the origin of the rearrangement and rearrangement-retrogression products, however, there is no general agreement.[27, 28a]

Cyanoethylation.[28b]   One of the most potent groups for the activation of a double bond towards the attack of anions is the cyano group. The simplest α,β-unsaturated organic cyanide, acrylonitrile, adds not only amines,[29] phenols,[30] hydrogen sulfide,[31] and alcohols,[32] but also compounds having reactive methylene or methinyl groups. These include carbocyclic compounds,[33] ketones,[34] aldehydes,[35] nitroparaffins,[36] and the haloforms.[37]   These addition reactions are called *cyanoethylation re-*

[27] Michael and Ross, *J. Am. Chem. Soc.*, **55**, 1632 (1933).

[28a] Holden and Lapworth, *J. Chem. Soc.*, **1931**, 2368.

[28b] For reviews of cyanoethylation see Bruson in Adams, *Organic Reactions*, Vol. V, p. 79, John Wiley and Sons, New York, 1949, and Saunders, *Ann. Repts. Chem. Soc. (London)*, **45**, 124 (1948).

[29] Ford, Buc, and Greiner, *J. Am. Chem. Soc.*, **69**, 844 (1947); British Patent 404,744 (1934), 457,621 (1936); Hoffmann and Jacobi, U. S. Patents 1,992,615 (1935), 2,017,537 (1935).

[30] German Patent 670,357 (1939); Langley and Adams, *J. Am. Chem. Soc.* **44**, 2326 (1922).

[31] German Patent 669,961 (1939); U. S. Patent 2,163,176.

[32] MacGregor and Pugh, *J. Chem. Soc.*, **1945**, 535.

[33] Bruson, *J. Am. Chem. Soc.*, **64**, 2457 (1942).

[34] Bruson and Reiner, *ibid.*, 2850.

[35] *Ibid.*, **66**, 56 (1944).

[36] Bruson and Reiner, *ibid.*, **65**, 23 (1943).

[37] Bruson, Niederhauser, Reiner, and Hester, *ibid.*, **67**, 601 (1945).

actions, since reaction always results in the attachment of a β-cyanoethyl group at the position of the reactive hydrogen atom. They are evidently special cases of the normal Michael condensation in which acrylonitrile is the acceptor molecule. The reaction of diethylacetaldehyde with acrylonitrile may be outlined as follows:

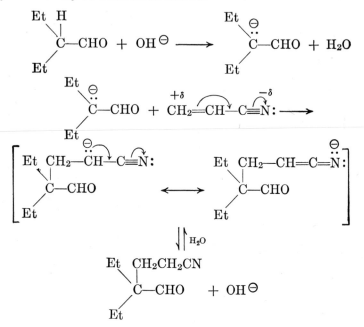

We may assume that the addition of amines or ammonia proceeds similarly through the ion R—N̈:H, or more probably through the ammonia or amine molecule:

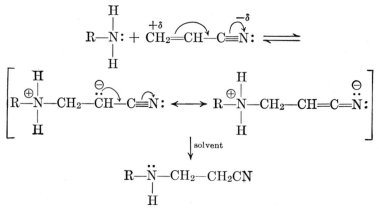

ADDITION REACTIONS IN WHICH THE TWO IONIC MECHANISMS OF ADDITION APPEAR TO BE TAKING PLACE SIMULTANEOUSLY

As might be expected, there are intermediate reactions in which the two ionic mechanisms of addition appear to be taking place simultaneously. For example, it has been found that the addition of halogens to maleic acid, fumaric acid, vinyl bromide, and allyl chloride is catalyzed by lithium chloride or lithium bromide.[38] It is evident, therefore, that although halogenation usually may be considered to be initiated and the rate controlled by the attack of a cation (p. 139), with these particular compounds the attack must be helped by the introduction of halide ion. Swedlund and Robertson [39] have pointed out that this behavior is not characteristic of all ethylenic systems, but only those to which strongly electron-attracting groups are attached. To such compounds the rate of addition initiated by a cation is slow (see p. 138) so that any catalytic effect upon the reaction initiated by an anion becomes apparent.

[38] Nozaki and Ogg, *J. Am. Chem. Soc.*, **64,** 697 (1942); *ibid.*, **704;** *ibid.*, **709.**
[39] Swedlund and Robertson, *J. Chem. Soc.*, **1947,** 632.

CHAPTER 8

NONCARBANION ADDITIONS TO CARBON-OXYGEN AND CARBON-NITROGEN MULTIPLE BONDS

GENERAL

In beginning our discussion of addition reactions at carbon-oxygen and carbon-nitrogen multiple bonds, it should be emphasized that these groups are undoubtedly better represented as resonance hybrids of the forms I and II (p. 14).

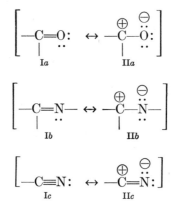

Furthermore, under the influence of a reagent, an electromeric shift may occur in the direction of II so as to increase further the electron-attracting character of the carbon atom and the electron-rich nature of the oxygen or nitrogen atom. In the extreme form of the resonance hybrid (II), there are both an atom with unshared electrons and a carbon atom with only six electrons in its outermost valence shell. Consequently, we might expect that there would be instances in which these groups initiate reactions by donating electrons to or accepting electrons from other reagents. If the oxygen atom of a carbonyl group acts as a donor,

we have the equation

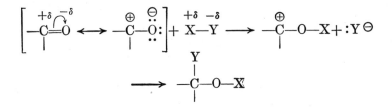

If the carbon atom initiates the addition by acting as an acceptor, we have

$$X—Y + \overset{+\delta}{\underset{|}{C}}\overset{-\delta}{=}\overset{}{O} \longrightarrow \overset{\oplus}{X} + Y—\overset{|}{\underset{|}{C}}—\overset{\ominus}{\underset{\cdot\cdot}{O}}: \longrightarrow Y—\overset{|}{\underset{|}{C}}—O—X$$

Although it is not always possible to determine which atom initiates an addition reaction, the establishment of the C—Y bond usually seems to be the most important step of the process, for near-by substituents which increase the positive character of the carbonyl carbon atom usually increase the reactivity of a carbonyl group towards addition reactions. Thus it is well known empirically that the reactivity of a carbonyl group generally decreases in the order:

$$\underset{R—\overset{}{\underset{}{C}}—H}{\overset{O}{\overset{||}{}}} > \underset{R—\overset{}{\underset{}{C}}—R'}{\overset{O}{\overset{||}{}}} > \underset{R—\overset{}{\underset{}{C}}—OR'}{\overset{O}{\overset{||}{}}} > \underset{R—\overset{}{\underset{}{C}}—NHR'}{\overset{O}{\overset{||}{}}} > \underset{R—\overset{}{\underset{}{C}}—\overset{\ominus}{\underset{\cdot\cdot}{O}}:}{\overset{O}{\overset{||}{}}}$$

We readily see that this is the order which would be predicted if we assume that it is the decreasing positive character of the carbonyl carbon atom which is responsible for the decreasing order of reactivity (p. 127). It is clear, however, that other factors besides the positive character of the carbonyl carbon atom play an important part in addition reactions. In Tables 1 and 2 we see that the general order of reactivity of certain carbonyl compounds with phenylmagnesium bromide is different from the order of reactivity of the same compounds with semicarbazide. Furthermore, even the order of reactivity of the carbonyl components with semicarbazide is changed as the pH is varied. It is apparent that unless a definite acidity and solvent are specified, any numerical values assigned to carbonyl compounds as relative reactivities are meaningless.

TABLE 1

RELATIVE REACTION RATES OF ALDEHYDES AND KETONES WITH
PHENYLMAGNESIUM BROMIDE

(Data from Kharasch and Cooper, *J. Org. Chem.*, **10**, 47 [1945])

Carbonyl Compound	Relative Reactivity
Acetone	15.5
Acetaldehyde	10.8
Benzaldehyde	5.4
Pinacolone	4.8
Cyclohexanone	1.0

TABLE 2

RATES OF FORMATION OF SEMICARBAZONES

Carbonyl Compound	Velocity Constant of Formation		
	Acetate Buffer *	Chloroacetate Buffer *	Water, pH7 †
Acetone	5.92	23.2	6.02
Acetaldehyde	.....	......	361
Benzaldehyde	5.1	145	2.05
Pinacolone	0.41	1.48	0.068
Cyclohexanone	24.9	fast	36

* Westheimer, *J. Am. Chem. Soc.*, **56**, 1964 (1934).
† Conant and Bartlett, *ibid.*, **54**, 2896 (1932).

Since the important step in most additions to carbon-oxygen or carbon-nitrogen multiple bonds is the establishment of the bond to the carbon atom, the presence of an acid should catalyze such reactions. The addition of a proton to a carbonyl group, for example, would render the carbonyl carbon atom more positive:

$$\overset{+\delta}{-C}\!\!=\!\!\overset{-\delta}{O} + H^{\oplus} \longrightarrow -\overset{\oplus}{C}\!-\!OH$$

In general, simple addition reactions are indeed acid-catalyzed. It is important to note, however, that the fragment which is to add to this carbon atom will invariably contain an atom with an unshared electron pair and it will also be capable of adding a proton:

$$\overset{\oplus}{H} + :\!\overset{\ominus}{A} \rightleftharpoons H\!-\!A$$

When a proton adds to :A$\ominus$, its electron-donating capacity is destroyed, and the concentration of reagent which can react with the carbonium ion is thereby reduced. The addition of acid therefore *increases* the acceptor capacity of the carbonyl group but at the same time *decreases* the concentration of reagent with which it can react. Consequently there is usually an optimum pH for addition reactions above which and below which the rate decreases. The point has been beautifully illustrated in the condensation of furfural with semicarbazide (Fig. 1). In strongly

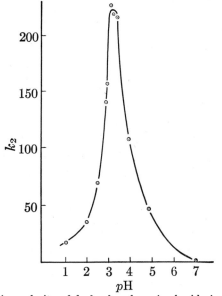

FIG. 1. Condensation velocity of furfural and semicarbazide in 0.5 M phosphate, citrate, and acetate buffers. (Data from Conant and Bartlett, *J. Am. Chem. Soc.*, **54**, 2893 [1932].)

basic solution the carbonyl group is not activated, and in strongly acidic solution the concentration of the reactive species (III) is low because of the equilibrium:

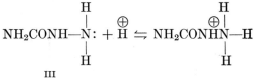

The reaction, therefore, proceeds best at pH 3.13.

ADDITIONS TO CARBONYL GROUPS

Hydration and Hemiacetal Formation. There is considerable evidence which indicates that when an aldehyde is dissolved in water or alcohols a reversible equilibrium is established between the aldehyde and its hydrate or hemiacetal:

$$\underset{\overset{|}{R}}{\overset{H}{|}}C{=}O + H_2O \rightleftarrows R{-}\underset{\underset{OH}{|}}{\overset{\overset{H}{|}}{C}}{-}OH$$

$$R{-}\overset{\overset{H}{|}}{C}{=}O + R'OH \rightleftarrows R{-}\underset{\underset{OR'}{|}}{\overset{\overset{H}{|}}{C}}{-}OH$$

The solution frequently becomes warm,[1,2] and its refractive index,[1] viscosity,[2] freezing point–composition curve,[3a] and ultraviolet absorption spectrum [3b] are not those which would be expected if no reaction took place.   Usually hydrates or hemiacetals of simple aldehydes are too unstable to be isolated, but a number of them are actually known and their physical properties have been determined.[4]   When the carbonyl group is attached to an electron-attracting group (making the carbonyl carbon atom abnormally positive), stable hydrates are frequently formed. Glyoxal, chloral, and ketomalonic acid are common examples.

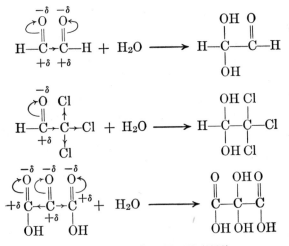

[1] Adkins and Broderick, *J. Am. Chem. Soc.*, **50**, 499 (1928).

[2] Müller, *Helv. Chim. Acta*, **17**, 1231 (1934).

[3] (a) McKenna, Tartar, and Lingafelter, *J. Am. Chem. Soc.*, **71**, 729 (1949); (b) Herold, *Z. Elektrochem.*, **39**, 566 (1933).

[4] *Schimmel and Co., Ann. Rept.*, **1933**, 71, (*C.A.*, **30**, 3774 [1936]).

Acetal formation involves the etherification of a hemiacetal. It is discussed in Chapter 11. Since a hemiacetal is formed so easily from a carbonyl compound and alcohol, it is not surprising to find that carbohydrates (polyhydroxy derivatives of aldehydes and ketones) frequently exist as cyclic structures in which a hemiacetal linkage is formed intramolecularly. Furthermore, since hemiacetal formation is a reversible process, many carbohydrates exhibit the phenomenon of mutarotation. The liberation of the free aldehyde (V) from the internal hemiacetal of the sugar (IV) destroys the optical activity of the hemiacetal carbon atom (in this case carbon 1), and reformation results in the formation of an equilibrium mixture of two diastereoisomers.

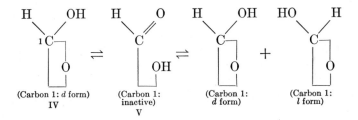

Insight into the mechanism of hemiacetal formation and hydrolysis has been gained by a careful study of mutarotation. In this reaction both the aldehyde and the alcohol are attached to the same molecule, and the rate of hydrolysis can be followed by optical or dilatometric methods. In water containing O^{18}, mutarotation is not accompanied by oxygen exchange at low temperatures.[5] The reaction is catalyzed by both bases and acids,[6] but apparently the presence of at least traces of both acids and bases in the reaction mixture is necessary. With tetramethylglucose, mutarotation does not occur either in the acidic solvent cresol or in the basic solvent pyridine, but it proceeds readily in a mixture of the two.[7] A plausible explanation [8] of this phenomenon is that, in acid-catalyzed hydrolysis, reversible addition of acid to the ethereal oxygen atom occurs readily (VI to VII) but a base is required to complete the reactions (VII, VIII, to IX).

[5] Goto, J. Chem. Soc. (Japan), **61**, 1283 (1940); (C.A., **37**, 4055 [1943]); ibid., **62**, 408 (1941), (C.A., **37**, 4055 [1943]).

[6] Bronsted and Guggenheim, J. Am. Chem. Soc., **49**, 2554 (1927).

[7] Lowry and Faulkner, J. Chem. Soc., **127**, 2883 (1925).

[8] Hammett, Physical Organic Chemistry, p. 337, McGraw-Hill Book Co., New York, 1940. See also Swain, J. Am. Chem. Soc., **70**, 1125 (1948).

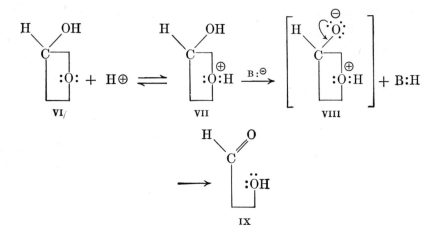

Similarly, with base-catalyzed hydrolysis, removal of the hydrogen atom of the hydroxyl group is a rapid reversible reaction (X to XI), but a proton must be abstracted from the solvent or added acid to complete the reaction (XI, XII, to XIII).

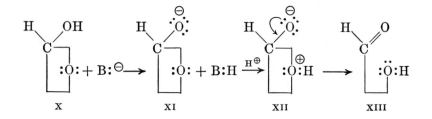

Cyanohydrin Formation. The rate-determining step in the formation of cyanohydrins is the addition of cyanide ion to the carbonyl group. The mechanism of the reaction can be illustrated by the following equations:

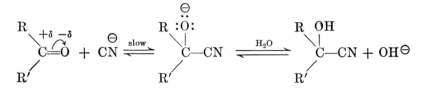

Undoubtedly acids enhance the acceptor capacity of the carbonyl group.

Their presence, however, converts the cyanide ion to undissociated hydrogen cyanide, and solutions which contain only undissociated hydrogen cyanide have been shown to react much more slowly with a carbonyl group than solutions of hydrogen cyanide which contain cyanide ion.[9] Thus the reaction between camphorquinone and hydrogen cyanide required eight to ten hours for completion. When a drop of aqueous alkali was added the reaction occurred in the course of a few seconds. When a quantity of mineral acid was present, no reaction took place during three weeks.

Bisulfite Addition Products and the Bucherer Reaction. The addition of sodium bisulfite to aldehydes and some ketones superficially appears to involve the addition of the elements $Na^{\oplus}$ and $HSO_3^{\ominus}$ to the carbonyl group. Kinetic studies, however, indicate that the reaction is complicated and probably involves sulfite rather than bisulfite ion.[10] One possible mechanism is the following:

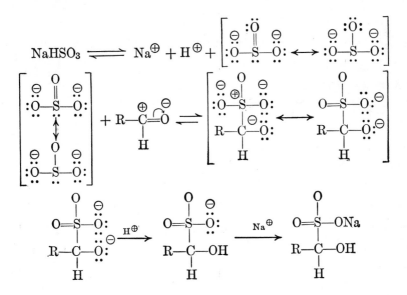

There can be no doubt that there is a carbon-sulfur bond in the bisulfite addition product. Fusion of iodomethane sulfonic acid (which itself can be converted into methane sulfonic acid) with potassium acetate leads to the same acetoxymethane sulfonic acid that can be obtained from the acetylation of the bisulfite addition product of formaldehyde: [11]

[9] Lapworth, *J. Chem. Soc.*, **83**, 996 (1903).

[10] Stewart and Donnally, *J. Am. Chem. Soc.*, **54**, 3561 (1932).

[11] Lauer and Langkammerer, *ibid.*, **57**, 2360 (1935).

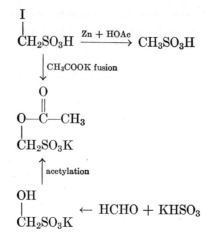

In the presence of aqueous ammonium bisulfite an equilibrium often exists between aromatic amines and aromatic hydroxy compounds. This reaction is called the Bucherer reaction [12] and its mechanism appears to involve the intermediate formation of a bisulfite addition complex. The mechanism which is most widely accepted is that of Fuchs and Stix,[13] illustrated here with 1-hydroxynaphthalene-4-sulfonic acid:

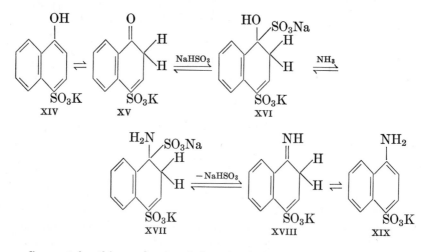

Support for this mechanism is based principally upon the fact that a number of aromatic hydroxy compounds form bisulfite addition com-

<hr />

[12] For a review of the Bucherer reaction, see Drake in Adams, *Organic Reactions*, Vol. I, p. 105, John Wiley and Sons, New York, 1942.

[13] Fuchs and Stix, *Ber.*, **55**, 658 (1922).

plexes [14] and the fact that the displacement of the hydroxyl group by the amino group (XVI to XVII) appears to occur in the aliphatic series. Thus the bisulfite addition product of formaldehyde readily forms aminomethane sulfonic acid when it is treated with aqueous ammonia: [15]

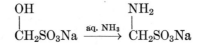

$$\begin{matrix} OH & & NH_2 \\ | & \xrightarrow{aq.\ NH_3} & | \\ CH_2SO_3Na & & CH_2SO_3Na \end{matrix}$$

The kinetics of the Bucherer reaction [16] is also consistent with the equations shown in formulas XIV to XIX.

From a theoretical point of view this is an extremely interesting reaction. The displacement of a hydroxyl group from a saturated carbon atom appears to be unknown in basic solution. The fact that aminomethane sulfonic acid can be isolated from the bisulfite addition product of formaldehyde on treatment with ammonia does not prove, of course, that a *direct* displacement, such as is indicated in XVI to XVII, actually occurred. Furthermore, it is quite clear that preliminary formation of an imine (XVIII) is not necessary for the reaction of aromatic amines with sodium bisulfite (steps XIX to XVIII to XVII, etc.). 1-Dimethylaminonaphthalene-4-sulfonic acid (XX) and 1-aminonaphthalene-4-sulfonic acid (XIX) show similar reaction kinetics [16a] when treated with sodium bisulfite, yet with the tertiary amine (XX) it is not possible to write an imino structure corresponding to XVIII.

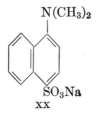

$$N(CH_3)_2$$

$$SO_3Na$$

XX

The Addition of Ammonia Derivatives.   Ammonia and almost all its derivatives appear to add to carbonyl groups by the donation of the free electron pair on nitrogen to the carbon atom of the carbonyl group, followed by the migration of a proton from the resulting positively charged nitrogen atom to the negative oxygen atom.   The reaction is catalyzed by acids, and often, where a primary amine is employed, water

[14] Drake in Adams, *Organic Reactions*, Vol. I, p. 107, John Wiley and Sons, New York, 1942; and Cowdrey, *J. Chem. Soc.*, **1946**, 1041.

[15] Raschig, *Ber.*, **59**, 865 (1926).

[16] (*a*) Cowdrey and Hinshelwood, *J. Chem. Soc.*, **1946**, 1036; (*b*) Cowdrey, *ibid.*, 1044, 1046.

splits out from the resulting addition product. The process may be generalized as follows for primary amines or ammonia:

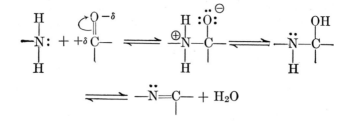

(1) *Semicarbazone* [17] *and hydrazone formation:*

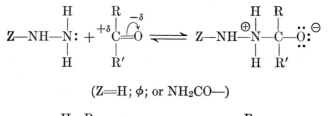

$$(Z=H; \phi; \text{ or } NH_2CO—)$$

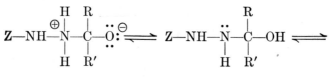

(2) *Oxime formation:*

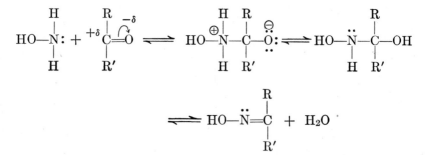

[17] Conant and Bartlett, *J. Am. Chem. Soc.*, **54**, 2881 (1932).

It is interesting that in neutral or acid solution, a comparative study of the kinetics of formation of d-carvone phenylhydrazone, semicarbazone, and oxime showed that they all follow the same course of reaction.[18]

With hydroxylamine, however, strong alkali has an accelerating effect upon oxime formation while it does not upon semicarbazone formation.[19] Presumably this is due to the formation of the ion $H\overset{\text{H}}{\underset{\cdot\cdot}{\text{O}\text{N}}}:\ominus$,

which like $\overset{\ominus}{C N}$ adds more readily to a carbonyl group than the undissociated molecule.

$$:\overset{\text{H}}{\underset{\text{H}}{N}}—OH \xrightarrow{\text{[base:]}\ominus} :\overset{\text{H}}{\underset{\text{H}}{N}}—\overset{\ominus}{\underset{\cdot\cdot}{O}}: + \text{base:H}$$

$$:\overset{\text{H}}{\underset{\text{H}}{N}}—\overset{\ominus}{\underset{\cdot\cdot}{O}}: \rightleftharpoons :\overset{\ominus}{\underset{\text{H}}{N}}—OH$$

(3) *Amide formation:*

$$R—\overset{O}{\overset{\|}{C}}—OH + NH_3 \rightleftharpoons [RCOO]\ominus + NH_4\oplus$$

$$\Updownarrow$$

$$R—\overset{OH}{\underset{NH_2}{\overset{|}{\underset{|}{C}}}}—OH \rightleftharpoons R—\overset{O}{\underset{NH_2}{\overset{\|}{\underset{|}{C}}}} + H_2O$$

(4) *Strecker synthesis:*

$$NH_4CN \rightleftharpoons HCN + NH_3$$

$$R—\overset{}{\underset{H}{\overset{|}{C}}}{=}O + NH_3 \rightleftharpoons R—\overset{NH_2}{\underset{H}{\overset{|}{\underset{|}{C}}}}—OH \rightleftharpoons R—\overset{NH}{\underset{H}{\overset{\|}{\underset{|}{C}}}} + H_2O \xrightarrow{\text{HCN}} R—\overset{NH_2}{\underset{H}{\overset{|}{\underset{|}{C}}}}—CN$$

[18] Stempel and Schaffel, *ibid.*, **66**, 1158 (1944).
[19] See Conant and Bartlett, *J. Am. Chem. Soc.*, **54**, 2894 (1932).

The Leuckart Reaction.   When high boiling carbonyl compounds are heated with formamide or ammonium formate the corresponding amino derivative is often obtained.[20a]   This reaction is usually called the Leuckart reaction.[20b]   One possible mechanism for it is the following:

$$HCOONH_4 \rightleftharpoons HCOOH + NH_3$$

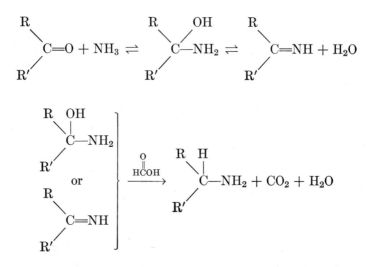

In support of this mechanism it has been found that the reaction is catalyzed by small amounts of Lewis acids such as ammonium sulfate or magnesium chloride.[21]   Ammonium formate rather than formamide appears to be the essential reactant.   At 120 to 130° in diethylene glycol solution, ammonium formate will bring about the transformation whereas formamide will not.[22]   The last step in the reaction sequence, the reduction of the ketone ammonia or imine by formic acid, is supported by the observation that benzalaniline and *p*-dimethylamino-phenylmethylcarbinol can be reduced by triethylammonium formate to benzylaniline and *p*-dimethylaminoethylbenzene, respectively.[22]

[20a] Goodson, Wiegand, and Splitter, *J. Am. Chem. Soc.*, **68**, 2174 (1946); Crossley and Moore, *J. Org. Chem.*, **9**, 529 (1944); Novelli, *J. Am. Chem. Soc.*, **61**, 520 (1939); Johns and Burch, *ibid.*, **60**, 919 (1938); Ingersoll, Brown, Kim, Beauchamp, and Jennings, *ibid.*, **58**, 1808 (1936).

[20b] For a review of the Leuckart reaction see Moore in Adams, *Organic Reactions*, Vol. V, p. 301, John Wiley and Sons, New York, 1949.

[21] Webers and Bruce, *J. Am. Chem. Soc.*, **70**, 1422 (1948).

[22] Alexander and Wildman, *ibid.*, 1187.

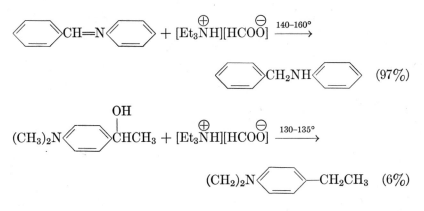

$$\left\langle\underset{}{\bigcirc}\right\rangle CH{=}N\left\langle\underset{}{\bigcirc}\right\rangle + [Et_3\overset{\oplus}{N}H][H\overset{\ominus}{C}OO] \xrightarrow{140-160°}$$

$$\left\langle\underset{}{\bigcirc}\right\rangle CH_2NH\left\langle\underset{}{\bigcirc}\right\rangle \quad (97\%)$$

$$\overset{\displaystyle OH}{\underset{\displaystyle |}{(CH_3)_2N\left\langle\underset{}{\bigcirc}\right\rangle CHCH_3}} + [Et_3\overset{\oplus}{N}H][H\overset{\ominus}{C}OO] \xrightarrow{130-135°}$$

$$(CH_2)_2N\left\langle\underset{}{\bigcirc}\right\rangle{-}CH_2CH_3 \quad (6\%)$$

The methylation of amines by formic acid and formaldehyde [23] is evidently a special case of the Leuckart reaction.

Addition of Hydride Ions. Although hydride ions and their reactions are well known to inorganic chemists, many organic chemists have received with considerable skepticism the postulation of the transfer of a hydrogen atom with a pair of electrons.

We have already seen that in acid solution many carbonium ion rearrangements may be interpreted as involving the intramolecular migration of an alkyl group with a pair of electrons to an electronically deficient atom (Chapter 3). A number of other reactions appear to involve a similar migration of a hydrogen atom with a pair of electrons (i.e., a hydride ion). Not only do these reactions proceed by the internal shift of a hydride ion (pp. 68, 145), but others are known in which an *inter*molecular transfer is involved (pp. 60, 146).

In basic solution there is convincing evidence, at least for one reaction, that an *intra*molecular hydride ion shift occurs. When phenylglyoxal is treated with barium deuteroxide, mandelic acid is formed which contains no deuterium attached to a carbon atom.[24] Furthermore, the reaction is first order in hydroxide ion and the glyoxal,[25] and there is no rearrangement in the carbon skeleton during the transformation.[24, 26] This can mean only that the transfer of the hydrogen atom with its pair of electrons to the carbonyl group must take place by an *intra*molecular path.

[23] Clarke, Gillispie, and Weisshaus, *ibid.*, **55**, 4571 (1933); Icke, Wisegarver, and Alles, *Org. Syntheses*, **25**, 89 (1945). See also Staple and Wagner, *J. Org. Chem.*, **14**, 559 (1949).

[24] Doering, Taylor, and Schoenwaldt, *J. Am. Chem. Soc.*, **70**, 455 (1948).

[25] Alexander, *ibid.*, **69**, 289 (1947).

[26] Neville, *ibid.*, **70**, 3499 (1948).

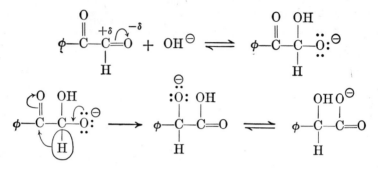

Other reactions which appear to involve hydride ion transfers are the Cannizzaro reaction, the Meerwein-Ponndorf-Verley reduction, and the reduction of carbonyl compounds with alcoholic alkali.

The Cannizzaro [27] **Reaction.** As the Cannizzaro reaction is usually carried out, an aldehyde is treated with strong aqueous alkali. An equimolecular mixture of the corresponding acid and alcohol is obtained from the two-phase reaction mixture. With some aldehydes, finely divided silver or silver oxide [28] must also be added to the alkali. In such heterogeneous systems there is good evidence that three different reaction courses are being followed and that at least one of them involves free radicals.[29] In methanol solution, however, the reaction is not influenced by small amounts of free radical initiators (benzoyl peroxide or sodium peroxide) or inhibitors (hydroquinone or diphenyl amine [25]). Under these conditions, the reaction can be interpreted as involving an intermolecular hydride ion transfer: [29, 30]

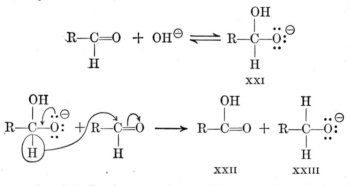

[27] For a review of the Cannizzaro reaction, see Geissman in Adams, *Organic Reactions*, Vol. II, p. 94, John Wiley and Sons, New York, 1944.

[28] Pearl, *J. Am. Chem. Soc.*, **68**, 429 (1946); *ibid.*, 1100; *J. Org. Chem.*, **12**, 79 (1947); *ibid.*, 85.

[29] Kharasch and Snyder, *ibid.*, **14**, 819 (1949).

[30] L. P. Hammett, private communication.

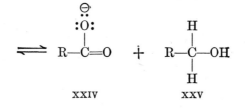

XXIV   XXV

Thus, the reaction with aromatic aldehydes is second order in aldehyde and first order in hydroxide ion,[31] and no deuterium becomes attached to carbon in the alcohol fragment when the reaction is carried out in deuterium oxide solution.[32] It is interesting that when the reaction is carried out with benzaldehyde in the cold and in the absence of excess alkali, benzyl benzoate has been isolated.[33] Although the point has not yet been settled, it seems probable that the ester is formed by a secondary reaction between the benzylate ion which is formed initially (XXIII) and two molecules of benzaldehyde: [29, 30]

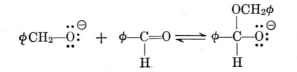

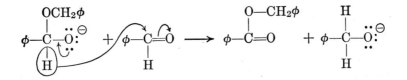

Another mechanism for the reaction has been suggested [34] but it has been impossible to obtain supporting evidence for it in an apparently favorable case.[35]

Hydroxyl-Carbonyl Group Equilibria.   When an alcohol and a carbonyl compound are brought together in basic solution, a reversible

[31] Tommila, *Ann. Acad. Sci. Fennicae*, Ser., **A59**, No. 8, 3 (1942), (*C.A.*, **38**, 6175 [1944]); Molt, *Rec. trav. chim.*, **56**, 233 (1937); Blanksma and Zaaijer, *ibid.*, **57**, 727 (1938); Lock and Eitel, *Monatsh.*, **72**, 392 (1939).

[32] Friedenhagen and Bonhoeffer, *Z. physik. Chem.*, **A181**, 379 (1938).

[33] Lachman, *J. Am. Chem. Soc.*, **45**, 2356 (1923).

[34] Geissman in Adams, *Organic Reactions*, Vol. II, p. 96, John Wiley and Sons, New York, 1944.

[35] Alexander, *J. Am. Chem. Soc.*, **70**, 2592 (1948).

equilibrium is formed (in addition to hemiacetals or hemiketals (p. 157)) between the starting materials and products which appear to have been formed from the oxidation of the alcohol and the reduction of the carbonyl compound. The best-known example of this kind of reaction is the Meerwein-Ponndorf-Verley reduction with aluminum alkoxides:[36]

There are, however, other examples. In the presence of potassium tertiary butoxide, quinine and benzophenone are equilibrated with quininone and benzhydrol.[37]   Benzyl,[38] methyl,[39] ethyl,[39, 40] propyl,[39] butyl,[39] and amyl[39] alcohols will reduce ketones to the corresponding secondary alcohols on heating at high temperatures with sodium or potassium hydroxide.   In all these cases it is probable that the reaction proceeds by the intermolecular transfer of a hydride ion from the alkoxide ion to the carbonyl group.

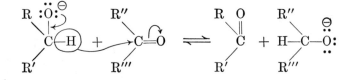

Experiments with deuterated optically active primary amyl alcohol, fluorenone, and sodium ethoxide, for example, showed a direct transfer of hydrogen from the hydroxyl carbon to the carbonyl carbon atom without intervention of the solvent.[41]   We should expect that, like all carbonyl additions, hydride addition reactions would be acid-catalyzed. Apparently, in aluminum isopropoxide and isopropyl alcohol the optimum acid strength of the solution has been reached.   Some alkoxide ions

[36] For a review of the reaction, see Wilds in Adams, *Organic Reactions*, Vol. II, p. 178, John Wiley and Sons, New York, 1944.

[37] Woodward, Wendler, and Brutschy, *J. Am. Chem. Soc.*, **67**, 1426 (1945).

[38] Palfray, Sabetay, and Mastagli, *Compt. rend.*, **203**, 1523 (1936).

[39] Hargreaves and Owen, *J. Chem. Soc.*, **1947**, 750.

[40] Rubin, *J. Am. Chem. Soc.*, **66**, 2075 (1944).

[41] Doering and Aschner, *Abstracts of Papers*, p. 21L, 112th Meeting of the American Chemical Society, New York, N. Y., September 1945.

must be present, and the acceptor capacity of the carbonyl carbon atom is enhanced by combination of the aluminum atom with the carbonyl oxygen atom:

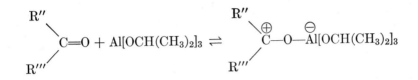

In connection with hydride ion transfers, it will be observed that addition should occur at a positive center. Since olefin additions are usually initiated by attack at a negative center, the Meerwein-Ponndorf-Verley reduction should occur preferentially at the carbonyl group of unsaturated carbonyl compounds. This is actually the case both in this reaction and in reductions carried out with lithium aluminum hydride.[42]

Addition of Sodium to Esters. When sodium is added to esters, different products are obtained, depending upon the solvents employed. In alcohol solution the Bouveault-Blanc reduction occurs and an alcohol is formed. In an inert solvent such as ether, acyloins are produced. These reactions are closely related and will be considered together.

Originally it was thought that chemical reductions brought about by dissolving metals in a suitable solvent proceeded by the intermediate formation of nascent hydrogen. It now seems much more probable that many such reductions proceed through a series of addition and displacement reactions.[43] The direct reaction of sodium with ethanol in the Bouveault-Blanc reduction, for example, is believed to be a side reaction which wastes sodium. The reaction of esters with sodium and alcohol may be explained in this way:[44] The direct addition of sodium to the carbonyl group produces a sodium ester ketal (XXVI), which is almost immediately decomposed by reaction with the alcohol present to give the addition product of an aldehyde and sodium alkoxide (XXVII). When the alcohol reacts too slowly with the sodium adduct (tertiary alcohols) or, where no alcohol is present, a free radical type reaction takes place which leads to a diketone (XXVIII to XXIX). Subsequent reaction of the aldehyde or the diketone with more sodium leads ultimately to the alkoxide derived from the ester (XXX) or to the acyloin (XXXI):

[42] Nystrom and Brown, *J. Am. Chem. Soc.*, **69**, 1197 (1947); Hochstein and Brown, *ibid.*, **70**, 3484 (1948); Martin, Schepartz, and Daubert, *ibid.*, 2601.

[43] See Campbell and Campbell, *Chem. Revs.*, **31**, 78 (1942).

[44] Hansley, *Ind. Eng. Chem.*, **39**, 55 (1947).

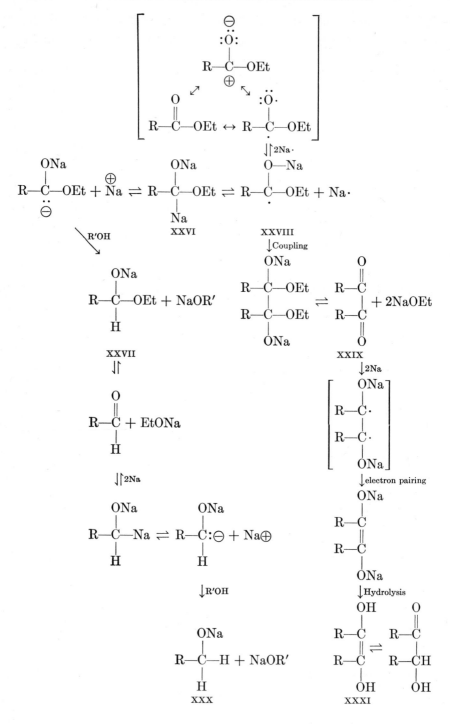

In the commercial utilization of the reduction of esters by sodium, a secondary alcohol such as methyl-isobutylcarbinol is employed. This particular alcohol reacts rather slowly with sodium but rapidly enough with the sodium ester ketal (XXVI) to keep acyloin formation from dominating the reaction.

ADDITIONS TO NITRILES

Addition of Alcohols, Water, and Amines. In general, additions to nitriles resemble additions to carbonyl groups with the exception that the primary addition products of simple molecules such as alcohols, water, and ammonia result in the formation of somewhat more stable compounds. Alcohols, for example, react with nitriles in the presence of an acidic catalyst to form salts of imino ethers:

$$R—C\equiv N: + H\oplus \rightleftharpoons [R—C:::\overset{\oplus}{N}—H \leftrightarrow R—\overset{\oplus}{C}::\overset{..}{N}—H]$$

$$\downarrow \text{ EtOH}$$

$$\underset{R—C=\overset{..}{N}H}{\overset{\overset{\oplus}{Et:\overset{..}{O}:H}}{|}} \rightleftharpoons \underset{\underset{\oplus}{R—C=NH}}{\overset{Et\overset{..}{O}: H}{|\quad|}}$$

Similarly, amines, present as sulfonates,[45] undergo the same type of acid-catalyzed addition to form amidine salts:

$$RNH_3\oplus + \phi SO_3\ominus \rightleftharpoons RNH_2 + \phi SO_3H$$

$$R—C\equiv N: + H\oplus \rightleftharpoons [R—C:::\overset{\oplus}{N}H \leftrightarrow R—\overset{\oplus}{C}::\overset{..}{N}H]$$

$$\downarrow \text{ RNH}_2$$

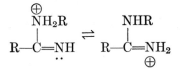

[45] Oxley and Short, *J. Chem. Soc.*, **1946**, 147.

With water, an amide is formed:

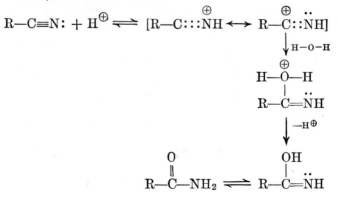

Frequently it is not possible to isolate the amide, for with simple molecules the corresponding amides are much more rapidly hydrolyzed by acids or bases than the nitriles themselves.[46]

One of the most interesting features of the hydrolysis of nitriles is the striking specificity of different acids in the reaction. At high acid strengths, hydrochloric acid is a much more effective reagent than sulfuric acid,[47] and anhydrous orthophosphoric acid appears to be even more potent.[48] The part the anion plays in the reaction is not completely

$$\underset{\mid}{\overset{\text{Cl}}{}}$$

clear, but possibly a reactive intermediate such as R—C=NH is formed which provides an alternative, perhaps more accessible, path to the amide. Kinetic data support this hypothesis.[47]

[46] Kilpi, Z. physik. Chem., **86,** 641 (1914); ibid., **740.**

[47] For a summary of the work which has been done on this subject, see Kilpatrick, J. Am. Chem. Soc., **69,** 42 (1947).

[48] See Baker and Taylor, Sidgwick's Organic Chemistry of Nitrogen, p. 313, Oxford University Press, London, England, 1942.

CHAPTER 9

CARBANION ADDITION TO CARBONYL GROUPS

There are a number of reactions which actually involve addition to carbon-oxygen or carbon-nitrogen multiple bonds but are often disguised by subsequent reactions or by the fact that the fragment which adds is often itself derived from a carbonyl compound. Thus both aldol formation (p. 176) and the Kolbe reaction (p. 197) appear to follow courses similar to the addition of hydrogen cyanide to benzaldehyde (p. 160), yet the structures of the end products are considerably different. As we have seen in Chapter 6, carbanions can be produced from a wide variety of starting materials. Under some conditions almost all of them will add to carbonyl groups. In nearly all the reactions in which the carbanion is derived from a compound containing a carbonyl group, the fundamental process may be diagrammed as follows:

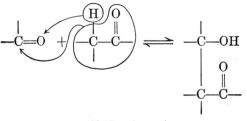

Aldol Reaction

In some cases, the initial reaction is followed by an elimination reaction resulting in the formation of an α,β-unsaturated carbonyl compound:

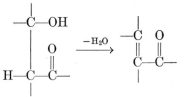

Perkin, Knoevenagel, and Claisen-Schmidt Condensations

175

When the carbonyl group is present in an ester, an alcohol is lost from the resulting hemiketal of the β-keto carbonyl compound which is formed:

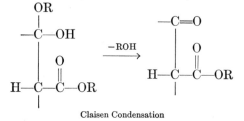

Claisen Condensation

Accordingly, these reactions may be divided into three major groups:

I. *Aldol reactions*, in which no subsequent elimination occurs and which lead to β-hydroxy carbonyl compounds (Aldol formation).

II. *The formation of α,β-unsaturated carbonyl compounds*, in which the initial addition reaction is followed by dehydration (Perkin, Knoevenagel, and Claisen-Schmidt condensations).

III. *Claisen condensations*, in which β-keto carbonyl compounds are formed by the loss of a negative ion from an incipient hemiketal (Claisen condensations, and Dieckmann ring closures).

In addition to these reactions in which the carbanions are supplied from carbonyl compounds, we will discuss in this chapter Grignard reactions, the benzilic acid rearrangement, the benzoin condensation, and the Kolbe synthesis of hydroxy aromatic acids. These reactions illustrate the addition of other kinds of carbanions to carbonyl groups. The benzilic acid rearrangement is an example of the *intramolecular* addition of a group with its pair of electrons to a carbonyl carbon atom.

ALDOL REACTIONS

Aldol reactions (as well as the initial steps in the formation of unsaturated carbonyl compounds and β-ketoesters) proceed through the following sequence of reactions:

$$[B:]\ominus + H-\overset{\displaystyle O}{\underset{\displaystyle |}{C}}-\overset{O}{\overset{\|}{C}} \rightleftharpoons BH + \left[\ominus:\overset{O}{\underset{|}{C}}-\overset{O}{\overset{\|}{C}} \leftrightarrow \overset{\ominus}{\underset{|}{C}}=\overset{:\ddot{O}:}{\underset{|}{C}} \right]$$

I

(*Continued on facing page*)

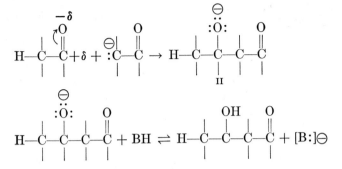

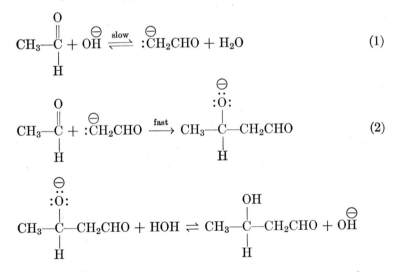

A base extracts an α-hydrogen atom from a molecule of the carbonyl compound to form the resonance hybrid (I). This anion adds through its carbanion form to a second molecule of the carbonyl compound to give the alkoxide intermediate (II). Since this intermediate is a relatively strong base, there will be competition between it and the original base for the proton which was extracted initially from the carbonyl compound to form the carbanion. For the formation of aldol, in which the base is usually sodium or potassium hydroxide, we have:

$$CH_3-\overset{\overset{\displaystyle O}{\|}}{\underset{\underset{\displaystyle H}{|}}{C}} + O\overset{\ominus}{H} \overset{slow}{\rightleftharpoons} \overset{\ominus}{:}CH_2CHO + H_2O \tag{1}$$

$$CH_3-\overset{\overset{\displaystyle O}{\|}}{\underset{\underset{\displaystyle H}{|}}{C}} + \overset{\ominus}{:}CH_2CHO \overset{fast}{\longrightarrow} CH_3-\overset{\overset{\displaystyle :\overset{\ominus}{O}:}{|}}{\underset{\underset{\displaystyle H}{|}}{C}}-CH_2CHO \tag{2}$$

$$CH_3-\overset{\overset{\displaystyle :\overset{\ominus}{O}:}{|}}{\underset{\underset{\displaystyle H}{|}}{C}}-CH_2CHO + HOH \rightleftharpoons CH_3-\overset{\overset{\displaystyle OH}{|}}{\underset{\underset{\displaystyle H}{|}}{C}}-CH_2CHO + O\overset{\ominus}{H}$$

With acetaldehyde, step 1 must be the slowest [1] since it has been shown that in spite of the fact that two molecules of aldehyde undergo reaction, the kinetics of the transformation is first order in aldehyde.[2] A slow initial step is in agreement with the fact that no deuterium becomes at-

[1] See Bell, *Trans. Faraday Soc.*, **37**, 717 (1941).
[2] Bell, *J. Chem. Soc.*, **1937**, 1637.

tached to carbon when the condensation is carried out in deuterium oxide solution.[3]   In other words, step 2 must proceed almost instantaneously, making step 1 essentially irreversible.   If step 1 were reversible, deuterium would be introduced at the α-carbon atom:

$$:\overset{\ominus}{C}H_2CHO + D_2O \rightleftharpoons CH_2DCHO + \overset{\ominus}{O}D \rightleftharpoons :\overset{\ominus}{C}HDCHO + HOD, \text{ etc.}$$

In all aldol reactions the rate relationship of these two steps is not necessarily the same.   The formation of diacetone alcohol from acetone, for example, proceeds with deuterium exchange.[4]   Consequently, we can conclude that for this reaction, step 2 proceeds at a much slower rate relative to step 1.

The Tollens' condensation is a crossed aldolization employing formaldehyde and an aldehyde or a ketone in the presence of a weak base. Since formaldehyde has no α-hydrogen atoms, it is an extremely reactive carbonyl acceptor (p. 155).   Consequently, reaction occurs readily with carbanions and leads to polymethylol derivatives: [5]

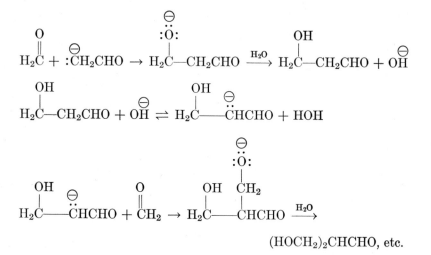

$$(HOCH_2)_2CHCHO, \text{ etc.}$$

Unless precautions are observed,[5] a crossed Cannizzaro reaction with formaldehyde occurs when all the α-hydrogen atoms are replaced by methylol groups.   Acetaldehyde, for example, leads to pentaerythritol: [6]

[3] Bonhoeffer and Walters, Z. physik. Chem., **A181**, 441 (1938).

[4] Walters and Bonhoeffer, ibid., **182**, 265 (1938).

[5] See Fitzky, U. S. Patent 2,275,586 (March 22, 1939).

[6] Schurink, Gilman-Blatt, Organic Syntheses, Collective Vol. I, p. 425, John Wiley and Sons, New York, 1941.

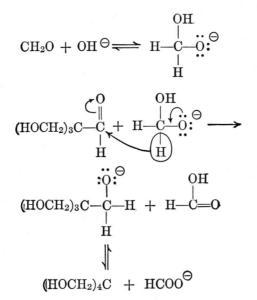

The formation of acetylenic carbinols from sodium acetylides and carbonyl compounds,[7] the addition of nitroparaffins to aldehydes,[8] and the Thorpe reaction are other transformations closely related to aldol reactions.

FORMATION OF α,β-UNSATURATED CARBONYL COMPOUNDS

The general sequence for the formation of α,β-unsaturated carbonyl compounds by condensation reactions may be illustrated as follows:

$$
\underset{\underset{|}{\overset{|}{CH_2}}}{} - \overset{O}{\underset{}{\overset{\|}{C}}} + [B:]^{\ominus} \rightleftharpoons :\overset{|}{\underset{|}{CH}} - \overset{O}{\overset{\|}{C}} + BH \tag{3}
$$

$$
\underset{\underset{|}{\overset{|}{CH_2}}}{} - \overset{O}{\overset{\|}{C}} + :\overset{|}{CH} - \overset{O}{\overset{\|}{C}} \rightarrow \underset{\underset{|}{\overset{|}{CH_2}}}{} - \overset{\overset{\ominus}{\overset{..}{:O:}}}{\underset{|}{C}} - \overset{|}{\underset{|}{CH}} - \overset{O}{\overset{\|}{C}} \tag{4}
$$

[7] See Jones, *Ann. Reps.*, **41**, 165 (1944).
[8] Bourland and Hass, *J. Org. Chem.*, **12**, 704 (1947).

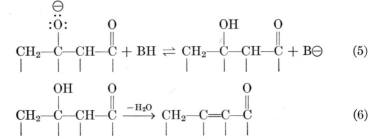

$$CH_2-\overset{:\overset{\ominus}{\overset{..}{O}:}}{\underset{|}{C}}-\overset{}{\underset{|}{CH}}-\overset{O}{\overset{||}{C}} + BH \rightleftharpoons CH_2-\overset{OH}{\underset{|}{C}}-\overset{}{\underset{|}{CH}}-\overset{O}{\overset{||}{C}} + B\ominus \qquad (5)$$

$$CH_2-\overset{OH}{\underset{|}{C}}-\overset{}{\underset{|}{CH}}-\overset{O}{\overset{||}{C}} \overset{-H_2O}{\longrightarrow} CH_2-\overset{}{\underset{|}{C}}=\overset{}{\underset{|}{C}}-\overset{O}{\overset{||}{C}} \qquad (6)$$

In this sequence, the steps are identical with those which were postulated for aldolization except that they are followed by a dehydration step. Consequently, these reactions are facilitated by reaction mixtures which are basic but contain a certain amount of acid (mostly present, of course, as its salt). This conclusion becomes clear if we ask ourselves how water is lost in the process. In Chapter 5 we saw that dehydration reactions usually require acid and proceed through the steps:

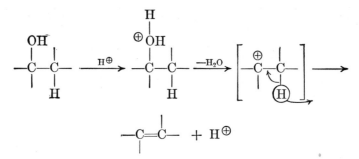

It is well known that the dehydration of aldol to crotonaldehyde is readily effected in the presence of a trace of mineral acid. Since aldols also undergo dehydration in the presence of base, there may be the possibility of a base-catalyzed dehydration:

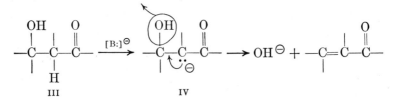

Normally alcohols are stable to strong bases, but with β-hydroxy carbonyl compounds (where the removal of an α-hydrogen atom occurs readily [III to IV]) the subsequent elimination of a hydroxyl group might follow.

The important point, however, is that no reasonable mechanism for the elimination of water can be written until step 5 is complete, and step 5 requires the presence of a proton donor (an acid). These considerations have been nicely verified in the Knoevenagel reaction (pp. 182, 183), where it has been found that a base alone is not as effective a catalyst as it is in the presence of acetic acid.

Perkin Reaction.[9]   When an aromatic aldehyde is heated with an anhydride of the type $(RCH_2CO)_2O$ and a salt of the corresponding acid, substituted β-arylacrylic acids are obtained. This reaction is usually called the Perkin reaction. Its mechanism may be outlined as follows:

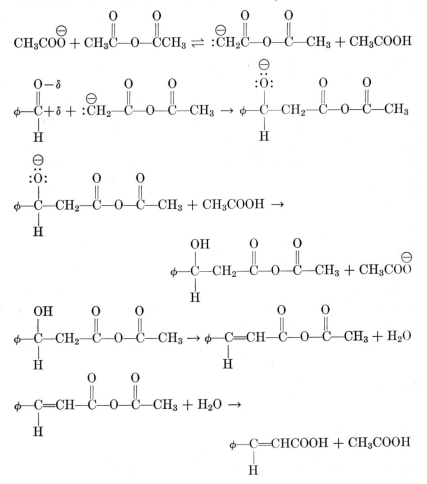

---

[9] For a review of the Perkin reaction, see Johnson in Adams, *Organic Reactions*, Vol. I, p. 210, John Wiley and Sons, New York, 1942.

For some time considerable confusion existed as to whether the salt or the anhydride condensed with the aldehyde,[9, 10] for when benzaldehyde was heated with acetic anhydride and sodium butyrate, ethylcinnamic acid was found to be the main product.[11] It is now quite clear, however, that it is the anhydride which undergoes condensation and that the sodium salt is simply the strongest commonly used base that will not destroy the anhydride. Thus acetic anhydride will condense with benzaldehyde in the presence of pyridine or triethyl amine whereas benzaldehyde, sodium acetate, and pyridine will not undergo the same reaction.[12] When an acid salt different from the anhydride is employed, an equilibrium

$$2RCOONa + (R'CO)_2O \rightleftharpoons (RCO)_2O + 2R'COONa$$

exists.[10] Condensation through $(RCO)_2O$ would, of course, give the impression that the Perkin reaction proceeded through the sodium salt (RCOONa).

It is interesting that in one case, at least, a condensation related to the Perkin reaction has been stopped at the "aldol" stage. When a mixture of benzaldehyde and ethyl acetate was added to an ether solution of sodium triphenyl methyl and the reaction mixture was worked up after one minute, a 26 per cent yield of the "aldol" (V) was obtained.[13] When the reaction was carried out over a longer period of time, ethyl cinnamate was formed.[14]

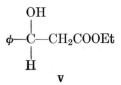

V

Knoevenagel Reaction. Aldehydes and ketones frequently react with active methylene compounds such as acetoacetic ester, malonic ester, and cyanoacetic ester to form α,β-unsaturated carbonyl compounds. This reaction usually is called the Knoevenagel reaction. As has been said, the process appears to proceed best in the presence of ammonia derivatives and acetic acid.[15] The reaction can be illustrated with the

[10] See Breslow and Hauser, **61**, 786 (1939).
[11] Fittig and Slocum, *Ann.*, **227**, 53 (1885).
[12] Kalnin, *Helv. Chim. Acta*, **11**, 977 (1928).
[13] Hauser and Breslow, *J. Am. Chem. Soc.*, **61**, 793 (1939).
[14] Müller, Gawlick, and Kreutzmann, *Ann.*, **515**, 110 (1934).
[15] (a) Cope, *J. Am. Chem. Soc.*, **59**, 2327 (1937); (b) Cope, Hofmann, Wyckoff, and Hardenbergh, *ibid.*, **63**, 3452 (1941).

condensation of methyl n-amyl ketone and methyl cyanoacetate: [15a]

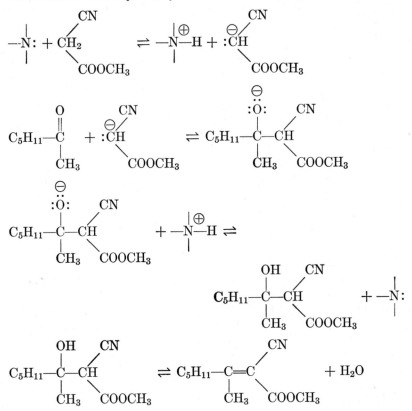

It is interesting that, of the number of catalysts and conditions investigated, acetamide in glacial acetic acid proved to be the best. Apparently in this sequence the dehydration step is extremely important.

There can be no doubt that the reaction is completely reversible at each step as these equations show. When methyl 1-methylheptylidine cyanoacetate (VI) was heated with water at 125° for 5 hours, the yield

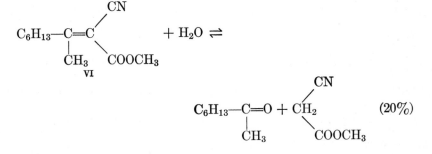

of methyl n-hexyl ketone was 20 per cent, and 70 per cent of the unsaturated ester was recovered.[15a]

The Claisen-Schmidt Reaction. When aromatic aldehydes are treated with aliphatic ketones in the presence of base, three reactions might be expected: a Cannizzaro reaction of the aromatic aldehyde; an aldol-type reaction of the ketone; or a crossed aldol reaction between the ketone and the aromatic aldehyde. In either of the last two possibilities dehydration might also occur. Undoubtedly all these reactions will take place in strong base, but by employing about 10 per cent aqueous sodium hydroxide, good yields are often obtained of α,β-unsaturated carbonyl compounds derived from a crossed aldol reaction between the aldehyde and the ketone. This reaction, generally called a Claisen-Schmidt reaction, can be illustrated by the synthesis of benzalacetophenone.[16]

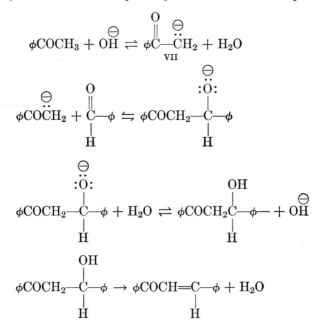

Although we might not have been able to make predictions concerning the relative rates of the Cannizzaro and the aldol reactions, we could have predicted that the crossed aldol reaction would proceed faster than the reaction between two molecules of acetophenone. Both aldol reactions would involve the same intermediate carbanion (VII), but benzaldehyde would be expected to be a better acceptor molecule than acetophenone (see p. 155).

[16] Kohler and Chadwell, in Gilman-Blatt, *Organic Syntheses*, Collective Vol. I, p. 78, John Wiley and Sons, New York, 1941.

CLAISEN CONDENSATIONS [17]

To most organic chemists the term *Claisen condensation* implies the self-condensation of esters in the presence of sodium ethoxide to give β-ketoesters. A Dieckmann condensation is a special Claisen condensation in which an ester of a dibasic acid undergoes intramolecular condensation to produce a cyclic β-ketoester. From the point of view of mechanism, however, this idea of a Claisen condensation is perhaps unnecessarily limited, for there are a number of extremely closely related reactions which involve compounds other than esters, and bases other than sodium ethoxide. In all these transformations, the essential feature of the reaction is the addition of a carbanion to a carbonyl group, followed by the loss of a negative ion from the seat of reaction.

The general steps in the self-condensation of esters in the presence of a base such as sodium ethoxide may be outlined as follows, using ethyl acetate as an example:

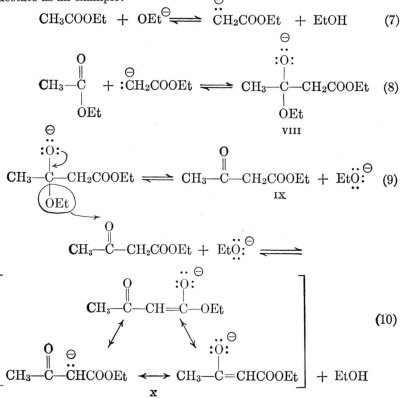

[17] For a review of the Claisen or acetoacetic ester condensation, see Hauser and Hudson, in Adams, *Organic Reactions*, Vol. I, p. 266, John Wiley and Sons, New York, 1942.

With these reactions, also, a carbanion is formed which undergoes addition to a carbonyl group. The difference between these reactions and those in which aldols or α,β-unsaturated carbonyl compounds are formed, however, is that an ethoxide ion (or, as we shall see later, another negative ion) is lost from the intermediate VIII forming the β-keto ester (IX). The last step, in which the sodio derivative (X) is formed, appears to be extremely important in order to displace the equilibrium of all these equations to favor the condensation product. It is significant, for example, that condensation cannot be effected with sodium ethoxide when the expected product is a β-ketoester which has no hydrogen atoms on the methylene carbon atom and, therefore, cannot form a sodio-derivative analogous to X. Thus ethyl isobutyrate will not undergo a Claisen condensation in the presence of sodium ethoxide to give $(CH_3)_2CHCOC(CH_3)_2COOEt$, although there appears to be no reason for steps 7 and 8 and 9 to fail. This view is particularly strengthened by the fact that ethyl isobutyrate *can* be made to condense with itself in the presence of sodium triphenylmethyl [18] or mesityl magnesium bromide [19] and with ethyl benzoate in the presence of sodium triphenylmethyl.[20] With these reactions, step 10 is apparently unnecessary because the step corresponding to 7 (equation 11) is effectively irreversible:

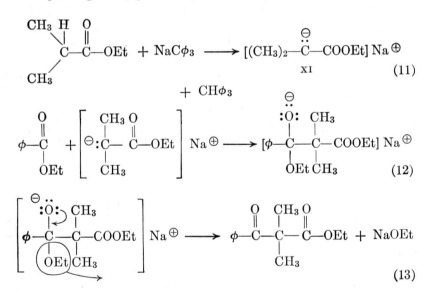

[18] Hauser and Renfrow, *J. Am. Chem. Soc.*, **59**, 1823 (1937).
[19] Spielman and Schmidt, *ibid.*, 2009.
[20] Renfrow and Hauser, *ibid.*, **60**, 463 (1938).

When sodium ethoxide is employed, all these steps are probably completely reversible since a number of β-ketoesters undergo retrogression in the presence of sodium ethoxide. Ethyl propionate, for example, forms ethyl α-propionylpropionate in the presence of sodium ethoxide, but when the ketoester is treated with alcoholic sodium ethoxide, it reverts to ethyl propionate.[21]

An inspection of the mechanism of the condensation of ethyl isobutyrate with ethyl benzoate reveals that the essential feature of the acceptor molecule (ethyl benzoate) is that it be able to lose a negative ion (ethoxide ion in this case) in step 13 to form the β-ketoester. Accordingly it has been found possible to carry out successful Claisen condensations between ethyl isobutyrate and other acceptor molecules such as benzoyl chloride, or benzoic anhydride.[22] For all of these reactions we may generalize step 13 as follows:

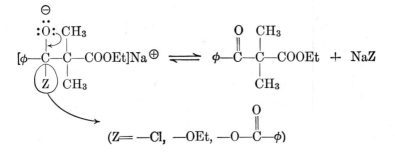

Similarly the carbanion (XI) need not have been derived from an ester. Methyl ketones in the presence of sodamide [23] can be acylated with esters to give β-diketones of the type $RCOCH_2COR'$. The mechanism appears to be:

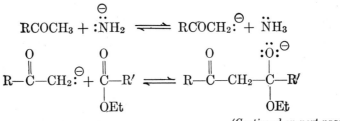

(Continued on next page)

[21] Dieckmann, *Ber.*, **33**, 2670 (1900).
[22] Hudson, Dick, and Hauser, *J. Am. Chem. Soc.*, **60**, 1960 (1938).
[23] Adams and Hauser, *ibid.*, **66**, 1220 (1944).

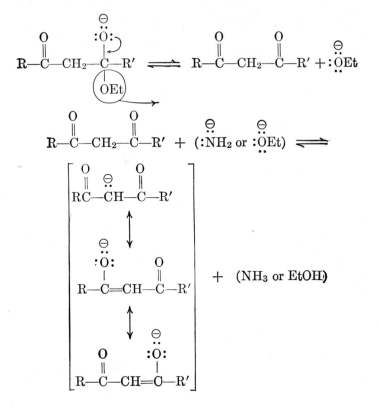

MISCELLANEOUS CARBANION ADDITIONS TO CARBONYL GROUPS

Grignard Reagents.[24]   In the majority of their reactions, Grignard reagents behave as if they dissociate under appropriate conditions into carbanions, dialkyl magnesium compounds, and free radicals:

$$R\cdot\ +\ \cdot MgX \rightleftharpoons \boxed{RMgX} \rightleftharpoons \overset{\ominus}{R}:\ +\ \overset{\oplus}{MgX}$$

$$\text{⇅}$$

$$\tfrac{1}{2}R_2Mg + \tfrac{1}{2}MgX_2$$

The equilibria are believed to be rapid and reversible.   In the presence of a polar group, such as the carbonyl group, the reagent appears to react through the ionic form:

[24] For an excellent discussion of the ionic nature of the Grignard reaction, see Evans and Pearson, *J. Am. Chem. Soc.*, **64**, 2865 (1942).

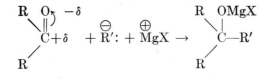

With certain reactive halides, esters, and ethers, displacement reactions occur:

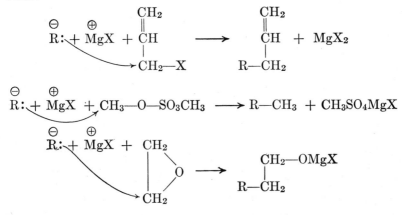

All these reactions resemble carbanion processes (pp. 175, 201).

In other instances, free radicals appear to be involved. When one mole of magnesium is added to two moles of triphenylmethyl bromide, the solution contains triphenylmethyl free radicals and hexaphenylethane but *no Grignard reagent.*[25] Addition of a second mole of magnesium produces the Grignard reagent in almost quantitative yield:

$$\left. \begin{array}{c} Mg + 2\phi_3CBr \rightarrow MgBr_2 + \phi_3\!-\!C\!-\!C\!-\!\phi_3 \\ \Updownarrow \\ \phi_3C\cdot + \phi_3C\cdot \end{array} \right\} \xrightarrow{Mg} 2\phi_3CMgBr$$

Other examples of the free radical nature of Grignard reagents include a number of coupling reactions which are catalyzed by traces of small quantities of metallic halides, particularly those of iron, nickel, and cobalt.[26]

There can be no doubt that a Grignard reagent exists in equilibrium with a molecule of dialkyl or diaryl magnesium and magnesium halide. The addition of dioxane will precipitate $RMgX$ and MgX_2 from an

[25] Gomberg and Bachmann, *J. Am. Chem. Soc.*, **52**, 2455 (1930).

[26] For a leading reference, see Kharasch, Morrison, and Urry, *ibid.*, **66**, 368 (1944).

ether solution of a Grignard reagent,[27, 28, 29] and this method can even be used for the preparation of R_2Mg compounds. Reasoning from analogy with the behavior of an ether solution of zinc chloride and ethylmagnesium bromide, in which exchange to diethyl zinc has been shown to be almost instantaneous, we can conclude that if MgX_2 were added to a solution containing R_2Mg the exchange to $RMgX$ would be almost instantaneous.[24] Since, however, few reagents are known that will react with R_2Mg but not with $RMgX$,[30] it is customary to discuss ionic Grignard reactions from the point of view of $R:\ominus$ and $\oplus MgX$.

A careful examination of the nature of Grignard reagents, however, makes it clear that we are not dealing with free carbanions. A Grignard reagent will conduct an electrical current, but transference studies indicate that there is magnesium *in the anion as well as in the cation* and that more equivalents of R plus X are transferred to the anode than faradays of electricity are used.[24] Furthermore, conductance experiments show that at moderate concentrations, the molar conductance of a Grignard reagent *increases* rapidly with concentration, in contrast to simple ionization phenomena in which molar conductance usually decreases with concentration.

The interpretation of these facts is that the overall formula for ionization involves not one but several molecules of $RMgX$. The ions are not simple ones but rather complexes of several units involving ether molecules, MgX_2 and R_2Mg. R_2Mg, $RMgX$, and MgX_2 are all acceptor molecules because magnesium has only four electrons in its valence shell and it can accommodate four more. At the same time $RMgX$, MgX_2, and Et_2O are donor molecules because each contains an atom with unshared electrons. The anions, therefore, which are produced by the agency of an electrical current are probably complexes of one or more of the following types:

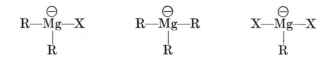

This view is in accordance with conductance data showing that several molecules of a Grignard reagent are necessary for the ionization reaction to occur.

[27] Schlenk and Schlenk, Jr., *Ber.*, **62**, 920 (1929).

[28] Cope, *J. Am. Chem. Soc.*, **57**, 2238 (1935).

[29] Noller and Raney, *ibid.*, **62**, 1749 (1940).

[30] Gilman, *Organic Chemistry*, p. 517, John Wiley and Sons, New York, 1943.

Since the cation $\overset{\oplus}{\text{MgX}}$ can accommodate six electrons about it and also carries a positive charge, it will undoubtedly be very highly solvated and not very mobile because of its attraction for solvent molecules. This is in agreement with transference data which indicate that there is a large transference of matter to the anode. Several possible structures for the cation are the following:

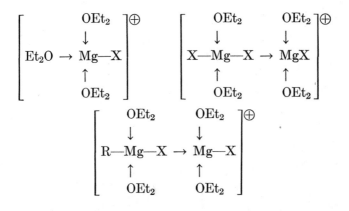

A careful study of the kinetics of the Grignard reaction with nitriles has verified the fact that the concept of a free carbanion is indeed an oversimplification of the actual course of a Grignard addition reaction.[31] Benzonitrile was found to react with *n*-butylmagnesium bromide in accordance with strictly second-order kinetics. Thus the slow solvolytic ionization of the reagent to a carbanion cannot be the rate-determining step of the transformation. Alternatively, it has been suggested that the preliminary step in Grignard addition reactions involves the displacement of one of the solvating ether molecules of the complex $RMgX \cdot 2Et_2O$ by a free electron pair of the carbonyl or nitrile group. For example:

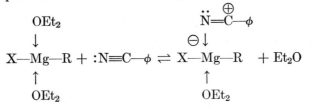

This reaction could then be followed by the intramolecular (equation 14)

[31] Swain, *J. Am. Chem. Soc.*, **69**, 2306 (1947).

or intermolecular (equation 15) transfer of an alkyl group to the positive carbon atom: [32]

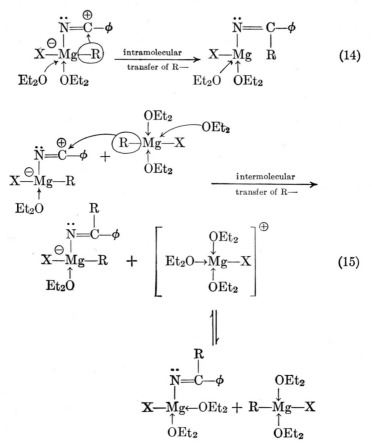

If this interpretation is correct, addition to nitriles must proceed by a rate-determining intramolecular transfer in order to satisfy second-order kinetics. In support of this hypothesis it has been pointed out that the rates of reaction of benzonitrile with different Grignard reagents are in the order:

[p-tolyl   or   α-naphthyl] > phenyl > p-chlorophenyl > methyl

[32] The idea of a complex coordinated through magnesium followed by an intramolecular shift seems to have been in the minds of many chemists for a long time. See particularly Hess and Rheinboldt, *Ber.*, **54**, 2043 (1921); Meisenheimer, *Ann.*, **442**, 180 (1925); and footnote 38.

So far as the data overlap, this is the sequence observed for the migrational aptitude of the different groups in the pinacol rearrangement (p. 47).

Although ketones react too rapidly with Grignard reagents for the kinetics to be studied, certain qualitative considerations suggest that Grignard additions to this group sometimes proceed by the intermolecular path. Benzophenone, for example, reacts rapidly with one equivalent or less of phenyl magnesium bromide to form a precipitate, but benzophenone is recovered by the addition of water.[33] With an excess of Grignard reagent, however, the precipitate rapidly dissolves to give complete reaction. As Swain has pointed out, in this instance we probably have *excess* uncomplexed Grignard reagent reacting directly with benzophenone already polarized by complex formation.

The Reformatsky reaction [34] can also be pictured as a kind of Grignard addition reaction in which magnesium is replaced by zinc, a metal less reactive than magnesium towards carbonyl groups. This reagent, too, is probably highly solvated since zinc diethyl in benzene is a nonconductor, but in ether the solution conducts readily. Presumably this is due to the solvation of the $RZn\oplus$ cation.[24] Here again we find that a considerable amount of aldehyde or ketone may be recovered from the reaction mixture upon hydrolysis of the addition complex, but in this reaction it is apparently due to an unusual tendency of the Reformatsky reagent to enolize the aldehyde or ketone.[35] Ethyl acetate may be isolated from the reaction mixture before hydrolysis, and this, of course, corresponds to the reaction of the reagent with an active hydrogen compound.

In many Grignard reactions there is no particular advantage of these rather complicated mechanisms over the simplification of writing the reaction as a carbanion addition or substitution reaction. In so doing, however, we should not forget that it is a short-hand representation which for some reactions may have no factual basis.

In certain instances a consideration of the actual mechanism of a Grignard addition provides considerable insight into the nature of a reaction. For example, 1,4-addition can be pictured as proceeding in part through a quasi six-membered ring: [36]

[33] See Gilman and Jones, *J. Am. Chem. Soc.*, **62**, 1243 (1940).

[34] For a review of the Reformatsky reaction, see Shriner in Adams, *Organic Reactions*, Vol. I, p. 1, John Wiley and Sons, New York, 1942.

[35] Newman, *J. Am. Chem. Soc.*, **64**, 2131 (1942).

[36] Lutz and Reveley, *ibid.*, **63**, 3184 (1941).

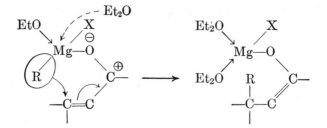

Since lithium belongs to the first group of the periodic table and probably does not undergo preliminary complex formation as readily as magnesium, this concept provides an explanation for the higher ratio of 1,2 to 1,4 addition with lithium alkyls than with Grignard reagents.[37] Similarly the enolization of ketones by Reformatsky or Grignard reagents can be explained by cyclic intermediates:

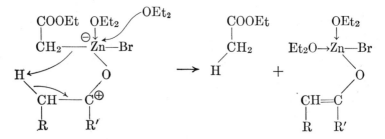

Reactions of allylic Grignard reagents (p. 287) may also be discussed advantageously from the point of view of preliminary complex formation.[38]

Benzoin Condensation. In the presence of alkali cyanides, magnesium,[39] or amalgamated aluminum,[39] aromatic aldehydes often dimerize to form α-hydroxy ketones:

$$2ArCHO \rightarrow ArCHOHCOAr$$

When the reaction is specifically catalyzed by cyanide ion it is usually referred to as the *benzoin condensation*.[40] Any mechanism for the transformation should be in accordance with these facts:

(1) The reaction is reversible.[41]

[37] Gilman and Kirby, *ibid.*, 2046.

[38] For another example, see Johnson, *ibid.*, **55**, 3029 (1933).

[39] Schorigin, Issaguljanz, and Gussewa, *Ber.*, **66**, 1431 (1933).

[40] For a review of the benzoin condensation, see Ide and Buck in Adams, *Organic Reactions*, Vol. IV, p. 269, John Wiley and Sons, New York, 1948.

[41] Buck and Ide, *J. Am. Chem. Soc.*, **53**, 2350, 2784 (1931).

(2) It follows the rate equation:

$$v = k[\phi CHO]^2[\overset{\ominus}{CN}]$$

(See footnote 42)

(3) It is not catalyzed by hydrogen cyanide or complex cyanides.[42]
(4) The rate is not affected by the addition of alkali.[42]
(5) The reaction fails when either strongly electron-attracting groups (NO_2)[43] or electron-releasing groups (—OH, —OCH_3, or —$N(CH_3)_2$)[44] are *ortho* or *para* to the aldehyde group.

The following mechanism[45] seems to account for these facts:

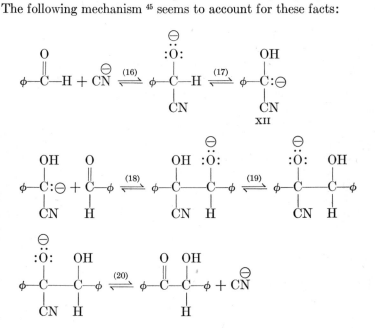

Third-order kinetics requires step 18 or 19 to be rate determining. Step 18 seems more probable since it involves the establishment of a carbon-carbon bond. Apparently the specific effect of the cyanide ion is to facilitate step 17, although it is perhaps surprising that this step is not sufficiently catalyzed by base to affect the kinetic order of the overall reaction. It is clear that in an acid medium (for example hydrogen cyanide) the carbanion of the cyanohydrin (XII) would not be expected.

[42] Stern, Z. physik. Chem., **50**, 513 (1904).
[43] Homolka, Ber., **17**, 1902 (1884).
[44] Irvine, J. Chem. Soc., **79**, 670 (1901); Raiford and Talbot, J. Am. Chem. Soc., **54**, 1092 (1932); Staudinger, Ber., **46**, 3535 (1913).
[45] Lapworth, J. Chem. Soc., **83**, 1004 (1903).

The effect of substituents in the benzene ring provides an interesting example of the dual nature of carbanion addition to carbonyl groups. When an electron-releasing group is conjugated with the aldehyde function, a resonance form such as (XIV) apparently lowers the usual positive charge on the carbonyl carbon atom to a point where the addition

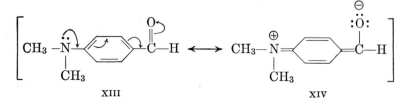

of the cyanohydrin carbanion (which might be formed) fails. Reaction 18 will therefore not proceed. In *p*-nitrobenzaldehyde, however, the acceptor capacity of the carbonyl group would be expected to be very good, but in the carbanion XV the electron pair necessary for combination with a second aldehyde molecule is partially relayed to the nitro group (XVI). The reaction, therefore, fails again at step 18, but this time because of poor donor ability.

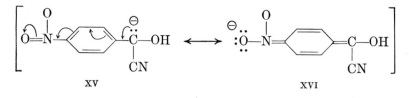

This interpretation makes it seem plausible that unreactive aldehydes which alone fail to undergo the benzoin condensation because of the presence of electron-releasing groups in the ring might add to more powerful acceptor aldehydes if they were introduced into the reaction mixture. Similarly we might expect aldehydes that are unreactive because of electron-withdrawing groups in the ring to combine with added aldehydes which would give more reactive carbanions. The first of these possibilities has been realized. A number of *mixed benzoins* have been prepared from aldehydes containing electron-releasing groups in the *para* position.[46] *p*-Nitrobenzaldehyde, however, does not seem to form benzoins of any kind.

One of the most interesting aspects of the formation of mixed benzoins is the structure of the product obtained. With *p*-dimethylaminobenzal-

[46] (*a*) Buck and Ide, *J. Am. Chem. Soc.*, **52**, 220 (1930); (*b*) *ibid.*, 4107; (*c*) *ibid.*, **54**, 3302 (1932).

dehyde and benzaldehyde, for example, we might get either XVII or XVIII.

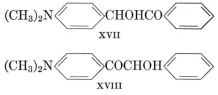

$(CH_3)_2N$⟨   ⟩CHOHCO⟨   ⟩

XVII

$(CH_3)_2N$⟨   ⟩COCHOH⟨   ⟩

XVIII

A careful study of our mechanism shows that since benzaldehyde functions as the acceptor molecule for the carbanion of p-dimethylaminobenzaldehyde cyanohydrin in the mixed reaction, the alcohol group will be adjacent to the benzene ring and the carbonyl group will be attached to the p-dimethylaminophenyl group (XVIII).[47]   In all the mixed benzoin condensations which have been carried out, the keto group is attached to the benzene ring containing the more electron-releasing substituent.[46c, 48]

Kolbe Reaction.   Thus far we have discussed a number of reactions which behave as if they were initiated by carbanions derived from carbonyl or organometallic compounds.   In Chapter 6 we pointed out that the resonance forms XX and XXI contribute significantly to the structure of a phenoxide ion.

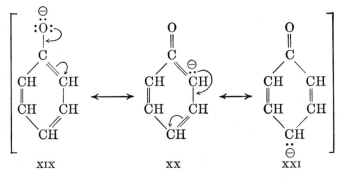

XIX   XX   XXI

A phenoxide ion, therefore, might be expected to undergo certain reactions characteristic of carbanions at the *ortho* and *para* positions.   One of the best-known examples of such a reaction is the Kolbe synthesis of salicylic acid in which the carbanion form of the phenoxide ion undergoes addition to the carbonyl group of carbon dioxide: [49]

[47] Jenkins, Bigelow, and Buck, *ibid.*, **52,** 5198 (1930).

[48] Buck and Ide, *ibid.*, **53,** 1912 (1931).

[49] Silin and Moshchinskaya, *J. Gen. Chem.* (U. S. S. R.), **8,** 810 (1938); (*C.A.*, **33,** 1306 [1939]).

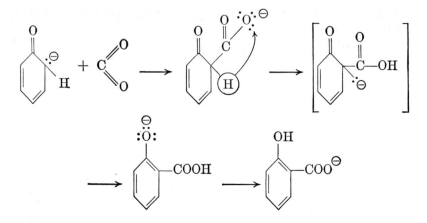

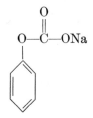

For some time this reaction has been written as an intramolecular re-arrangement, since the first product which can be isolated from the reaction is sodium phenylcarbonate:

$$
\underset{\text{O}}{\overset{\text{O}}{\parallel}}\\
\text{O—C—ONa}
$$

In one instance, however, there seems to be little doubt that the reaction proceeds essentially as shown above. In a careful study of the carbonation of sodium β-naphthoxide [49] it was found that at 40 to 60° sodium β-naphthylcarbonate (**XXII**) was indeed first formed. At 120° the reversible reaction 21,

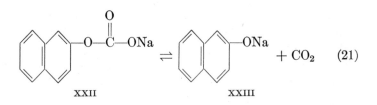

was shifted to the right as evidenced by a corresponding increase of reaction pressure. Subsequently **XXIV** was formed in 92 to 94 per cent

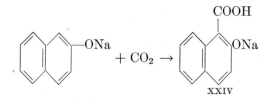

XXIV

yield.   It is interesting that **XXIV** and not **XXV** was formed from the reaction.

XXV

The Benzilic Acid Rearrangement.   When benzil is treated with sodium hydroxide, benzilic acid is formed and the reaction appears to proceed by the intramolecular *addition* of a group with an electron pair to the carbonyl carbon atom.   A mechanism which seems quite plausible for the reaction is the following.[50]   It is identical mechanistically with the glyoxal-glycolic acid rearrangement (p. 167).

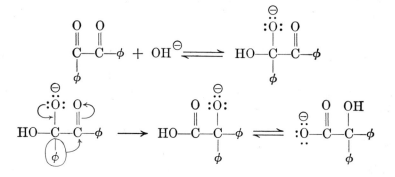

In support of this mechanism it has been found that the reaction is strictly first order in hydroxide ion (but not phenoxide ion),[51] and that hydroxide ion adds rapidly and reversibly to benzil.[52]

It would seem that, in an anhydrous medium, alkoxides should lead to esters of benzilic acid if this mechanism is correct:

[50] Ingold, *Ann. Rep. Chem. Soc.*, **25**, 124 (1928).
[51] Westheimer, *J. Am. Chem. Soc.*, **58**, 2209 (1936).
[52] Roberts and Urey, *ibid.*, **60**, 880 (1938).

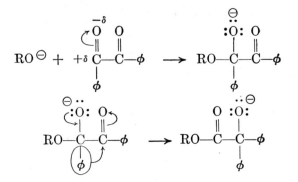

In benzene solution, when sodium *tert*-butoxide was employed, only the α-hydroxy acids could be isolated from a number of aliphatic α-diketones.[53]   The exact significance of this fact is not clear.

[53] Oakwood, Pohland, and Burhans, *Abstracts of Papers*, 105th meeting of the American Chemical Society, p. 27M, Detroit, Michigan, April 1943.

CHAPTER 10

CARBANION DISPLACEMENT REACTIONS

In Chapter 4 we pointed out that S_N2 type displacements are characteristic of reagents which contain an atom with an unshared pair of electrons. Thus hydroxide ion, alkoxides, amines, halide ions, and carboxylate ions commonly effect displacements at a saturated carbon atom. Carbanions also bring about the same reaction:

$$-\overset{|}{\underset{|}{C}}:\ominus \; + \; -\overset{|}{\underset{|}{C}}-X \; \rightarrow \; -\overset{|}{\underset{|}{C}}-\overset{|}{\underset{|}{C}}- \; + \; :\overset{\ominus}{X}$$

$$X = \text{halogen}, \; -OSO_3R, \; \text{or} \; -\overset{\oplus}{N}R_3$$

Almost all alkylations carried out in basic media are carbanion displacement reactions. The following syntheses are examples.

Acetoacetic and Malonic Ester Syntheses

$$\underset{\underset{COOEt}{|}}{CH_3COCH_2} \; + \; NaOEt \; \rightleftharpoons \; [\underset{\underset{COOEt}{|}}{CH_3CO\overset{\ominus}{C}H}:]\overset{\oplus}{Na} \; + \; EtOH$$

$$[\underset{\underset{COOEt}{|}}{CH_3CO\overset{\ominus}{C}H}:] \; + \; R-X \; \rightarrow \; \underset{\underset{COOEt}{|}}{CH_3COCHR} \; + \; \overset{\ominus}{X}, \; \text{etc.}$$

Alkylations with Quaternary Ammonium Salts [1]

$$(EtOOC)_2CH_2 \; + \; NaOEt \; \rightleftharpoons \; [(EtOOC)_2\overset{\ominus}{C}H:]\overset{\oplus}{Na} \; + \; EtOH$$

$$[(EtOOC)_2\overset{\ominus}{C}H:] \; + \; \underset{\underset{\phi}{|}}{CH_2}-\overset{\overset{CH_3}{|}}{\underset{\underset{CH_3}{|}}{\overset{\oplus}{N}}}-\phi \; \rightarrow \; (EtOOC)_2CH-\underset{\underset{\phi}{|}}{CH_2} \; + \; :\overset{\overset{CH_3}{|}}{\underset{\underset{CH_3}{|}}{N}}-\phi$$

Alkylations with Alkene Oxides [2]

---

[1] Snyder, Smith, and Stewart, *J. Am. Chem. Soc.*, **66**, 200 (1944).

[2] Grigsby, Hind, Chanley, and Westheimer, *J. Am. Chem. Soc.*, **64**, 2606 (1942); Glickman and Cope, *ibid.*, **67**, 1012 (1945).

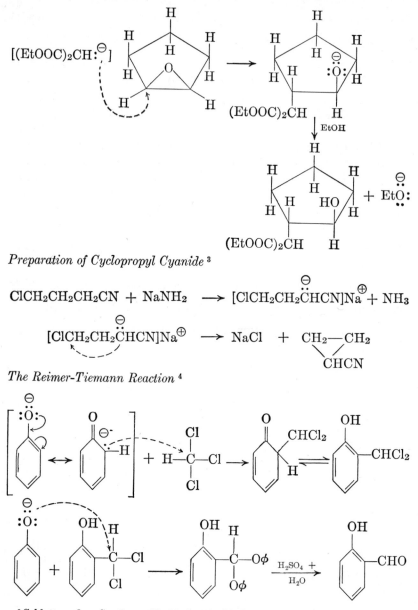

Preparation of Cyclopropyl Cyanide [3]

$$ClCH_2CH_2CH_2CN + NaNH_2 \longrightarrow [ClCH_2CH_2\overset{\ominus}{\underset{\cdot\cdot}{C}}HCN]Na^{\oplus} + NH_3$$

$$[Cl\overset{\curvearrowleft}{CH_2CH_2}\overset{\ominus}{\underset{\cdot\cdot}{C}}HCN]Na^{\oplus} \longrightarrow NaCl + \begin{array}{c}CH_2{-}CH_2 \\ \diagdown\diagup \\ CHCN\end{array}$$

The Reimer-Tiemann Reaction [4]

[3] Schlatter, *Org. Syntheses*, **23**, 20 (1943); McCloskey and Coleman, *ibid.*, **24**, 36 (1944).

[4] For a discussion of the Reimer-Tiemann reactions and a number of leading references, see Fieser in Gilman, *Organic Chemistry*, p. 190, John Wiley and Sons, New York, 1943.

The Wurtz Reaction. One of the best-known methods for the preparation of hydrocarbons is the reaction of organic halides with metallic sodium:

$$2RX + 2Na \xrightarrow{\text{inert solvent}} R\text{---}R + 2NaX$$

The process is usually called the Wurtz reaction if alkyl halides are employed, the Fittig reaction if aryl halides are used, or the Wurtz-Fittig reaction if it is carried out with a mixture of alkyl and aryl halides. Although all the reactions lead to more than one product when a mixture of two different halides is employed, the Wurtz-Fittig reaction shows a remarkable tendency to unite two dissimilar fragments. n-Butylbenzene, for example, can be prepared from bromobenzene and n-butyl bromide in yields of 65 to 70 per cent.[5]

There has been much discussion as to whether these reactions proceed by free radical or ionic paths. Certainly a heterogeneous reaction conducted in a nonpolar environment would not be expected to follow an ionic course, and indeed the appearance of benzene, biphenyl, o-phenylbiphenyl, and triphenylene (I) from the reaction of bromobenzene with sodium does suggest a free radical reaction.[6]

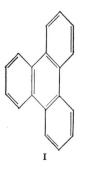

I

It has been pointed out by Morton, however, that although a free radical mechanism has been neither proved nor disproved, it is nevertheless possible to interpret the Wurtz reaction on the basis of the two steps, A and B.[7]

[5] Read, Foster, Russell, and Simril, *Org. Syntheses*, **25**, 11 (1945).

[6] Bachmann and Clarke, *J. Am. Chem. Soc.*, **49**, 2089 (1927); Blum-Bergmann, *ibid.*, **60**, 1999 (1938).

[7] Morton, Davidson, and Hakan, *ibid.*, **64**, 2242 (1942); Morton, Davidson, and Newey, *ibid.*, 2240.

(Step A)

$$RCH_2CH_2X + 2Na \rightarrow [RCH_2\overset{\ominus}{C}H_2{:}]\overset{\oplus}{N}a + NaX$$

(Step B)

$$[RCH_2\overset{\ominus}{C}H_2{:}]\overset{\oplus}{N}a + R'CH_2CH_2X \rightarrow$$

(a) $RCH_2CH_2CH_2CH_2R' + NaX$ (displacement)

(b) $RCH_2CH_3 + R'CH{=}CH_2 + NaX$ (elimination)

(c) $RCH_2CH_2X + R'CH_2\overset{\ominus}{C}H_2{:}$ (exchange)

In step A a carbanion is formed. In step B the carbanion reacts with a molecule of halide by one of three routes: (a) a displacement reaction at a carbon atom, (b) an elimination process, or (c) a displacement reaction at a halogen atom. Each of the products shown in step B has been isolated from the reaction mixture and there is experimental evidence for each of the steps indicated. We can conclude, for example, that step A occurs in a Wurtz reaction and that organosodium compounds do exist, since carbonation of a typical reaction mixture leads to considerable quantities of the corresponding carboxylic acid.[8] Furthermore, the coupling reaction

$$2RNa \rightarrow R{-}R + 2Na$$

does not take place. As larger and larger amounts of sodium were employed, the yield of organosodium compounds approached 100 per cent, but at the same time the yield of the hydrocarbon R—R dropped to zero.[8]

Evidence for the S_N2 character of route a in step B has been gained by a study of the reaction of benzyl sodium with (+) 2-bromobutane.[9] A major portion of the optical activity (>74 per cent) is retained during the process, and inversion of configuration apparently takes place:

$$[\phi\overset{\ominus}{C}H_2{:}] + H{-}\underset{\underset{CH_2CH_3}{|}}{\overset{\overset{CH_3}{|}}{C}}{-}Br \rightarrow \phi CH_2{-}\underset{\underset{CH_2CH_3}{|}}{\overset{\overset{CH_3}{|}}{C}}{-}H + \overset{\ominus}{B}r \quad (69\%)$$

$\qquad\qquad\qquad\quad$ d $\qquad\qquad\qquad$ l (probably)

[8] Morton and Richardson, *ibid.*, **62**, 123 (1940).

[9] Letsinger, *ibid.*, **70**, 406 (1948).

It is not yet clear why complete racemization occurs when the reaction is carried out with n-butyl sodium.

It is a consequence of route b in step B that if a halide should be added to a preformed organosodium compound, any olefin which might result should be derived from the *halide*. Similarly any saturated hydrocarbon of the structure RCH_2CH_3 should originate from the *organosodium compound*.

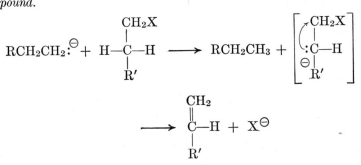

Test of these conclusions is obscured by the simultaneous operation of a metal-halogen interchange (c), which can be interpreted as a carbanion displacement at a halogen atom:

$$RCH_2\overset{\ominus}{CH_2}: + X\!-\!CH_2CH_2R' \rightarrow RCH_2CH_2X + :\overset{\ominus}{C}H_2CH_2R'$$

There is, however, indirect evidence that these conclusions are correct. Thus in a series of reactions of amyl sodium or octyl sodium with a number of alkyl halides, pentane or octane predominated over pentene or octene in every instance.[10]

That a metal-halogen interchange, (c), does take place under conditions of the Wurtz reaction has been shown by the isolation of amyl iodide in 47% yield from the reaction of amyl sodium with methyl iodide.[10]

In conclusion it should be pointed out that the unusual success of the Wurtz-Fittig reaction in coupling two unlike halides can be understood if we assume that phenyl sodium predominates over the alkyl sodium in the first phase of the reaction and that phenyl sodium reacts preferentially with alkyl halides in the second phase of the reaction. These assumptions seem very reasonable, since aromatic halides are always more inert to displacement reactions than alkyl halides and ethyl sodium has been shown to react even with benzene to give phenyl sodium and ethane.[11] Consequently, when a solution of ethyl bromide and bromo-

[10] Morton, Davidson, and Newey, *ibid.*, **64**, 2240 (1942).

[11] Schorigin, *Ber.*, **41**, 2723 (1908).

benzene is allowed to react with sodium, phenyl sodium should predominate over ethyl sodium in the mixture.

The Haloform Reaction.[12]   The term *haloform reaction* generally includes all those processes in which a haloform is obtained from an organic compound by the action of a hypohalite.[12]   The reaction is characteristic of acetaldehyde, methyl ketones, and those compounds which might be expected to lead to acetaldehyde or methyl ketones under the conditions of the reaction.   Since, however, all these processes seem to have in common the transformation

$$R-\overset{O}{\overset{\|}{C}}-CH_3 + 3NaOX \rightarrow RCOONa + HCX_3 + 2NaOH$$

our discussion of the mechanism will be limited to this particular reaction.

As Fuson and Bull have pointed out, there is much evidence which indicates that the formation of a haloform from a methyl ketone proceeds in two stages.   First, the ketone is halogenated to a trichloromethyl ketone:

$$R-\overset{O}{\overset{\|}{C}}-CH_3 \xrightarrow{X_2} R-\overset{O}{\overset{\|}{C}}-CH_2X \rightarrow R-\overset{O}{\overset{\|}{C}}-CHX_2 \rightarrow R-\overset{O}{\overset{\|}{C}}-CX_3$$

and this reaction is followed by alkaline cleavage:

$$R-\overset{O}{\overset{\|}{C}}-CX_3 \xrightarrow{NaOH} R-\overset{O}{\overset{\|}{C}}-ONa + HCX_3$$

The halogenation process may be regarded as a carbanion displacement reaction on a halogen molecule in equilibrium with the hypohalite: [13]

$$NaOX + NaX + H_2O \rightleftharpoons X_2 + 2NaOH$$

$$R-\overset{O}{\overset{\|}{C}}-CH_3 + :O\overset{\ominus}{H} \rightleftharpoons R-\overset{O}{\overset{\|}{C}}-\overset{\ominus}{C}H_2: + H_2O$$

$$R-\overset{O}{\overset{\|}{C}}-\overset{\ominus}{C}H_2: + :\overset{..}{X}:\overset{..}{X}: \rightarrow R-\overset{O}{\overset{\|}{C}}-CH_2X + :\overset{..}{\underset{..}{X}}:\overset{\ominus}{}$$

(*Continued on facing page*)

[12] For a review of the haloform reaction, see Fuson and Bull, *Chem. Revs.*, **15**, 275 (1934).

[13] Hammett, *Physical Organic Chemistry*, Chapter VIII, pp. 96–98, McGraw-Hill Book Co., New York, 1940.

$$R\text{—}\overset{\overset{\displaystyle O}{\|}}{C}\text{—}CH_2X + :\overset{\ominus}{O}H \rightleftharpoons R\text{—}\overset{\overset{\displaystyle O}{\|}}{C}\text{—}\overset{\ominus}{\underset{\cdot\cdot}{C}}HX + H_2O, \text{ etc.}$$

Presumably the slow step in the sequence is the formation of the carbanion, since rate studies have shown that in basic solution iodine and bromine react with acetone at the same rate.[14] Similarly, at a pH less than 9, acetophenone is brominated or chlorinated in the α-position at the same rate.[15] With each ketone the rate of reaction is *independent of the concentration of halogen present* but directly proportional to the concentration of base.

This same study [15] showed further that in the reaction of hypobromite or hypoiodite with acetone, carbanion formation is so slow that it controls completely the overall rate of polyhalogenation. Consequently monobromoacetone and dibromoacetone must form carbanions much more readily than acetone itself. This is in agreement with the point of view that S_N2 reactions (in this instance at a hydrogen atom) should be favored by electron withdrawal from the seat of reaction (p. 89).

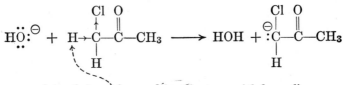

(attack here favored by electron withdrawal)

The cleavage stage of the haloform reaction may be regarded as a hydroxide ion displacement reaction at the keto group, although again we cannot be sure that preliminary addition at the carbonyl group does not take place (p. 90):

$$\overset{\cdot\cdot}{H}\overset{\ominus}{O}: + \overset{\overset{\displaystyle O}{\|}}{\underset{\underset{\displaystyle R}{|}}{C}}\text{—}CX_3 \rightarrow \left[HO\text{—}\overset{\overset{\displaystyle O}{\|}}{\underset{\underset{\displaystyle R}{|}}{C}} + :\overset{\ominus}{C}X_3 \right] \rightarrow :\overset{\ominus}{\underset{\cdot\cdot}{O}}\text{—}\overset{\overset{\displaystyle O}{\|}}{\underset{\underset{\displaystyle R}{|}}{C}} + HCX_3$$

This interpretation seems particularly attractive since a *methyl ester* has been isolated as the first hydrolysis product of a haloform reaction carried out in aqueous methanol. Thus 5-methoxy-8-acetotetralin (II) gave 5-methoxy-8-carbomethoxytetralin (III) when the hypohalite mix-

[14] Bartlett, *J. Am. Chem. Soc.*, **56**, 967 (1934).
[15] Bartlett and Vincent, *ibid.*, **57**, 1596 (1935).

ture reaction was kept cold:[16]

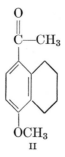

II

The formation of this intermediate appears to result from the equilibrium

$$:\overset{\ominus}{\underset{..}{O}}H + CH_3OH \rightleftharpoons CH_3\overset{\ominus}{\underset{..}{O}}: + H_2O$$

followed by displacement of the trichloromethyl carbanion from the trichloromethyl ketone by methoxide ion:

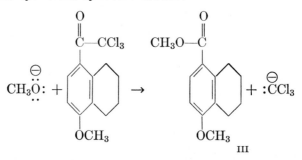

III

The formation of the ester rather than the acid seems to be another instance of the fact that, in competition with other ions or molecules, hydroxide ion is sometimes a rather poor nucleophilic agent (p. 90).

Summary of Carbanion Reactions. In concluding our discussion of carbanion processes, we might summarize the reactions of compounds which can furnish carbanions by considering the products formed when esters are treated with strong base.[17] There are four positions available for attack:

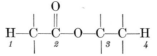

[16] Arnold, Buckles, and Stoltenberg, *ibid.*, **66**, 208 (1944).
[17] Hauser, Saperstein, and Shivers, *ibid.*, **70**, 606 (1948).

When reaction occurs at *1*, an equilibrium is established resulting in the formation of an ester-carbanion:

$$[B:]^\ominus + H-\overset{\displaystyle O}{\underset{|}{C}}-\overset{\displaystyle \|}{\underset{|}{C}}-O-\overset{|}{\underset{|}{C}}-\overset{|}{\underset{|}{C}}-H \rightleftharpoons BH + \begin{bmatrix} :\overset{\ominus|}{C}-\overset{\displaystyle O}{\underset{|}{C}}-O-\overset{|}{\underset{|}{C}}-\overset{|}{\underset{|}{C}}-H \\[2em] \overset{\ominus}{\underset{\displaystyle :\ddot{O}:}{}} \quad \updownarrow \\[2em] C{=}\overset{|}{C}-O-\overset{|}{\underset{|}{C}}-\overset{|}{\underset{|}{C}}-H \end{bmatrix}$$

Depending upon its structure and the experimental conditions employed, this species may undergo a carbanion addition ("Claisen Condensation," p. 185) or a carbanion substitution reaction ("Alkylation," p. 201).

Attack of base at the carbonyl carbon atom (*2*) usually results in the displacement of a substituted alkoxide ion:

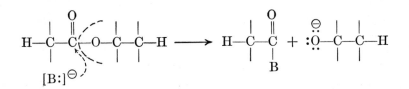

Thus hydroxide ion leads to saponification (p. 231); another alkoxide ion leads to transesterification (p. 231); and carbanions give keto compounds or tertiary alcohols (Grignard reaction).

Positions *1* and *2* constitute the two most common points of attack in an ester molecule, but in certain instances, a displacement reaction at position *3*:

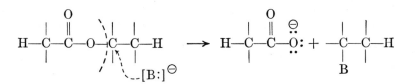

or an elimination reaction initiated by an attack at position *4* has been observed:

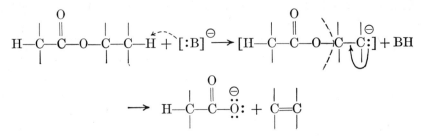

Thus, when there are no α-hydrogen atoms and the carbonyl group is hindered (as in allyl mesitoate), displacement at position 3 has been effected with phenylmagnesium bromide. Allylbenzene was formed in 70 per cent yield.[18] The mechanism of the displacement process is complicated. With crotyl mesitoate (IV) (and probably allyl mesitoate) a cyclic mechanism seems to be involved [19] since the transformation gave only crotylbenzene (VI) and none of the isomeric α-methylallylbenzene. With α-methylallyl mesitoate, where a six-membered ring analogous to V is sterically hindered,[20] a mixture of crotyl- and α-methylallylbenzenes

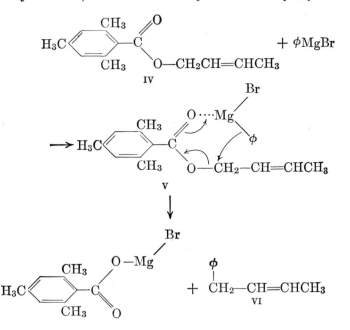

[18] Arnold, Bank, and Liggett, *ibid.*, **63**, 3444 (1941); see also Arnold and Liggett, *ibid.*, **64**, 2875 (1942).

[19] Arnold and Liggett, *ibid.*, **67**, 337 (1945).

[20] Arnold and Searles, *ibid.*, **71**, 2021 (1949).

was obtained.[21]   In this alkylation there is a striking similarity among the products and ratio of products obtained from the reaction of phenyl-magnesium bromide with crotyl chloride and α-methallyl chloride.   Accordingly, it seems probable that the same intermediate (essentially a butenyl carbonium ion) is involved in each case [21] (see p. 278):

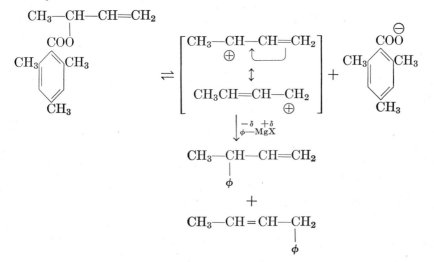

Support for the idea of a preliminary ionization in this transformation is to be found in the reaction of triphenylmethyl acetate with methyl magnesium iodide.   1,1,1,Triphenylethane is formed in a yield of 68 per cent.[22]   A similar sequence may be written for this reaction:

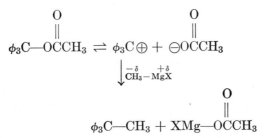

It is particularly noticeable that these unusual Grignard reactions are found with compounds which would be expected to form extremely stable carbonium ions (see p. 42).

β-Elimination (attack at position 4) has been realized by treatment of α,β-diphenylethyl mesitoate (VII) with phenylmagnesium bromide.[17] Stilbene and mesitoic acid were obtained in yields of 80 to 90 per cent:

[21] Wilson, Roberts, and Young, *ibid.*, 2019.
[22] Fieser and Heymann, *ibid.*, **64**, 376 (1942).

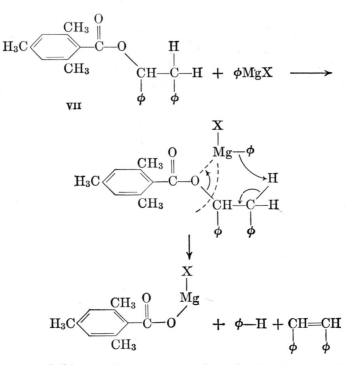

The success of this reaction appears to depend not only upon the absence of a hydrogen atom α to the carboxyl group and a very hindered carbonyl group, but also upon activation of the hydrogen atom (4) by a phenyl group.

CHAPTER 11

FORMATION AND CLEAVAGE OF ETHERS

Williamson Synthesis. One of the best-known syntheses for the preparation of ethers consists in treating an alkyl halide with a metal alkoxide or phenoxide:

$$RONa + R'X \rightarrow ROR' + NaX$$

This reaction is usually called the Williamson synthesis of ethers. In a modification of it, the alkyl halide may be replaced by a sulfonic ester or a dialkyl sulfate.

Undoubtedly the transformation is a displacement reaction which normally proceeds by an S_N2 mechanism:

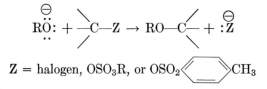

$$Z = \text{halogen, } OSO_3R, \text{ or } OSO_2\langle\underline{\quad}\rangle CH_3$$

Thus the reaction of sodium eugenoxide with various alkyl iodides in dry alcohol solution was shown to be in accord with second-order kinetics.[1] The reaction of sodium ethoxide with optically active 2-bromo or 2-chlorooctane proceeded with complete inversion,[2] and etherification of ethanol containing O^{18} with diethyl sulfate and alkali indicated that the ethyl group came from the sulfuric ester and that the alkoxide fragment was derived from the alcohol.[3]

$$CH_3CH_2O^{18}H + (CH_3CH_2)_2SO_4 \rightarrow$$

$$CH_3CH_2O^{18}CH_2CH_3 + HOSO_3CH_2CH_3$$

Although the Williamson synthesis usually proceeds by S_N2, halides are known whose rate of etherification is independent of the concentration of alkoxide ion in a solution of the corresponding alcohol. Triphenylmethyl chloride and α-phenylethyl chloride are examples (p. 83).

---

[1] Woolf, *J. Chem. Soc.*, **1937**, 1173.

[2] Hughes, Ingold, and Masterman, *ibid.*, 1200.

[3] Lauder and Green, *Trans. Faraday Soc.*, **44**, 808 (1948).

Again it is clear that if we are to apply the general principles of displacement reactions to making predictions about the Williamson synthesis (p. 85), we must know whether the reaction proceeds by S_N1, by S_N2, or by the simultaneous operation of both processes.

Formation and Cleavage of Ethers in Acidic Media.   When alcohols are treated with acids, dehydration (p. 105) or etherification often occurs. Diethyl ether, for example, is prepared commercially by passing ethanol into a mixture of sulfuric acid and alcohol maintained at 140°.   By modifying this method somewhat, satisfactory yields of certain mixed ethers have been obtained.[4]   In other instances etherification proceeds extremely readily.   Triphenylcarbinol is etherified by boiling with methanol[5] (unless it is carefully freed of traces of acid),[6] and benzhydrol is reported to form dibenzhydryl ether by refluxing it with water.[7] Again, traces of acid are probably responsible for reaction.

Reactions of this kind appear to be carbonium ion processes (p. 36):

$$\text{ROH} + \text{H}\oplus \rightleftharpoons \underset{\oplus}{\text{R}-\overset{\text{H}}{\underset{\cdot\cdot}{\text{O}}}-\text{H}} \rightleftharpoons \text{R}\oplus + :\overset{\text{H}}{\underset{\cdot\cdot}{\text{O}}}-\text{H}$$

$$\text{R}\oplus + :\overset{\text{R}}{\underset{\cdot\cdot}{\text{O}}}-\text{H} \rightleftharpoons \underset{\cdot\cdot}{\text{R}-\overset{\oplus\overset{\text{R}}{|}}{\text{O}}-\text{H}} \rightleftharpoons \text{R}-\overset{\text{R}}{\underset{\cdot\cdot}{\text{O}}}: + \text{H}\oplus$$

Originally it was believed that etherification with sulfuric acid proceeded through the intermediate formation of alkyl sulfuric acids ($ROSO_3H$), since these products sometimes could be isolated from the reaction mixture.   It now seems clear, however, that alkyl sulfuric acids are formed only as by-products in the reaction and are not actually intermediates in the etherification process.   Thus, ethyl tert-butyl ether was prepared in yields of 95 per cent by heating a mixture of tert-butyl and ethyl alcohols containing 15 per cent sulfuric acid at 70°, yet titration of the cooled reaction mixture showed no evidence of the formation of an alkyl sulfuric acid.[4]   Furthermore, the yield of diethyl ether was 95 per cent when ethanol was passed through concentrated sulfuric acid heated to 140°, but when the reaction was carried out with ethyl sulfuric acid at the same temperature, much sulfur dioxide was evolved and the yield dropped to 70 per cent.[4,8]   We can, therefore, conclude that the

[4] Norris and Rigby, *J. Am. Chem. Soc.*, **54**, 2088 (1932).

[5] Strauss and Hüssy, *Ber.*, **42**, 2177 (1909).

[6] Hatt, *J. Chem. Soc.*, **1938**, 483.

[7] Stobbe and Zeitschel, *Ber.*, **34**, 1967 (1901).

[8] Barbet, British Patents 100,406 (1915) and 101,724 (1916).

function of sulfuric acid is to promote the formation of carbonium ions. This view is supported by the fact that other Lewis' acids such as zinc chloride, boron trifluoride, and aluminum chloride also convert alcohols to ethers.[9]

Acetals are ethers of hemiacetals (p. 158). Often they are formed by heating aldehydes in alcoholic solution containing a trace of acid. The mechanism of the reaction is probably the following:

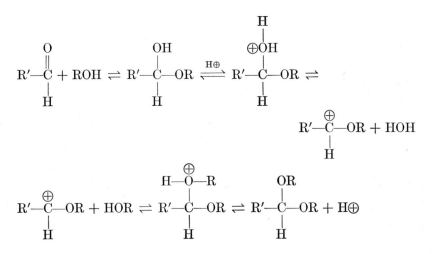

Experimentally it is known that it is easier to prepare an acetal than a simple ether. This is in accord with the mechanism presented for etherification since the carbonium ion involved in this sequence is stabilized by resonance,

$$\left[\begin{array}{ccc} R'-\overset{\oplus}{\underset{H}{C}}-\overset{..}{\underset{..}{O}}-R & \longleftrightarrow & R-\underset{H}{C}=\overset{\oplus}{\underset{..}{O}}-R \end{array} \right]$$

and thus would be expected to be formed more readily than R⊕.

Another very useful method for the preparation of acetals or ketals is based upon the use of orthoesters.[10] The reaction is usually carried out by heating the carbonyl compound with ethyl orthoformate in ethanol solution containing a small amount of ammonium chloride or dry hy-

[9] For a summary of the reagents which have been employed to effect etherification, see Van Alphen, *Rec. trav. chim.*, **49**, 754 (1930).

[10] Claisen, *Ber.*, **29**, 1007 (1896).

drogen chloride. A mechanism for the reaction is the following:

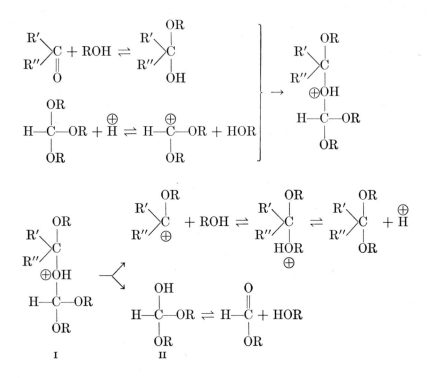

I   II

An interesting aspect of this reaction is that decomposition of the oxonium ion (I) produces the "hemiacetal" of ethyl formate (II). It is presumably the dissociation of this product into ethanol and ethyl formate that forces the main reaction toward completion. The fact that the oxygen atom is found in the formate ester when an aldehyde is treated with ethyl thioorthoformate [11] supports the view that cleavage of the oxonium ion (I) occurs as it is shown.

The synthesis of orthoesters from nitriles [12] is another example of acid-catalyzed etherification. In this reaction, a nitrile is treated with dry hydrogen chloride and an alcohol to form an iminoester hydrochloride. The dry iminoester hydrochloride is then allowed to react with an alcohol and an orthoester is produced. A possible mechanism for the reaction is the following:

[11] Post, *J. Org. Chem.*, **5**, 244 (1940).

[12] Taylor and Baker, *Sidgwick's Organic Chemistry of Nitrogen*, p. 154, Oxford University Press, London, 1942.

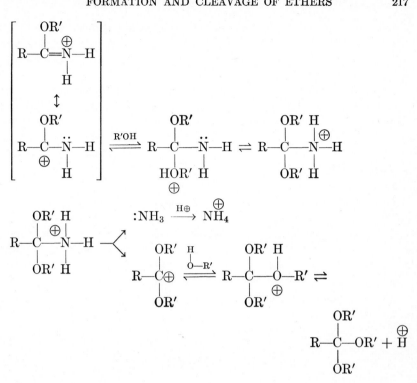

Here again equilibrium is displaced toward the polyether by removal of one of the by-products (NH_3) from the reaction sequence.

Examination of the equations on p. 214 will show that all the steps are considered to be reversible. Consequently, the cleavage of ethers is generally regarded as a carbonium ion process proceeding through the reverse steps:

$$R—\overset{..}{\underset{..}{O}}: + \overset{\oplus}{H} \rightleftharpoons R—\underset{\oplus}{O}—H \rightleftharpoons R\oplus + \underset{R}{\overset{R}{O}}—H$$

$$R\oplus + :\overset{..}{\underset{..}{O}}—H \rightleftharpoons R—\underset{\oplus}{O}—H \rightleftharpoons R—O + \overset{\oplus}{H}$$

A number of consequences of practical interest have been verified for this sequence. Ethers which would be expected to form carbonium ions readily should be easily cleaved. Acetals and highly branched[4] or benzyl ethers[13] are indeed unusually sensitive to acids. A polar solvent

[13] Goldsworthy and Robinson, *J. Chem. Soc.*, **1938**, 56.

should favor the reaction. We find, for example, that an aqueous halogen acid dissolved in acetic acid is a better reagent for the cleavage of ethers than a solution prepared from the anhydrous hydrogen halide and acetic acid.[14]

Although the carbonium ion representation of aqueous acid-catalyzed etherification and cleavage is quite useful for correlating much important information, the actual course of the reaction must be more complex than it has been indicated here. The very fact that there is so great a difference in the rate at which ethers are hydrolyzed by the halogen acids $(HCl:HBr:HI = 1:6:\infty)$ is a clear indication that the function of the acid is not simply to provide protons for the reaction.

In anhydrous media cleavage occurs more slowly than in aqueous media, and the process resembles an S_N2 displacement rather than a carbonium ion reaction. Thus the first products in the cleavage of an unsymmetrical ether by a halogen acid are the *less* highly branched halide and the *more* highly branched alcohol.[15] This would be the expected result of a collision between a protonated ether molecule and, for example, a halide ion, since attack should occur at the less substituted position:

$$X^\ominus + \underset{\underset{CH(CH_3)_2}{|}}{\overset{\overset{CH_3}{\nearrow}}{\underset{}{O}}} \overset{+\delta}{\cdots\cdots} HX^{-\delta} \longrightarrow X{-}CH_3 + \underset{\underset{CH(CH_3)_2}{|}}{OH} + X^\ominus$$

If a carbonium ion were involved, we should expect the halide to be derived from the more stable, and therefore the more highly branched, alkyl group. It is also pertinent that anisole is not cleaved by dry hydrogen chloride or hydrogen bromide in carbon tetrachloride solution unless a small amount of pyridine, dimethylaniline, or aniline is added.[16] Furthermore, the presence of these bases increases the rate of cleavage of ethers in acetic acid solution. All these experiments imply that more than two molecules participate in the formation of the transition complex leading to etherification or cleavage (see p. 83).

Epoxides. Except towards strong acids, simple ethers are generally inert. In an epoxide, however, the carbon-oxygen-carbon system is subjected to considerable strain, and we find that these compounds are reactive synthetic intermediates. Study of the reactions of epoxides has

---

[14] See Lüttringhaus and Sääf, *Angew. Chem.*, **51**, 916 (1938).

[15] Baril, Manning, and Newman, *Abstracts of Papers*, p. 41M, 98th Meeting of the American Chemical Society, Boston, Massachusetts, September 1939.

[16] Walvekar, Phalnikar, and Bhide, *J. Indian Chem. Soc.*, **20**, 131 (1943).

provided considerable insight into the mechanism of neighboring displacement reactions (p. 96).

Epoxides are usually prepared in the laboratory by the reaction of olefins with organic peracids or by the reaction of halohydrins with alkali. The mechanism of the first of these processes has not been completely elucidated,[17a] but the second involves an ionic reaction whose mechanism has already been discussed (p. 96). The synthesis of phenylmethyl glycidic ester [17b] appears to proceed by a related sequence:

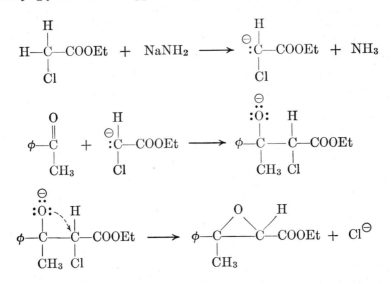

In their reaction with bases, epoxides appear to undergo typical S_N2 attack. Ammonia,[18] amines,[19] alkoxides,[20] and sodio derivatives [21] react at the less substituted carbon atom (except in vinyl systems, see p. 222), and at least in one case which has been studied inversion of configuration results (p. 202).

Grignard reagents also react with epoxides to give products which appear to have been formed by carbanion attack at the less substituted

[17a] Swern, *Chem. Revs.*, **45**, 1 (1949).

[17b] Allen and Van Allen, *Org. Syntheses*, **24**, 82 (1944). For a review of the Darzens glycidic ester condensation of which this synthesis is an example, see Magerlein in Adams *Organic Reactions*, Vol. V, p. 413, John Wiley and Sons, Inc., New York, 1949.

[18] Castro and Noller, *J. Am. Chem. Soc.*, **68**, 203 (1946).

[19] Emerson, *ibid.*, **67**, 516 (1945).

[20] Chitwood and Freure, *ibid.*, **68**, 680 (1946).

[21] Easton, Gardner, and Stevens, *ibid.*, **69**, 2941 (1947); Russell and VanderWerf, *ibid.*, 11; Glickman and Cope, *ibid.*, **67**, 1012 (1945); Grigsby, Hind, Chanley, and Westheimer, *ibid.*, **64**, 2606 (1942).

carbon atom: [22]

$$RMgX + CH_2\overset{O}{\diagdown}CHCH_3 \rightarrow RCH_2{-}\overset{OH}{\underset{|}{C}}HCH_3$$

A careful study of the transformation, however, has revealed that the process is different from most Grignard reactions in that a molecule of dialkyl magnesium is probably an essential reactant. Thus addition of one mole of ethyl magnesium bromide to one mole of ethylene oxide gives an addition complex which *is the same as that obtained by passing ethylene oxide into an ethereal solution of magnesium bromide.*[23] Apparently the first mole of ethylene oxide reacts almost exclusively with the magnesium bromide, in equilibrium with the Grignard reagent and diethyl magnesium, to form an addition complex. Hydrolysis of the reaction mixture at this point gives 60 to 70 per cent ethylene bromohydrin but little or no *n*-butyl alcohol. These reactions may be represented by the following equations: [22, 23, 24, 25]

$$2CH_3CH_2MgBr \rightleftharpoons MgBr_2 + (CH_2CH_3)_2Mg$$

$$\Big\downarrow {\scriptstyle 2CH_2\overset{O}{\diagup\diagdown}CH_2}$$

$$Mg(OCH_2CH_2Br)_2 + (CH_3CH_2)_2Mg$$

$$2HOCH_2CH_2Br \xleftarrow{\;H_2O\;}$$

In order to obtain *n*-butyl alcohol, the reaction mixture must be heated or a second mole of ethylene oxide must be added:

$$(CH_3CH_2)_2Mg + Mg(OCH_2CH_2Br)_2 \longrightarrow$$

$$Mg(OCH_2CH_2CH_2CH_3)_2 + MgBr_2$$

$$\Big\downarrow {\scriptstyle H_2O}$$

$$HOCH_2CH_2CH_2CH_3$$

or

$$(CH_3CH_2)_2Mg + 2CH_2\overset{O}{\diagup\diagdown}CH_2 \longrightarrow (CH_3CH_2CH_2CH_2O)_2Mg$$

$$\Big\downarrow {\scriptstyle H_2O}$$

$$HOCH_2CH_2CH_2CH_3$$

[22] Huston and Bostwick, *J. Org. Chem.*, **13**, 331 (1948).
[23] Huston and Agett, *ibid.*, **6**, 123 (1941).
[24] Huston and Langham, *ibid.*, **12**, 90 (1947).
[25] Cottle and Hollyday, *ibid.*, 510.

Individually, both of these reactions have been shown to proceed readily.[24]

A further complication in the reaction of Grignard reagents with epoxides is that isomeric products are often formed. Thus ethylene oxide reacts with n-butylmagnesium bromide to give a mixture of 1-hexanol and 2-hexanol:[25]

$$n\text{-BuMgBr} + \text{CH}_2\!\!\overset{\displaystyle O}{\diagup\!\!\diagdown}\!\!\text{CH}_2 \rightarrow \text{CH}_3\text{CH}_2\text{CH}_2\text{CH}_2\text{CH}_2\text{CH}_2\text{OH} \quad (65\%)$$

$$+$$

$$\overset{\displaystyle \text{OH}}{\underset{\displaystyle |}{}}$$
$$\text{CH}_3\text{CH}_2\text{CH}_2\text{CH}_2\overset{|}{\text{C}}\text{HCH}_3 \quad (10\%)$$

Apparently this is due to the decomposition of the addition complex to form a carbonyl compound, followed by subsequent reaction of the carbonyl compound with the Grignard reagent. Acetone, for example, is one of the products formed when the propylene oxide addition complex is heated.[22]

$$\overset{\displaystyle \text{CH}_3}{\underset{\displaystyle |}{}}$$
$$[\text{BrCH}_2\overset{|}{\text{C}}\text{HO}\!-\!]_2\text{Mg} \overset{\Delta}{\rightarrow} \text{CH}_3\text{COCH}_3 + \text{HBr} + \text{MgO} + \text{CH}_3\text{CH}\!\!=\!\!\overset{\displaystyle \text{Br}}{\underset{\displaystyle |}{\text{C}}}\text{H}$$

In acid solution, attack at the more highly branched carbon atom tends to occur. Thus when propylene oxide was treated with ethanol, sodium ethoxide directed the reaction almost quantitatively to the formation of the primary ether. Addition of sulfuric acid to the reaction mixture, however, led to the formation of both isomers in approximately equal amounts:[20]

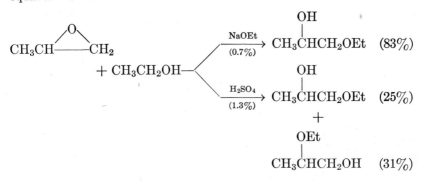

In studies with *cis* and *trans* isomers of 2-butene epoxide,[26] it was found that in aqueous perchloric acid solution the *cis* isomer gave the *dl* glycol whereas the *meso* glycol was formed from the *trans* isomer. Consequently, inversion must have occurred during the reaction and the carbonium ion could have had no completely separate existence. For the *cis* isomer this transformation can be illustrated as follows:

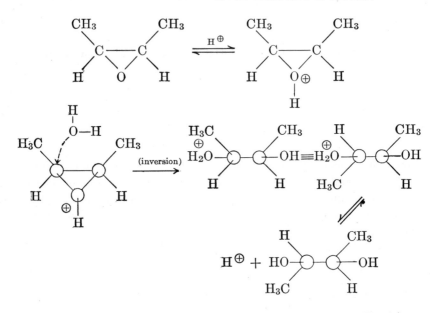

(This is only one isomer of a *dl* pair)

In concluding our discussion of the reactions of epoxides, the methanolysis of 3,4-epoxy-1-butene might be mentioned. This reaction has been studied in detail, and it illustrates very nicely some of the principles of epoxide reactions which we have considered. In the presence of sulfuric acid the only product isolated was 2-methoxy-3-buten-1-ol (III).[27, 28] When sodium methoxide was employed as the catalyst, the major product of the reaction was 1-methoxy-3-buten-2-ol (IV),[28] but some 2-methoxy-3-buten-2-ol was also obtained.

$$CH_3OH + CH_2{=}CH{-}CH{\overset{O}{\diagdown}}CH_2 \xrightarrow{(H_2SO_4)} CH_2{=}CH{-}\overset{\displaystyle OCH_3}{\underset{III}{CH}}{-}CH_2OH$$

[26] Wilson and Lucas, *J. Am. Chem. Soc.*, **58**, 2396 (1936).

[27] Kadesch, *ibid.*, **68**, 41 (1946).

[28] Bartlett and Ross, *ibid.*, **70**, 926 (1948).

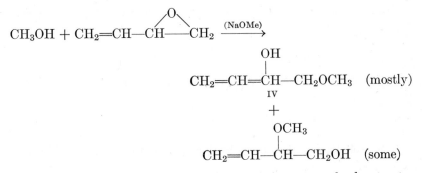

$$CH_3OH + CH_2=CH-CH-CH_2 \xrightarrow{(NaOMe)}$$

$$\underset{IV}{CH_2=CH=CH-CH_2OCH_3} \quad (mostly)$$
$$+$$
$$CH_2=CH-\overset{OCH_3}{\underset{|}{CH}}-CH_2OH \quad (some)$$

The abnormally selective acid methanolysis is apparently due to stabilization of the intermediate transitory carbonium ion by resonance (p. 42).

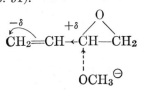

$$\left[CH_2=CH-\overset{\oplus}{CH}-\overset{OH}{\underset{|}{CH_2}} \longleftrightarrow \overset{\oplus}{CH_2}-CH=CH-\overset{OH}{\underset{|}{CH_2}} \right]$$

In the base-catalyzed reaction, more of a mixture resulted than perhaps might have been expected (see p. 219) because attack at the secondary carbon atom was facilitated by the polarizability of the adjacent vinyl group (p. 91).

$$\overset{-\delta}{CH_2}=CH-\overset{+\delta}{CH}-CH_2$$
$$\underset{OCH_3^{\ominus}}{|}$$

CHAPTER 12

ESTERIFICATION AND HYDROLYSIS [1]

It is well known that esterification and hydrolysis are equilibrium processes:

$$RCOOH + R'OH \underset{\text{hydrolysis}}{\overset{\text{esterification}}{\rightleftharpoons}} RCOOR' + H_2O$$

Undoubtedly the same intermediates are involved in the forward and reverse reactions. Since it is much easier experimentally to study hydrolysis than esterification, much of what is known about the process is based upon hydrolysis experiments. Accordingly, this discussion deals mostly with the hydrolysis of esters.

In general, hydrolysis may be carried out in acidic or basic media.

ACID HYDROLYSIS

In considering the acid hydrolysis of esters, we should remember that esters are weak bases. Most of them show a molar freezing point depression of two when they are dissolved in 100 per cent sulfuric acid. Presumably the two species arise from the reaction (see p. 36):

$$R'COOR + H_2SO_4 \rightleftharpoons [R'COOR]\overset{\oplus}{H} + H\overset{\ominus}{S}O_4$$

There might seem to be some confusion as to the oxygen atom with which the proton is associated. From our discussion of polarizability (p. 28) and the reactivity of carbonyl groups (p. 156), we should expect the proton to be found on the keto-oxygen atom:

$$\left[\begin{array}{cc} \oplus : \overset{..}{O}H & OH \\ \| & | \\ R'-C-OR & \leftrightarrow & R'-C-OR \\ & & \oplus \end{array} \right]$$

In discussing esterification and hydrolysis, however, most authors prefer to show the proton on the ethereal oxygen atom and to consider this form

---

[1] For an excellent review from which much of this material was adapted, see Day and Ingold, *Trans. Faraday Soc.*, **37**, 686 (1941).

as being a necessary and a sufficient intermediate for reaction:

$$\begin{array}{c} \text{O} \quad \text{H} \\ \parallel \quad \mid \\ \text{R}'\text{—C—OR} \\ \oplus \end{array}$$

Actually, these two views are not incompatible. Although addition probably occurs predominately at the keto-oxygen atom, nevertheless it seems reasonable to suppose that an equilibrium exists between the two cations:

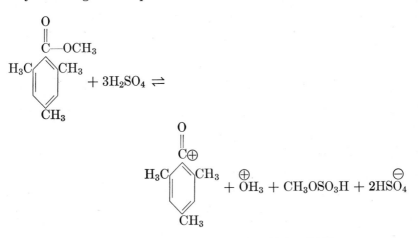

If such an equilibrium exists, it can indeed be assumed that reaction occurs only when the proton is on the ethereal oxygen atom. That addition does take place at the ethereal oxygen in certain cases has been shown unequivocally with the methyl ester of 2,4,6-trimethylbenzoic acid. This compound gives a fivefold freezing point depression in sulfuric acid,[2] which can mean only that dissociation has occurred, probably according to the equation:

[2] Newman, Kuivila, and Garret, *J. Am. Chem. Soc.*, **67**, 705 (1945).

After proton addition has taken place at the ethereal oxygen atom of an ester, bond rupture may occur between the acyl group and the oxygen atom,

Acyl-Oxygen Fission

or between the alkyl group, R, and the oxygen atom,

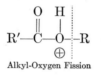

Alkyl-Oxygen Fission

These two possibilities have been called *acyl-oxygen fission* and *alkyl-oxygen fission*.[1] These names will be used throughout this discussion. Furthermore, rupture may be spontaneous (unimolecular), or the attack of water or solvent molecules may be detected in the rate equation of the process (bimolecular). The situation may be diagrammed as follows:

I. Bimolecular acyl-oxygen fission

II. Unimolecular acyl-oxygen fission

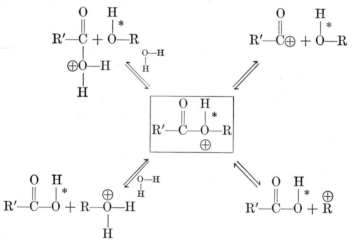

III. Bimolecular alkyl-oxygen fission

IV. Unimolecular alkyl-oxygen fission

* *The asterisk used in these formulas marks the location of the ethereal oxygen atom shown in the central box as it progresses through the different courses of reaction which are indicated.*

Of these possibilities, only route III is not well known. One example, however, appears to be the hydrolysis of highly strained lactones in weakly acidic media (p. 103).

Again, it is not possible to predict the effect of substituents on the hydrolysis of esters without a knowledge of the route which is being followed. In the following paragraphs each path is discussed separately.

I. Bimolecular Acid-Catalyzed Reactions Involving Acyl-Oxygen Fission. Almost all hydrolysis or esterification reactions involving primary or secondary alcohols occur without breaking the bond between the alkyl group R and the ethereal oxygen atom. Evidence for this prevalence of acyl-oxygen fission is the following:

1. Direct esterification of optically active 2-octanol with acetic acid in the absence of mineral acid resulted in the complete preservation of optical activity.[3]
2. No rearranged products were formed during the formation and hydrolysis of neopentyl acetate [4] or α-methylallyl acetate.[5] If free carbonium ions had been obtained by an alkyl-oxygen fission, we should expect rearrangement products (see pp. 44, 57).
3. The esterification of benzoic acid with methyl alcohol containing O^{18} gave, as a by-product, water containing only O^{16}:[6]

$$\phi CO \vdots OH + CH_3O^{18} \vdots -H \rightarrow \phi COO^{18}CH_3 + H_2O$$

4. The methanol obtained from the acid hydrolysis of methyl hydrogen succinate in water containing O^{18} contained none of the heavy isotope:[7]

$$HOOC(CH_2)_2CO \vdots -OCH_3 + H_2O^{18} \rightarrow$$
$$HOOC(CH_2)_2COO^{18}H + CH_3OH$$

The attack of water upon the protonated ester during hydrolysis has been demonstrated with methyl acetate. By employing acetone as a solvent and having present only enough water to react with the ester,

[3] Hughes, Ingold, and Masterman, J. Chem. Soc., 1939, 840.
[4] Quayle and Norton, J. Am. Chem. Soc., 62, 1170 (1940).
[5] Ingold and Ingold, J. Chem. Soc., 1932, 758.
[6] Roberts and Urey, J. Am. Chem. Soc., 60, 2391 (1938).
[7] Datta, Day, and Ingold, J. Chem. Soc., 1939, 838.

hydrolysis was shown to be first order in ester and first order in water.[8] Since it is well known that the rate of hydrolysis of esters is also dependent upon the concentration of the acid employed as a catalyst, we have the complete rate equation:

$$\text{Rate} = k[\text{ester}][\overset{\oplus}{\text{H}}][\text{H}_2\text{O}]$$

In aqueous solution, when the concentration of water is approximately constant, the equation reduces to

$$\text{Rate} = k_1[\text{ester}][\overset{\oplus}{\text{H}}]$$

A large number of esters have been shown to undergo hydrolysis according to this relationship.

A mechanism which seems to coordinate these facts is the following:

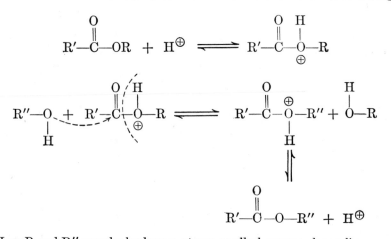

Here R and R'' may be hydrogen atoms or alkyl groups, depending upon whether we are considering esterification, hydrolysis, or acid-catalyzed ester interchange.[9]

It is impossible to state *a priori* the effect substituents will have on the velocity of this reaction, since electron release will favor formation of the protonated complex, but it will hinder the nucleophilic attack of R''OH on such a complex. Any substituent, however, would be expected to have a greater effect in R' than in R, since R' is directly attached to the seat of reaction whereas R is separated from it by the oxygen atom. Experimentally it is found that electron-releasing groups in R and R' de-

[8] Friedman and Elmore, *J. Am. Chem. Soc.*, **63**, 864 (1941).

[9] Harfenist and Baltzly, *ibid.*, **69**, 362 (1947). See also Farkas, Schächter, and Vromen, *ibid.*, **71**, 1991 (1949).

crease the velocity of the reaction.[9, 10] Steric hindrance also appears to play an important role, for the rate of reaction decreases markedly as R, R', or R'' becomes highly branched.

II. **Unimolecular Acid-Catalyzed Reactions Involving Acyl-Oxygen Fission.** At least one instance is known in which decomposition of the protonated complex does not seem to depend upon the attack of water or an alcohol molecule. It is the formation or hydrolysis of esters of 2,4,6-trimethylbenzoic acid in sulfuric acid solution. Since cryoscopic studies have shown that the acid gives a molar freezing point depression of four (p. 39), and the ester five (p. 225), we must conclude that decomposition of the protonated complex to the acyl carbonium ion

$$
\begin{matrix}
\text{O} \\
\parallel \\
\end{matrix}
$$

$(R'—C\oplus)$ has already occurred. This conclusion is supported by the observations that a freshly prepared solution of methyl 2,4,6-trimethylbenzoate gave a quantitative yield of 2,4,6-trimethylbenzoic acid on being poured into ice water.[11] A similar solution of the acid gave a 78 per cent yield of the ester when poured into methanol.[12] The equations are:

$$
\begin{matrix}
\text{O} & \text{H} & & \text{O} & \text{H} & & \text{O} \\
\parallel & | & & \parallel & | & & \parallel & & \oplus \\
\text{R'—C}\oplus & + & \text{O—H} & \rightleftharpoons & \text{R'—C—O—H} & \rightleftharpoons & \text{R'—C—OH} & + & \text{H} \\
& & & & \oplus & & & &
\end{matrix}
$$

$$
\begin{matrix}
\text{O} & \text{H} & & \text{O} & \text{H} & & \text{O} \\
\parallel & | & & \parallel & | & & \parallel & & \oplus \\
\text{R'—C}\oplus & + & \text{O—R''} & \rightleftharpoons & \text{R'—C—O—R''} & \rightleftharpoons & \text{R'—C—O—R''} & + & \text{H} \\
& & & & \oplus & & & &
\end{matrix}
$$

Under comparable conditions, benzoic acid or ethyl benzoate dissolves in the sulfuric acid but is recovered unchanged by the addition of methanol or water.

It is evident that this course of reaction would be expected only in strongly acidic, highly polar solvents, and with esters or acids capable of high electron release in R' which can stabilize the acyl carbonium ion

$$
\begin{matrix}
\text{O} \\
\parallel \\
\end{matrix}
$$

$R'—C\oplus$. Indeed, we find that the hydrolysis of methyl 2,4,6-trimethylbenzoate shows the properties of a *bimolecular reaction in aqueous alcoholic solution containing a trace of acid*. Also the electron-releasing

---

[10] For a number of leading references, see Day and Ingold, *Trans. Faraday Soc.*, **37**, 700 (1941).

[11] Treffers and Hammett, *J. Am. Chem. Soc.*, **59**, 1711 (1937).

[12] Newman, *ibid.*, **63**, 2431 (1941).

capacity of three methyl groups is necessary for complete ionization in sulfuric acid solution. Thus, the molar freezing point depression of 2,6-dimethylbenzoic acid is about 3.5 rather than 4.0.[11]

IV. Unimolecular Acid-Catalyzed Reactions Involving Alkyl-Oxygen Fission. If unimolecular alkyl-oxygen fission occurred during the hydrolysis of an ester, a carbonium ion would be formed and it should undergo reactions characteristic of this species. Thus we should observe partial racemization of the alcohol obtained, and occasionally olefins (p. 105), ethers (p. 214), or rearranged products (p. 57) might be formed as by-products in the reaction. All these expectations have been realized. Thus, in contrast to experiments in which only acetic acid was employed (p. 227), the esterification of optically active 2-octanol with acetic acid in the presence of sulfuric acid showed a small but definite partial racemization.[3] A number of other optically active secondary alcohols showed the same behavior.[13] Similarly, the hydrolysis of certain allyl esters resulted in rearrangement (p. 233). All these results indicate that the alkyl-oxygen bond is not retained intact during reaction. Ethers have been isolated from the alcoholysis of *tert*-butyl esters. When a solution of *tert*-butyl benzoate was boiled for four days in anhydrous methanol, 61 per cent *tert*-butyl methyl ether was isolated.[14] Under the same conditions, *tert*-butyl alcohol and methanol did not react in the presence of benzoic acid. It was also found that *tert*-butyl 2,4,6-trimethylbenzoate could be hydrolyzed by allowing the ester to stand in methanol solution containing dry hydrogen chloride for one-half hour and then pouring the reaction mixture onto ice. When the methyl ester was treated in the same way no reaction occurred, so it is evident that the hydrolysis which apparently involves alkyl-oxygen fission is indeed facilitated by the group which would be expected to form a carbonium ion readily.

The supposition that a carbonium ion is formed as an intermediate in these reactions is still further supported by the observation that when *tert*-butyl esters are treated with sulfuric acid in dioxane solution, isobutylene is formed, and the process is completely reversible.[15] Similarly, the reaction of *tert*-butyl benzoate with acetic acid in the presence of *p*-toluenesulfonic acid gave a small amount of isobutylene.[16]

---

[13] Kenyon, Partridge, and Phillips, *J. Chem. Soc.*, **1936**, 85; Hills, Kenyon, and Phillips, *ibid.*, 582; Balfe, Hills, Kenyon, Phillips, and Platt, *ibid.*, **1942**, 556; Balfe, Daughty, Kenyon, and Poplett, *ibid.*, 605; Balfe, Downer, Evans, Kenyon, Poplett, Searle, and Tarnoky, *ibid.*, **1946**, 797; Balfe, Evans, Kenyon, and Nandi, *ibid.*, 803; Balfe, Kenyon, and Wicks, *ibid.*, 807.

[14] Cohen and Schneider, *J. Am. Chem. Soc.*, **64**, 3382 (1941).

[15] Altschul, *ibid.*, **68**, 2605 (1946); *ibid.*, **70**, 2569 (1948).

[16] Cohen, *ibid.*, **66**, 1395 (1944).

BASIC HYDROLYSIS

In basic hydrolysis there is only one positive center at which attack would be expected to occur. It is the carbonyl carbon atom:

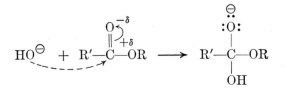

Decomposition of this addition complex could then occur either by the loss of a hydroxide ion (i.e., by a reversal of the step by which it was formed) or by the separation of an alkoxide ion:

In saponification procedures the second of these reactions proceeds to completion because equilibrium is displaced by a proton exchange between the acid and the alkoxide ion. When the base employed is an alkoxide ion, however, transesterification occurs:

The formation of amides from esters appears to be a closely related process.[17] Here we may suppose that the reaction proceeds similarly through an amide ion:

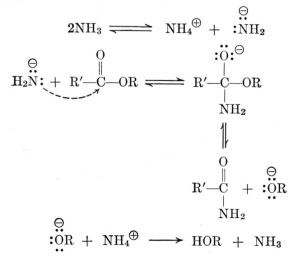

or alternatively through the neutral ammonia molecule:

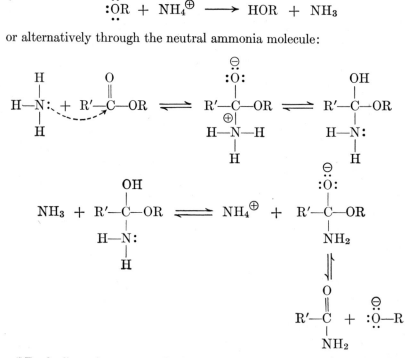

[17] For leading references, see Gordon, Miller, and Day, *ibid.*, **70**, 1946 (1948), and **71**, 1245 (1949).

For the saponification of esters, evidence similar to that on p. 227 indicates that the reaction usually proceeds with acyl-oxygen fission. The most self-contained proof again has been obtained by the use of O^{18}. The alkaline hydrolysis of amyl acetate in water containing this isotope showed that the amyl alcohol which was formed contained only O^{16}: [18]

$$CH_3COOC_5H_{11} + H_2O^{18} + NaOH \rightarrow CH_3COO^{18}Na + C_5H_{11}OH$$

Saponification is kinetically first order in ester and first order in hydroxide ion. Taken as a whole, then, the reaction may be regarded as a displacement process in which the rate-determining step involves the attack of hydroxide ion and the separation of an alkoxide ion. In agreement with this point of view, the reaction is aided by electron withdrawal from the carbonyl group and hindered by electron release or an increase in the bulk of R.[10]

It is interesting to note that there are certain esters for which none of these mechanisms of hydrolysis is completely satisfactory. It has been found, for example, that the hydrolysis of optically active α-methyl cinnamyl or α,γ-dimethylallyl hydrogen phthalate gave a racemized product in weakly alkaline solution but an optically active product in the presence of more concentrated alkali: [19]

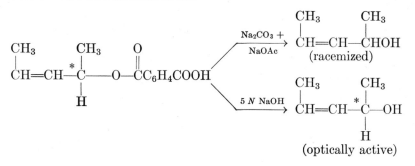

Similarly, α-phenyl-γ-methallyl hydrogen phthalate led to rearranged products in weak aqueous alkali: [20]

[18] Polanyi and Szabo, *Trans. Faraday Soc.*, **30**, 508 (1934).

[19] Kenyon, Partridge, and Phillips, *J. Chem. Soc.*, **1936**, 85; Hills, Kenyon, and Phillips, *ibid.*, 582.

[20] Kenyon, Partridge, and Phillips, *ibid.*, **1937**, 216.

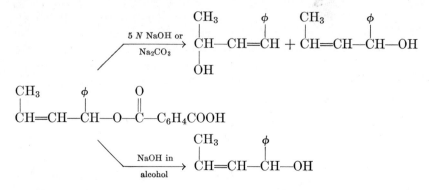

It is evident that in both these reactions alkyl-oxygen fission occurred, but the exact mechanism of the hydrolysis is not clear. The reactions in weak alkali seem characteristic of carbonium ions, but such intermediates are rather improbable in an alkaline medium.

CHAPTER 13

SUBSTITUTION ON THE BENZENE NUCLEUS

From the point of view of organic syntheses, no aspect of aromatic substitution reactions is as important as the position an entering group will take in a ring which is already substituted. In spite of the attention which this problem has received, predictions still can be made with moderate certainty only when the molecules are simple and the important functional groups are directly attached to the aromatic nucleus. In these instances, most orientations can be understood by a consideration of the mechanism whereby reaction occurs and the factors governing the distribution and mobility of electrons (Chapter 2). Accordingly, it is the object of this chapter to outline the general mechanism by which ionic substitution occurs on a benzene ring, to discuss briefly some of the qualitative factors which influence the position of substitution, and to set down some of the important facts concerning each of the more common substitution processes.

GENERAL ASPECTS OF SUBSTITUTION ON A BENZENE NUCLEUS

Mechanism. As we shall see in later discussions of the individual ionic substitution processes, there is much evidence which indicates that substitution on a benzene ring generally proceeds through the steps:

$$A:Z + catalyst \rightleftharpoons \overset{\ominus}{A}:[catalyst] + \overset{\oplus}{Z}$$

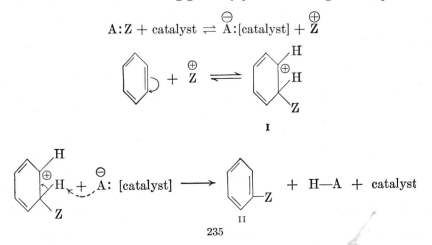

235

Usual electron-seeking attack at the olefinic linkage gives the carbonium ion (I). In this species a proton is eliminated from an adjacent carbon atom (p. 44), and the substituted benzene derivative (II) results. Elimination of a proton occurs, rather than the addition of an anion (Chapter 7), because restoration of the aromatic ring produces a species which is more stabilized by resonance than the dihydrobenzene derivative (III):

III

When the resonance stabilization which can be gained by elimination of a proton is small, however, subsequent addition of an anion occasionally does occur. Phenanthrene, for example, can be brominated in the dark to give either 9,10-dibromophenanthrene [1] or 9-bromophenanthrene (see p. 247).

The Effect of Various Groups on the Electron Distribution of an Aromatic Ring at the Moment of Reaction. Since attack on a benzene ring in substitution reactions is led by an electron-seeking species, it would be expected to occur at a point where the electron density is the highest. Consequently, electron-releasing groups attached to the benzene ring will facilitate the attack of $Z\oplus$, and electron-attracting groups will hinder the reaction. This of course is the same way in which substituents affect addition to simple olefinic bonds (p. 138). Accordingly, if we disregard for the moment steric hindrance, the problem of orientation can be restated as the problem of determining the point in an aromatic nucleus where the electron density becomes greatest as the electron-seeking reagent ($Z\oplus$) approaches the benzene ring.

It is well known that substituents can be broadly classed as *ortho-para* or *meta* directing. The explanation of this fact becomes clear if we observe that any structure written with a charge in the *ortho* position is actually a resonance hybrid of two other almost equivalent resonance forms. One of these has a charge in the *para* position, and the other has a charge in the other *ortho* position. Thus when the substituent is electron repelling and cannot enter into resonance with the benzene ring, we have the extreme structures:

[1] Price, Arntzen, and Weaver, *J. Am. Chem. Soc.*, **60**, 2838 (1938).

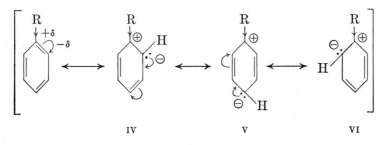

IV   V   VI

When the substituent is only electron attracting, the electron deficiency can be relayed similarly into the *para* and other *ortho* position:

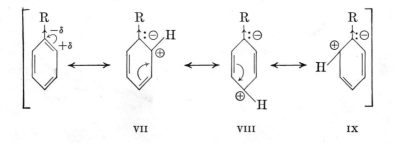

VII   VIII   IX

It is evident that in none of these resonance structures is the relative electron density of the *meta* position either increased or decreased except by the proximity of the charge in the *ortho* or *para* position. Consequently, with the tertiary butyl group, which appears to release its shared electron pair slightly toward an adjacent group (see p. 12),[2] the *ortho* and *para* positions are electron rich. With the electron-attracting trichloromethyl group, however, the *ortho* and *para* positions have a lower electron density than the *meta* position, and the compound is nitrated preferentially in the *meta* position (64.5 per cent).[3]

When the first atom of the side chain possesses an unshared electron pair, or when it is capable of becoming electronically deficient, resonance structures such as IV to VI and VII to IX become particularly important owing to the formation of partial double bonds between these atoms and the aromatic nucleus (see p. 15). The extreme resonance structures are the following:

[2] For one possible explanation of the origin of the permanent polarization of *t*-butylbenzene, see Berliner and Bondhus, *J. Am. Chem. Soc.*, **70**, 854 (1948).

[3] Holleman, *Chem. Revs.*, **1**, 187 (1925).

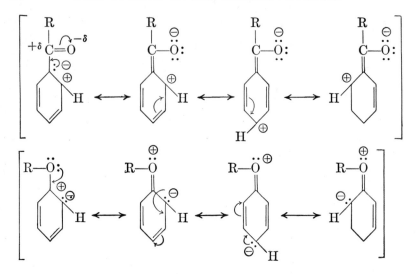

The potentially electronically deficient carbonyl carbon atom effects a decreased charge density in the *ortho* and *para* positions. Conversely, the charge density is increased when the aromatic nucleus is directly attached to an atom with an unshared electron pair.

The principal difficulty in predicting the position of highest electron density in the aromatic nucleus is that it is not yet possible to compare quantitatively the relative magnitudes of permanent polarization, resonance, and the polarizability of conjugated systems when they operate in opposition to each other. In Table 1 are summarized the electrical factors which operate for a number of simple substituents and the observed orientation which these groups exert when they are attached to a benzene ring.

Again we find that resonance appears to outweigh permanent polarization (p. 89). When two of these groups are in opposition we can make only good guesses as to the position a new substituent will take (see p. 243).

Throughout this discussion the tacit assumption has been made that orientation is dependent only upon the position at which the highest electron density can be developed and therefore that the position of substitution will be independent of the substituting reagent. This is a simplifying assumption which is usually qualitatively correct. It is not always, however, for occasionally striking differences are observed. Thus *p*-acetylaminodiphenyl ether is nitrated [4] *ortho* to the acetylamino group,

[4] Oesterlin, *Monatsh.*, **57**, 38 (1931).

TABLE 1

ELECTRICAL FACTORS IN OPERATION FOR RING SUBSTITUENTS AND THEIR COMBINED
EFFECT UPON SUBSTITUTION

Groups	Permanent Polarization (I_s)	Resonance (M)	Polarizability of Conjugated System (E)	Orientation *
$-C(CH_3)_3$	Electron repelling	None †	None †	o, p
$-CCl_3$	Electron attracting	None	None	m
$-\overset{\ominus}{\overset{..}{\underset{..}{O}}}:$	Electron repelling	Electron releasing	Electron releasing	o, p
$-\overset{..}{\underset{..}{O}}R, -\overset{..}{N}R_2,$				
$-\overset{..}{N}HCOCH_3,$ $-\overset{..}{N}HSO_2R,$ $-\overset{..}{\underset{..}{X}}:$ (halogen)	Electron attracting	Electron releasing	Electron releasing	o, p
$-C\equiv N, -NO_2,$ $\overset{O}{\underset{\parallel}{-C-}}$	Electron attracting	Electron attracting	None ‡	m
$-\overset{\oplus}{N}R_3, -\overset{\oplus}{N}H_3$	Electron attracting	None	None	m
$-CH_3,$ $-CH_2R,$ $-CHR_2$	Electron repelling	Electron releasing (hyperconjugation)	Electron releasing (hyperconjugation)	o, p

* See Fieser in Gilman, *Organic Chemistry*, p. 203, John Wiley and Sons, New York, 1943.

† See, however, footnote 2.

‡ See p. 16.

but brominated [5] in the *para* position of the other ring:

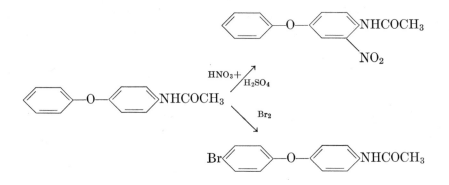

Furthermore the effect of the reaction mixture upon the molecule being substituted must also be considered. It is well known that an aromatic amine is converted into a substituted ammonium ion in acidic media and that this is the species which is actually responsible for the *meta* orientation frequently observed (p. 9). It is often forgotten, however, that many compounds other than amines are bases in strong acid solution so that the species undergoing substitution may actually be a cation. *p*-Tolyl carbonate, for example, is nitrated principally in the *ortho* position with fuming nitric acid but in the *meta* position in a mixture of fuming nitric and fuming sulfuric acid: [6]

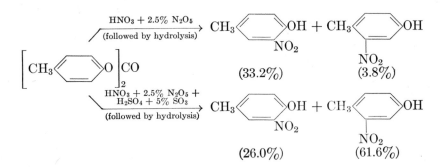

Presumably in sulfuric acid solution one of the species undergoing nitration is a cation such as X or XI.

[5] Bennett and Chapman, *Ann. Rep. Progress Chem.* (Chemical Society of London), **27**, 142 (1930).

[6] Lucas and Liu, *J. Am. Chem. Soc.*, **55**, 1273 (1933).

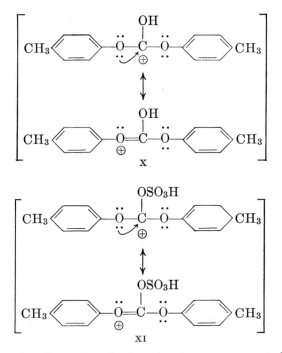

It is interesting that when the functional groups are not directly attached to the aromatic ring, orientation cannot be predicted from a consideration of the point of highest electron density. Cinnamic acid (XII),[7] ω-nitrostyrene (XIII),[8] and 2-phenylethenesulfonyl chloride (XIV),[9] all orient predominantly *ortho-para*, although we should expect these positions to be electronically deficient.

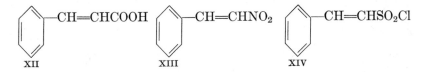

In ω-nitrostyrene, for example, we should expect the resonance forms XV to XVIII to contribute importantly to the structure of the molecule, and we should therefore expect substitution to occur in the *meta* position. The reason for the *ortho-para* orientation of these compounds is not clear: *

[7] Underwood and Kochmann, *ibid.*, **48**, 254 (1926); Müller, *Ann.*, **212**, 124 (1882).
[8] Baker and Wilson, *J. Chem. Soc.*, **1927**, 842.
[9] Bordwell and Rohde, *J. Am. Chem. Soc.*, **70**, 1191 (1948).
* For one explanation, see reference 9.

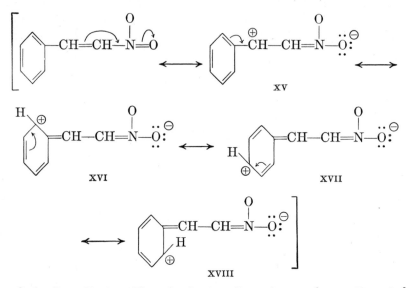

Ortho-Para Ratio. Thus far in our discussion we have attempted only to classify substituents as either *ortho-para* or *meta* directing. It is of interest, therefore, to examine the *ortho-para* class in the hope of being able to predict whether the *ortho* or the *para* isomer will be favored.

Since there are two *ortho* positions but only one *para* position, we should expect twice as much *ortho* as *para* substitution if a given substituent affected each position equally. Actually, however, *para substitution is almost always favored*, and the *ortho-para* ratio is less than 2 (see Table 2). Again the basis for this behavior is not completely clear. However, given the fact that *para* substitution is favored, it is possible to make certain generalizations about the way the *ortho-para* ratio will be affected by different substituents present on the aromatic ring.

First it seems reasonable that as the size of a substituent becomes larger, *para* substitution will be favored. This is indeed found to be the case as the alkyl group of an alkyl benzene increases in size from methyl to *tert*-butyl.[10] Similarly, as size of the attacking reagent becomes larger, *para* substitution should be favored. It is presumably this factor which is responsible for the fact that the chlorination of chlorobenzene goes 39 per cent *ortho* and 55 per cent *para* whereas bromination gives 11 per cent *o*-bromochlorobenzene and 87 per cent of the *para* isomer (Table 2). Second, when a substituent is strongly electron attracting (by permanent polarization) the near-by *ortho* positions should be more strongly deactivated than the more distant *para* position and the *ortho-*

[10] See LeFevre, *J. Chem. Soc.*, **1933**, 980.

TABLE 2

ORTHO-PARA RATIO IN SUBSTITUTION REACTIONS

(Data from Holleman, *Chem. Revs.*, **1**, 187 [1925])

		Product			
Compound	Operation	% o	% m	% p	o/p
Toluene	Nitration	56	3	41	1.4
Toluene	Sulfonation	32	6	62	0.5
Chlorobenzene	Chlorination	39	6	55	0.7
Chlorobenzene	Bromination	11	1.6	87	0.1
Chlorobenzene	Nitration	30		70	0.4
Chlorobenzene	Sulfonation			100	0.0
Bromobenzene	Nitration	37.6		62.1	0.6
Benzyl chloride	Nitration	40.9	4.2	54.9	0.7
Benzal chloride	Nitration	23.3	33.8	42.9	0.5
Acetanilide	Nitration	4.5		95.5	0.1
Benzanilide	Nitration		2.9	97.1	0.0
Phenol	Chlorination	49.8		50.2	1.0
Phenol	Bromination	9.8		90.2	0.1
Phenol	Nitration	40.0		60.0	0.7

para ratio should again decrease.[11] Thus, in spite of the fact that the size of the substituent increases in the halobenzene series from fluorobenzene to iodobenzene, *ortho* nitration becomes increasingly more pronounced in descending the series.[11] We have already seen that the electron-attracting power of the halogens also decreases in the same order (p. 8). By a judicious application of these two principles, many good guesses may be made as to the position a third substituent will take when two groups are already present in an aromatic ring.

Orientation When More Than One Group Is Present in a Benzene Ring. When more than one group is present in a benzene ring, it is difficult to predict orientation. With *p*-ethyl- and *p*-isopropyltoluene, substitution occurs predominantly *ortho* to the methyl group.[10, 12] This fact could have been predicted either on the basis of a more important hyperconjugation contribution of the methyl group or on the basis of steric hindrance.

Hyperconjugation is usually considered to be of less importance than resonance which involves an unshared electron pair (pp. 15, 31). Consequently, we have another generalization, first pointed out by Robin-

[11] Lapworth and Robinson, *Mem. Proc. Manchester, Lit. Phil. Soc.*, **72**, 43 (1927).
[12] LeFevre, *J. Chem. Soc.*, **1933**, 977; *ibid.*, **1934**, 1501; Ganguly and LeFevre, *ibid.*, 852, 1697.

son,[13] that a group having an unshared electron pair on an atom adjacent to the benzene ring will control orientation when it is opposed by an alkyl group. Although there are some exceptions,[14] the principle is often useful. Thus in the nitration of the acetylaminotoluenes, the following results have been obtained: [15]

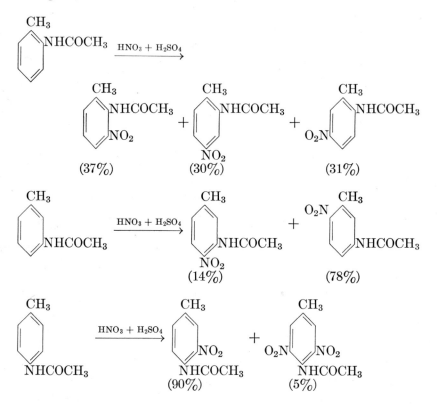

It is clear that in each instance the acetylamino group controlled the orientation. In the nitration of the *meta* isomer, the fact that the nitro group entered predominantly *para* to the acetylamino group can be interpreted either as a consequence of steric hindrance or deactivation of the adjacent position by the acetylamino group. In Table 3 are summarized the products obtained from a number of substitution reactions in which there is more than one substituent already present on the aromatic nucleus.

[13] Robinson, *Outline of an Electrochemical Theory of the Course of Organic Reactions*, p. 41, Institute of Chemistry of Great Britain and Ireland, London, England, 1932.

[14] Brady, Quick, and Welling, *J. Chem. Soc.*, **127**, 2264 (1925).

[15] McGookin and Swift, *J. Soc. Chem. Ind.*, II, **58**, 152 (1939).

TABLE 3

Compound	Operation	Position of Entering Group	Reference
o-Chlorotoluene	Nitration	CH_3— ring with Cl (18.9%), (17.0%), (20.7), (43.4%)	(16)
m-Chlorotoluene	Nitration	CH_3— ring with Cl, (8.8%), (32.3%), (58.9%)	(16)
p-Chlorotoluene	Nitration	CH_3— ring —Cl, (58%), (42%)	(16)
o-Chlorophenol	Nitration	HO— ring with Cl, —NO_2 (principally)	(3)
o-Chloronitro-benzene	Chlorination	Cl— ring(O_2N) —Cl $+$ Cl— ring(O_2N, Cl)	(3)
m-Hydroxybenzoic acid	Nitration	O_2N— ring(OH) —COOH, ring(HO, NO_2) —COOH, ring(OH)(NO_2) —COOH	(3)
p-Cresol	Nitration	HO— ring(NO_2) —CH_3 (only)	(3)
o-Chloroacetanilide	Nitration	CH_3CONH— ring (39%), (59%), Cl 1.9%	(17)
m-Chloroacetanilide	Nitration	CH_3CONH— ring (44.2%), (55%), Cl	(17)
p-Chloroacetanalide	Nitration	CH_3CONH— ring(NO_2) —Cl (only)	(17)
o-Acetoxyacet-anilide	Nitration	CH_3CONH— ring(CH_3COO) (23%), (48%)	(18)

TABLE 3 (*Continued*)

Compound	Operation	Position of Entering Group	Reference
o-Methoxyacetanilide	Nitration	$CH_3\overset{\overset{\displaystyle O}{\|\|}}{C}-NH$⟨(13%)⟩(74%) OCH_3	(18)
m-Chlorobromobenzene	Nitration	(37%) Cl⟨⟩(62%) (1%) Br	(19)
m-Iodochlorobenzene	Nitration	(37%) Cl⟨⟩(63%) (2%) I	(19)
m-Bromoiodobenzene	Nitration	(46%) I⟨⟩(52%) (2%) Br	(19)
p-Chlorobromobenzene	Nitration	(54.8%) (45.2%) Br⟨⟩Cl	(19)
p-Fluorochlorobenzene	Nitration	(79.3%) (20.7%) Cl⟨⟩F	(19)
p-Dimethylaminobenzoic acid methochloride	Nitration	$(CH_3)_2N$⟨⟩$COOH$ NO_2 (after hydrolysis)	(20*a*)
o-Alkoxyanilines	Bromination	Br H_2N⟨⟩Br OR	(21)
o-Alkoxyacetanilides	Chlorination	CH_3CONH⟨⟩Cl OR	(21)
m-Aminophenol	Sulfonation	H_2N⟨⟩SO_3H OH	(20*b*)
p-Aminophenol	Bromination	Br HO⟨⟩NH_2 Br	(21)
p-Alkoxyacetanilides	Bromination or chlorination	X CH_3CONH⟨⟩OR	(21)

TABLE 3 (*Continued*)

Compound	Operation	Position of Entering Group	Reference
p-Alkoxyanilines	Bromination	Br H₂N⟨◯⟩OR Br	(21)
p-Hydroxyacet-anilide	Bromination	Br CH₃CONH⟨◯⟩OH Br	(21)

SUBSTITUTION PROCESSES

Halogenation. Perhaps no single study has contributed more to our knowledge of aromatic substitution reactions than the study of halogenation. For a long time aromatic substitution has been regarded as a process of addition to one of the olefinic bonds, followed by elimination of water or a hydrogen halide. Phenanthrene, for example, will add bromine to form a crystalline dibromide. On gentle heating, this material is transformed into 9-bromophenanthrene: [22]

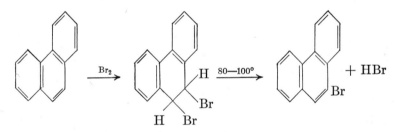

A careful study of the reaction, however, has revealed that the formation of the dibromide is not a necessary intermediate in the formation of the 9-bromo derivative. Consequently, aromatic substitution need not proceed through an addition-elimination mechanism.[23]   Thus it has been

[16] Wibaut, *Rec. trav. chim.*, **32**, 243 (1913).
[17] de Bruyn, *Rec. trav. chim.*, **36**, 161 (1917).
[18] See Ingold, *Ann. Rep. Progress Chem.* (Chemical Society of London), **23**, 138 (1926).
[19] See Ingold, *ibid.*, **25**, 141 (1928).
[20] (*a*) Zaki and Tadros, *J. Chem. Soc.*, **1941**, 562.   (*b*) Miller, Mosher, Gray, and Whitmore, *J. Am. Chem. Soc.*, **71**, 3559 (1949).
[21] See Theilacker, *Ber.*, **71**, 2065 (1938).
[22] See Price, *J. Am. Chem. Soc.*, **58**, 1834 (1936).
[23] Price, *ibid.*, **58**, 2101 (1936).

found that bromine will *add* rapidly and reversibly to phenanthrene but that the principal reaction is a photochemical process [22,24,1] which is inhibited by molecular iodine.[23] *Substitution by bromine,* however, is catalyzed by the addition of a halogen carrier such as ferric chloride or molecular iodine. The effect of these catalysts cannot be simply to facilitate the elimination of hydrogen bromide from the dihalide, since no *hydrogen bromide is evolved from phenanthrene dibromide when it is allowed to stand with molecular iodine.* Since the reaction will proceed in the dark in the presence of carriers, it seems extremely probable that the bromination of phenanthrene is an ionic process which proceeds essentially through the steps:

$$Br\text{—}Br + I_2 \rightleftharpoons [BrI_2]^{\ominus} + Br^{\oplus}$$

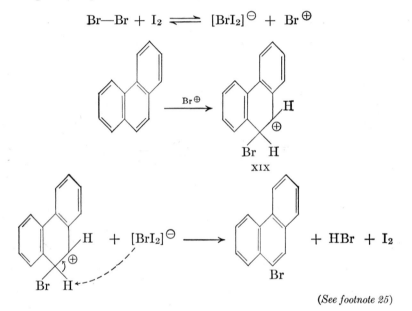

XIX

(*See footnote 25*)

The fact that both phenanthrene and phenanthrene dibromide react at the same rate in the presence of *iodine and bromine* to give 9-bromophenanthrene [23] suggests that the same intermediates are involved in

[24] Kharasch, White, and Mayo, *J. Org. Chem.,* **2,** 574 (1938).

[25] This mechanism was originally proposed by Pfeiffer and Wizinger, *Ann.,* **461,** 132 (1928). The equations shown here, however, represent only one of several possible paths for reaction. Kinetic analyses (see footnote 28 and Robertson, Allan, Haldane, and Simmers, *J. Chem. Soc.,* **1949,** 933) indicate that more than one process is taking place at once. Thus the reactive intermediate Br $\oplus$ can be generated from other sources such as Br_2, Br_4, IBr_3 also present in the reaction mixture. Similarly it seems probable that species such as IBr_3, Br_2, and $I_3 \ominus$ may also act with $BrI_2 \ominus$ as proton acceptors in the last step of the sequence.

both reactions. As we have already seen (p. 105) acid-catalyzed elimination reactions are assumed to involve an intermediate such as XIX.

Although a stable dibromide cannot be isolated for a similar study of the bromination of benzene, the kinetics of the iodine catalyzed bromination of benzene is identical with that of phenanthrene.[26] Consequently it is very probable that the mechanism of the halogenation of benzene is the same as that proposed for phenanthrene. The kinetics of chlorination,[27] bromination,[28] and iodination by iodine chloride [29] are also in agreement with this interpretation. The halogenation of phenols, however, appears to be a different, more complex process.[30]

It is clear from the mechanism proposed for halogenation that the purpose of halogen carriers is to develop a positively charged ion from the halogen molecule:

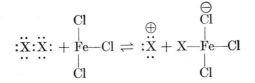

Similarly, when iodine monochloride is the halogenating agent employed, iodine rather than chlorine will be introduced into the benzene ring as a result of the unequal charge distribution between the dissimilar halogen atoms:

$$\overset{+\delta}{\overset{..}{\underset{..}{:I}}} \quad \overset{-\delta}{\overset{..}{\underset{..}{:Cl:}}}$$

Although some chlorination occasionally occurs even with iodine monochloride,[29] it is not clear why iodine monobromide is a brominating agent for phenol and aniline.[31]

Nitration. When mixed acid is employed, the nitration of benzene derivatives appears to take place through the following steps:

[26] Price and Arntzen, *J. Am. Chem. Soc.*, **60**, 2837 (1938).

[27] de la Mare and Robertson, *J. Chem. Soc.*, **1943**, 279.

[28] Robertson, de la Mare, and Johnston, *ibid.*, 276. de la Mare and Robertson, *ibid.*, **1948**, 100; Bradfield, Davies, and Long, *ibid.*, **1949**, 1389.

[29] Lambourne and Robertson, *ibid.*, **1947**, 1167.

[30] Soper and Smith, *ibid.*, **1926**, 1582; Painter and Soper, *ibid.*, **1947**, 342; Li, *J. Am. Chem. Soc.*, **64**, 1147 (1942).

[31] Militzer, *J. Am. Chem. Soc.*, **60**, 256 (1938).

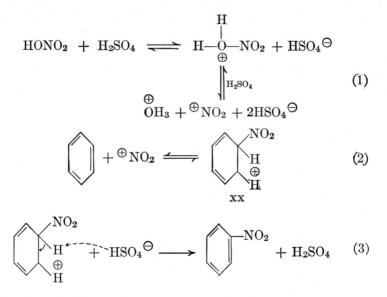

Equation 2 is the usual one written for the characteristic attack at an olefinic bond, and there is good evidence for equations 1 and 3. Thus there can be no doubt that the species $\oplus NO_2$ (called a *nitronium ion*) exists in a sulfuric acid solution of nitric acid. This has been deduced from ultraviolet absorption spectra,[22] Raman spectra,[32] vapor pressure data,[32, 33] freezing point measurements [33, 34] and electrolysis experiments.[33, 35] That $\oplus NO_2$ is the reactive species is indicated by the fact that the Raman line characteristic of the ion appears only at those concentrations of water, nitric acid, and sulfuric acid which are sufficiently concentrated for the nitration of nitrobenzene.[33] Other supporting evidence has been gained by a comparison of the rate of nitration of nitrobenzene and the percentage ionization of tri-*p*-nitrophenylcarbinol, a substance known to ionize in sulfuric acid solution to give a carbonium ion $(O_2NC_6H_4)_3C\oplus$:

$$(O_2NC_6H_4)_3C\text{—}OH + 2H_2SO_4 \rightleftharpoons (O_2NC_6H_4)_3C\overset{\oplus}{} + \overset{\oplus}{O}H_3 + 2HS\overset{\ominus}{O_4}$$

Since the two curves parallel each other through a wide range of acid strength, it seems highly probable that both reactions are preceded by the same kind of ionization.[36a]

[32] Brand, *J. Chem. Soc.*, **1946**, 880.
[33] Bennett, Brand, and Williams, *ibid.*, 869.
[34] Gillespie, Graham, Hughes, Ingold, and Peeling, *Nature*, **158**, 480 (1946).
[35] Bennett, Brand, and Williams, *J. Chem. Soc.*, **1946**, 875.
[36a] Westheimer and Kharasch, *J. Am. Chem. Soc.*, **68**, 1871 (1946).

The evidence for step 3 is indirect but nevertheless interesting. Inspection of the equations 1 to 3 will show that nitration depends not only on the attack of $\oplus NO_2$ upon a benzene ring, but also upon removal of a proton from the intermediate XX.[36b] The most important acceptor of a proton is certainly the bisulfate ion $(HSO_4)\ominus$,[37] and consequently the rate of step 3 should be increased by the addition of water:

$$H_2O + H_2SO_4 \rightleftharpoons \overset{\oplus}{OH_3} + \overset{\ominus}{HSO_4}$$

This reaction, however, will tend to reverse step 1. *Thus there should be an optimum concentration of water in the sulfuric acid of a nitrating mixture above which and below which the rate of nitration should decrease.* For many nitration reactions, aqueous sulfuric acid of about 90 per cent concentration has been found to be optimal.[36, 38] Furthermore, when the concentration of sulfuric acid is greater than 90 per cent (and the concentration of bisulfate ion is therefore too small), addition of $HSO_4\ominus$ should increase the rate of reaction. Conversely, when the concentration of sulfuric acid is lower than 90 per cent, the rate of reaction should be decreased by the addition of $HSO_4\ominus$ through the reversal of equation 1. Both these consequences have been verified.[36, 38, 39a]

From this discussion it can be seen that the usefulness of sulfuric acid in a nitrating mixture depends upon the fact that sulfuric acid provides an ideal balance between the ionization of nitric acid into the ion $\oplus NO_2$ and the subsequent removal of a proton from one of the intermediates. That it does not act simply as an absorbent for the water formed during the reaction has been shown by the fact that the introduction of phosphorus pentoxide into the reaction mixture causes no change in the reaction rate.[39b]

In the absence of sulfuric acid, the nitration of certain reactive benzene derivatives appears to proceed through a preliminary nitrosation step rather than the sequence outlined above. Thus phenol,[40] anisole,[41] and

[36b] For evidence that this is not so for all nitrations, see Melander, *Nature*, **163**, 599 (1949).

[37] Sulfuric acid and the ion $HS_2O_7\ominus$ also appear to act as electron acceptors. See footnote 38.

[38] Bennett, Brand, James, Saunders, and Williams, *J. Chem. Soc.*, **1947**, 474; Bennett, *Chem. and Industry*, **15**, 235 (1949).

[39a] For a different interpretation see Gillespie, Hughes, Ingold, Millen and Reed, *Nature*, **163**, 599 (1949).

[39b] Martinsen, *Z. physik. Chem.*, **59**, 622 (1907).

[40] Martinsen, *ibid.*, **50**, 385 (1905).

[41] Schramm and Westheimer, *J. Am. Chem. Soc.*, **70**, 1782 (1948).

naphthalene [42] are nitrated only when the nitric acid contains some oxides of nitrogen. Preliminary nitrosation is indicated with anisole by the fact that the products obtained by the nitration of p-nitrosoanisole under a wide variety of conditions parallel those obtained from the mixture of anisole under the same conditions.[41]

Sulfonation.[43] In concentrated sulfuric acid solution, it has been shown experimentally that there is sulfur trioxide present.[44] Consequently we may consider sulfuric acid or sulfur trioxide as the reactive species in sulfonation processes. One mechanism which has been suggested involving sulfuric acid,[45] is based upon a preliminary ionization similar to that which has been proposed for nitration:

$$2\text{HO}\!-\!\overset{\text{O}}{\underset{\text{O}}{\text{S}}}\!-\!\text{OH} \text{ (or } \text{HO}\!-\!\overset{\text{O}}{\underset{\text{O}}{\overset{\|}{\text{S}}}}\!-\!\text{OH)} \;\rightleftharpoons\; \text{H}\!-\!\overset{\text{H}}{\underset{\oplus}{\text{O}}}\!-\!\overset{\text{O}}{\underset{\text{O}}{\text{S}}}\!-\!\text{OH} + \text{HSO}_4{}^{\ominus}$$

$$\Big\Downarrow \text{H}_2\text{SO}_4$$

$$\overset{\oplus}{\text{OH}}_3 + {}^{\oplus}\text{SO}_3\text{H} + 2\text{HSO}_4{}^{\ominus}$$

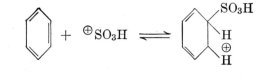

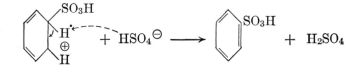

Alternatively, sulfur trioxide itself may be the electron-seeking reagent:

[42] Titov, *J. Gen. Chem.* (U.S.S.R.), **17**, 382 (1947); (*C.A.*, **42**, 545 [1948]).

[43] For reviews of sulfonation, see (*a*) Suter and Weston in Adams, *Organic Reactions*, Vol. III, p. 141, John Wiley and Sons, New York, 1946; (*b*) Fisk, *Ind. and Eng. Chem.*, **40**, 1671 (1948).

[44] Baumgarten, *Die Chimie*, **55**, 115 (1942).

[45] Price, *Chem. Revs.*, **29**, 51 (1941).

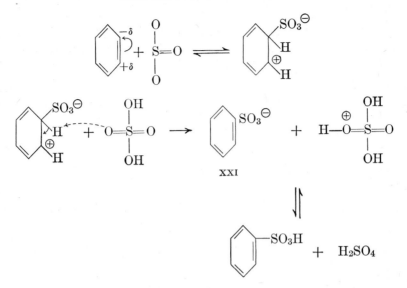

XXI

Although the second of these two reaction sequences seems preferable and has received some support from desulfonation studies,[46] it seems probable that there is actually no physical distinction between the two in aqueous sulfuric acid. The difference between the first mechanism (which involves $\oplus SO_3H$ and $HSO_4\ominus$) and the second (which involves SO_3 and H_2SO_4) depends upon the assignment of a proton to one of the two reaction intermediates. Since all these species may be solvated or highly hydrogen bonded, such a distinction seems to lack physical justification. The kinetics of sulfonation of p-nitrotoluene in aqueous sulfuric acid is consistent with either reaction sequence.[47] In fuming sulfuric acid (oleum), the rate of sulfonation is directly proportional to the concentration of sulfur trioxide.[46]

Although sulfonation resembles nitration and halogenation in many respects, there are certain important differences. The two most noticeable of these differences are the reversibility of sulfonation processes and the striking sensitivity of orientation to changes in the reaction temperature. Amino derivatives offer a further complication in that considerable amounts of *ortho* and *para* derivatives are often obtained. Thus at low temperatures, aniline gives a mixture of o, m, and p-aminobenzenesulfonic acid,[48] whereas dimethylaniline gives an almost equal

[46] Baddeley, Holt, and Kenner, *Nature*, **154**, 361 (1944).
[47] Cowdrey and Davies, *J. Chem. Soc.*, **1949**, 1871.
[48] Alexander, *J. Am. Chem. Soc.*, **68**, 969 (1946).

mixture of *p*- and *m*-dimethylaminobenzenesulfonic acid.[49]   At high temperatures, sulfonation gives only the *para*-substituted derivatives in either case:

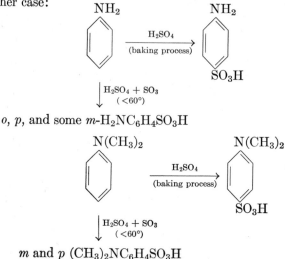

o, *p*, and some *m*-$H_2NC_6H_4SO_3H$

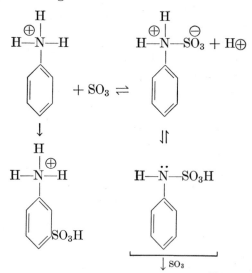

m and *p* $(CH_3)_2NC_6H_4SO_3H$

With aniline the explanation for these rather unusual results seems to be that in sulfuric acid solution sulfur trioxide forms undissociated phenylsulfamic acid from the substituted ammonium salt [48] and that this species is sulfonated together with the anilinium ion:

(Continued on facing page)

[49] Kurakin, *Zhur. Obschei Khim.* (*J. Gen. Chem.*), **18**, 2089 (1948); (*C.A.*, **43**, 3803 [1949].)

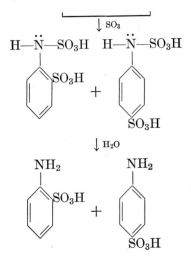

The orientation of phenylsulfamic acid would be expected to be *ortho-para*, since there is an unshared electron pair on the nitrogen atom adjacent to the benzene ring. Dimethylaniline forms no complex with sulfur trioxide [48] and consequently the formation of the *para* isomer may be interpreted as a reaction proceeding through the small amount of dimethylaniline in equilibrium with the substituted ammonium salt:

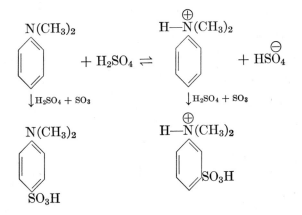

Free dimethylaniline would also be expected to orient *ortho-para* because of the free electron pair on the nitrogen atom.

At elevated temperatures when sulfonation is carried out with concentrated sulfuric acid, kinetic data [50] again are consistent with the for-

[50] Alexander, *ibid.*, **69**, 1599 (1947).

mation of phenylsulfamic acid. Dimethylaniline, however, appears to require dissociation into the free base before reaction will occur, since the high-temperature sulfonation of dimethylaniline cannot be carried out with concentrated sulfuric acid unless water is allowed to escape from the reaction mixture.[50] The fact that no sulfonation takes place when the ions alone are present suggests that sulfonation must be preceded by the dissociation:

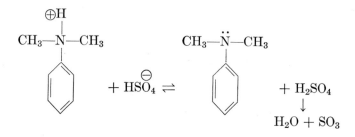

An example of the interesting sensitivity of sulfonation processes to temperature changes is the well-known sulfonation of naphthalene. At temperatures below 80°, α-naphthalenesulfonic acid is formed. At 160 to 165°, the β-isomer is produced either by direct sulfonation or by heating the α-isomer with sulfuric acid:

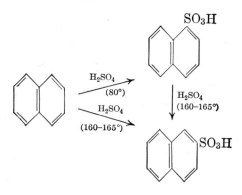

Isomerization here is due to the reversible nature of the sulfonation process. The α-position appears to be sulfonated more rapidly than the β-position, but at elevated temperatures desulfonation also occurs more rapidly at the α-position than in the β-position. Consequently an equilibrium is established which favors the concentration of the β-isomer.[51]

[51] Lantz, *Compt. rend.*, **201**, 149 (1935); *Bull. soc. chim.* [5], **2**, 2092 (1935).

At 160 to 162°, equilibrium is established in 1 to $1\frac{1}{2}$ hours, and the ratio of the α to the β-isomer is 15/85.[52] It is interesting that desulfonation of the α-isomer commences at 70° whereas the β-isomer requires a temperature of 113 to 115°.[53] It is probable, therefore, that, given a sufficient amount of time, sulfonation between the temperatures of 70 to 115° would produce only the β-isomer.

Jacobsen Rearrangement. When a polyalkylated benzene is allowed to remain in contact with sulfuric acid, a rearranged polylalkylbenzene sulfonic acid is often obtained. Reactions of this kind are usually called Jacobsen rearrangements.[54] The reaction of durene with sulfuric acid is an example:

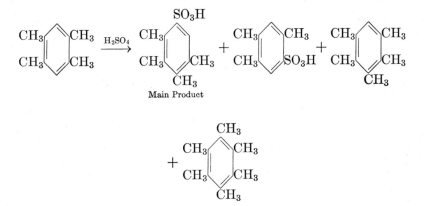

Main Product

Rearrangement appears to be a property of the sulfonic acids themselves and not of the hydrocarbons, since durenesulfonic acid rearranges in contact with phosphorus pentoxide, but durene itself will not.[55] Similarly, the sulfonic acid from pentamethylbenzene will rearrange in a desiccator over sulfuric acid, whereas the hydrocarbon will not.[54]

An explanation for this transformation has been proposed[56] based upon the steps illustrated in formulas XXII to XXIX.

[52] Spryskov and Ovsyankina, *J. Gen. Chem.* (U.S.S.R.), **16**, 1057 (1946); (*C.A.*, **41**, 2720 [1947]).

[53] Spryskov, *ibid.*, **16**, 2126 (1946); (*C.A.*, **42**, 894 [1948]).

[54] For a review of the Jacobsen rearrangement, see Smith in Adams, *Organic Reactions*, Vol. I, p. 370, John Wiley and Sons, New York, 1942.

[55] Smith and Cass, *J. Am. Chem. Soc.*, **54**, 1614 (1932).

[56] Arnold and Barnes, *ibid.*, **66**, 960 (1944).

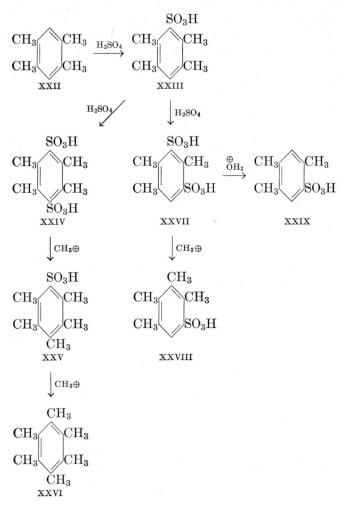

Although there is no proof for the mechanism, many of the data known about the reaction can be interpreted in terms of three general steps: (1) sulfonation (XXII to XXIV); (2) formation of a *m*- or *p*-disulfonic acid with the elimination of an alkyl carbonium ion if one of these positions is occupied (XXIII to XXVII and XXIII to XXIV); and (3) displacement of the *more hindered* sulfonic acid group by the eliminated carbonium ion (XXIV to XXVI and XXVII to XXVIII) or an oxonium ion (XXVII to XXIX). In agreement with (3) it has been found that the most hindered sulfonic acids are the most readily desulfonated.[57]

[57] Smith and Guss, *ibid.*, **62**, 2634 (1940).

The Jacobsen rearrangement of 6-*n*-propyl-7-methyltetralin (XXX) gives 5-*n*-propyl-6-methyltetralin (XXXIV).[58] The formation of a *n*-propyl product only is of particular interest for it implies that the re-arrangement did not involve a *n*-propyl carbonium ion. Such a car-bonium ion would be expected to rearrange at least in part during the re-action and to lead to the introduction of an isopropyl group. Further-more, if we follow through what seems to be the alternative route (XXX to XXXIV), the conclusion is reached that initial sulfonation must have occurred in the 5-position between the tetramethylene ring and the *n*-propyl group in preference to the less hindered 8-position.

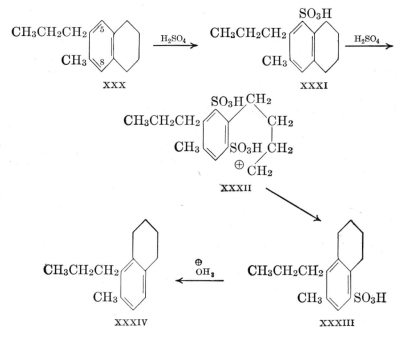

This result is somewhat surprising in view of the usual reluctance of a sulfonic acid group to enter a hindered position.[43a]

Friedel-Crafts Reaction. Aromatic alkylations or acylations which are catalyzed by anhydrous aluminum chloride are generally called Friedel-Crafts reactions.[59] The general mechanism for these reactions

[58] Smith and Chien-Pen, *ibid.*, **70**, 2209 (1948).

[59] For reviews of the Friedel-Crafts reaction, see (*a*) Calloway, *Chem. Revs.*, **17**, 327 (1935); (*b*) Price, *ibid.*, **29**, 37 (1939); (*c*) Nightingale, *ibid.*, **25**, 329 (1939); (*d*) Price in Adams, *Organic Reactions*, Vol. III, p. 1, John Wiley and Sons, New York, 1946; (*e*) Groggins, *Ind. Eng. Chem.*, **40**, 1608 (1948); (*f*) Francis, *Chem. Revs.*, **43**, 257 (1948). (*g*) Berliner in Adams, *Organic Reactions*, Vol. V, p. 229, John Wiley and Sons, New York, 1949.

consists in the formation of a carbonium ion, followed by the attack of this positively charged species upon the aromatic nucleus. Thus for alkylation we have

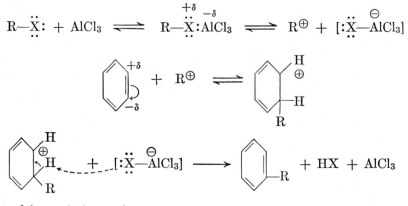

and for acylation we have

$$R-\overset{O}{\overset{\|}{C}}-\overset{..}{\underset{..}{X}}: + AlCl_3 \rightleftharpoons [R-\overset{+\delta\,O}{\overset{\|}{C}}-\overset{..}{\underset{..}{X}} : AlCl_3]^{-\delta} \rightleftharpoons R-\overset{O}{\overset{\|}{C}}\oplus + [:\overset{..}{\underset{..}{X}}-\overset{\ominus}{AlCl_3}]$$

or

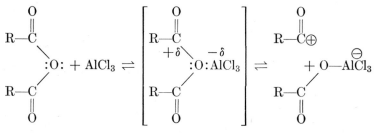

followed by

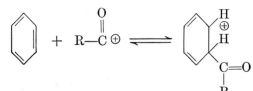

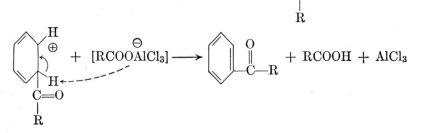

For both alkyl halides and acyl halides there is evidence of a preliminary ionization into a carbonium ion and $[\overset{\ominus}{X—AlCl_3}]$. As was mentioned in Chapter 3, solutions of an aluminum halide and an alkyl halide conduct an electrical current and aluminum migrates to the anode compartment (p. 40). When an alkyl halide and benzene are mixed with a different halide of aluminum, the off-gas from the reaction is found to contain both hydrogen halides.[60] Thus with benzyl chloride and benzyl bromide the following results were obtained:

$$C_6H_5CH_2Cl + AlBr_3 + C_6H_6 \rightarrow \begin{array}{l} 25.67\% \text{ HCl} \\ 74.33\% \text{ HBr} \end{array}$$

$$C_6H_5CH_2Br + AlCl_3 + C_6H_6 \rightarrow \begin{array}{l} 79.41\% \text{ HCl} \\ 20.59\% \text{ HBr} \end{array}$$

On the basis of the formation of the ion $[:\overset{\ominus}{\underset{..}{X}—AlX'_3}]$, the values of 25 and 75 per cent would be expected. Similarly, when the reaction is carried out with tert-butyl chloride or acetyl chloride and aluminum chloride containing radioactive chlorine, radioactivity is found almost equally distributed between the off-gas and the nonvolatile reaction mixture.[61] All these results support the view that the first step in the process is the formation of an ionized addition complex between the alkyl or acyl halide and aluminum halide.

Although there has been some confusion about the exact nature of the subsequent steps in the reaction (because of the formation of a complex between aluminum chloride and benzene [62]), it now seems probable that such complexes play no important part in the Friedel-Crafts reaction. By employing gallium trichloride (which is soluble in carbon disulfide solution), it has been possible to determine the equilibrium constant for the reaction:

$$C_3H_7Cl + GaCl_3 \rightleftharpoons [C_3H_7Cl \cdot GaCl_3]$$

and to show that the rate of alkylation of benzene with this reaction mixture is directly proportional to the concentration of the complex and of the aromatic hydrocarbon.[63] Consequently, we may conclude that any further function of the catalyst in activating the benzene molecule itself is probably negligible.

It is evident that the function of aluminum chloride in the Friedel-

[60] Korshak and Kolesnikov, *J. Gen. Chem.* (U.S.S.R.), **14**, 1092 (1944); (*C.A.*, **40**, 4033 [1946]).

[61] Fairbrother, *J. Chem. Soc.*, **1937**, 503.

[62] Nightingale, *Chem. Revs.*, **25**, 358 (1939).

[63] Ulich and Heyne, *Z. Electrochem.*, **41**, 509 (1935).

Crafts process is to generate carbonium ions from the alkyl or acyl halides. It would be expected, then, that a number of other combinations of starting materials and reagents which lead to carbonium ions should be capable of effecting acylation or alkylation. Indeed we find that olefins (p. 35), alcohols (p. 36), ethers (p. 36), and esters (p. 37) can be used as starting materials for aromatic alkylation reactions in the presence of such catalysts as boron trifluoride, sulfuric acid, or anhydrous hydrogen fluoride.[59d] Acylations can be carried out with acids (p. 37),[64] acid halides (p. 230), and acid anhydrides (p. 37). The Fries reaction [65] (in which phenolic esters are converted to hydroxy aromatic ketones by means of aluminum chloride) appears to be an example of a typical acylation reaction in which the ester itself acts as the source of an acyl carbonium ion:

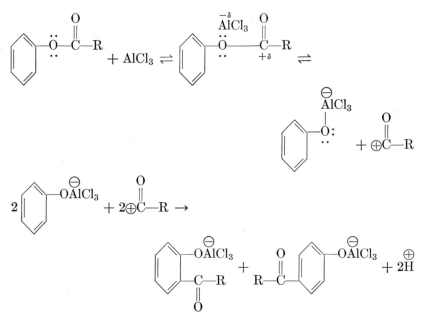

That the reaction is not an intramolecular rearrangement has been shown by the fact that a mixture of products is obtained when aluminum chloride is added to a solution of o-chloro-p-tolyl acetate and p-tolyl benzoate.[66] Evidence for a common intermediate in this reaction and

[64] Simons, Randall, and Archer, *J. Am. Chem. Soc.*, **61**, 1795 (1939).

[65] For a review of the Fries reaction, see Blatt in Adams, *Organic Reactions*, Vol. I, p. 342, John Wiley and Sons, New York, 1942.

[66] Rosenmund and Schnurr, *Ann.*, **460**, 56 (1928). See also Baltzly and Philips, *J. Am. Chem. Soc.*, **70**, 4191 (1948), and Ogata, Kometani, and Oda, *Bull. Inst. Phys. Chem. Research* (Tokyo), **22**, 828 (1943); (*C.A.*, **43**, 7924 [1949]).

the usual Friedel-Crafts reaction is that acetyl chloride has been isolated when 2,4,6-trichlorophenyl acetate is treated with aluminum chloride.[67]

One rather interesting aspect of the Friedel-Crafts reaction is that trialkylation of benzene often leads to a symmetrical 1,3,5-isomer rather than a 1,2,4-derivative as would be expected from the *ortho-para* orientation of the alkyl group introduced initially. Since alkylation by the Friedel-Crafts method has been shown to be a reversible reaction,[68] this anomalous orientation has been explained on the basis that both alkylation and dealkylation occur readily in the *ortho* and *para* positions. Simultaneously, however, some alkylation occurs in the *meta* position but no dealkylation.[68] If the reaction mixture is allowed to stand in contact with aluminum chloride for some length of time, then principally *meta* trialkyl derivatives will be formed:

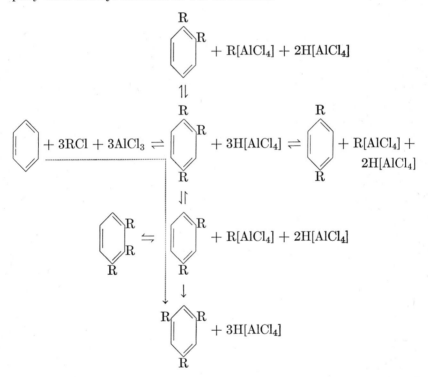

The observation that 1,2,4-trialkyl derivatives will often rearrange to the corresponding 1,3,5-isomers [68] supports this view. It is not clear, however, why no isomerization of the propyl group is observed in the

[67] Cox, *J. Am. Chem. Soc.*, **52**, 352 (1930).

[68] See Price in Adams, *Organic Reactions*, Vol. III, pp. 9–10, John Wiley and Sons, New York, 1946.

transformation of *p*-di-*n*-propylbenzene to *m*-di-*n*-propylbenzene and
1,3,5-tri-*n*-propylbenzene at 100° by the action of aluminum chloride.[69]

Acylations with Nitriles.   With particularly reactive aromatic nuclei
such as phenols, a Friedel-Crafts type reaction may be effected with
nitriles in the presence of an acid catalyst such as hydrogen chloride,
aluminum chloride, or zinc chloride.   The reaction is usually called the
Houben-Hoesch synthesis.[70a]   When hydrogen cyanide is employed, the
process leads to aromatic aldehydes even with a number of aromatic

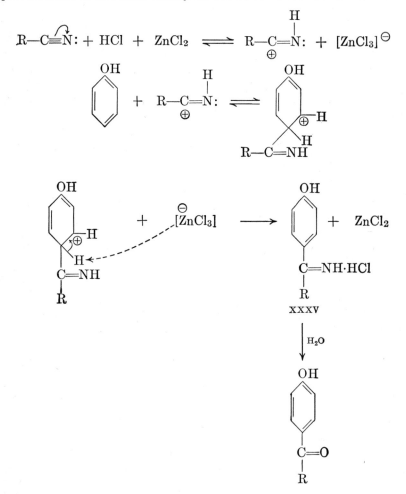

[69] Baddeley and Kenner, *J. Chem. Soc.*, **1935**, 305.

[70a] For a review of this reaction see Spoerri and Du Bois in Adams, *Organic Reactions*, Vol. V, p. 387, John Wiley and Sons, New York, 1949.

hydrocarbons.[70b, 71, 72] This modification is often called the Gattermann synthesis of aldehydes. These reactions may be formulated (p. 264) as proceeding through a carbonium ion formed by the addition of the acid to the nitrogen atom of the nitrile (p. 174), followed by hydrolysis of the resulting imino hydrochloride.

It is interesting that while the aldehyde synthesis probably proceeds by this mechanism with dry hydrogen chloride as the catalyst,[71] when aluminum chloride is present the reactive intermediate is a complex of aluminum chloride and two molecules of HCN (AlCl$_3$·2HCN).[70, 71] Since the resulting nitrogen containing intermediate corresponding to XXXV is hydrolyzed to an aldehyde, the same end product is obtained. This is of considerable practical importance, however, for two moles of hydrogen cyanide and two moles of aluminum chloride are required to introduce one aldehyde group.[70, 71, 72]

[70b] Hinkel, Ayling, and Beynon, *J. Chem. Soc.*, **1935**, 674.

[71] Hinkel, Ayling, and Beynon, *ibid.*, **1936**, 184.

[72] Niedzielski and Nord, *J. Am. Chem. Soc.*, **63**, 1462 (1941); *J. Org. Chem.*, **8**, 147 (1943).

CHAPTER 14

DIAZONIUM REACTIONS AND THE WOLFF-KISHNER REDUCTION

Diazotization. In almost all its reactions, nitrous acid attacks a point of high electron density. The nitrosation of methylaniline and dimethylaniline are examples:

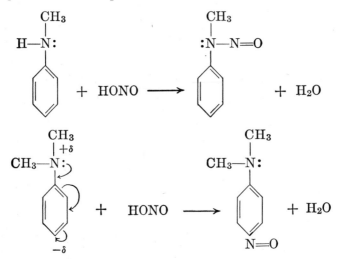

These reactions are, in general, acid-catalyzed.[1,2] Although the chemistry of nitrous acid is still not completely understood, it seems quite plausible[3] that the function of a stronger mineral acid is to facilitate the ionization:

$$H—\overset{..}{\underset{..}{O}}—N{=}O + \overset{\oplus}{H} \rightleftharpoons H—\underset{\oplus}{\overset{H}{\overset{|}{O}}}—\overset{..}{N}{=}O \rightleftharpoons H_2O + {\oplus}N{=}O$$

[1] Taylor, *J. Chem. Soc.*, **1928**, 1099; *ibid.*, 1897; Taylor and Price, *ibid.*, **1929**, 2052; Abel, Schmid, and Sidon, *Z. Elektrochem.*, **39**, 863 (1933).

[2] Hantzsch and Schümann, *Ber.*, **32**, 1691 (1899); Schmid and Muhr, *ibid.*, **70B**, 421 (1937).

[3] Kenner, *Chemistry and Industry*, **1941**, 445. See also Hodgson and Norris, *J. Soc. Dyers and Colourists*, **65**, 226 (1949).

Salts containing the ion $\oplus$NO are known,[4] and such an ion would be expected to attack a point of high electron density. Accordingly, diazotization of aromatic amines may be written:

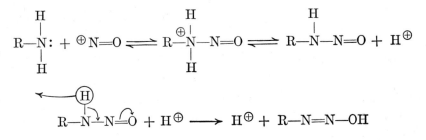

In the presence of excess acid, the protonated diazonium hydroxide dissociates into a diazonium ion and water:

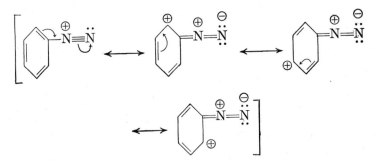

Undoubtedly the same reaction occurs with aliphatic primary amines and nitrous acid. With aryl amines, however, the diazonium ion is stabilized by the resonance forms,

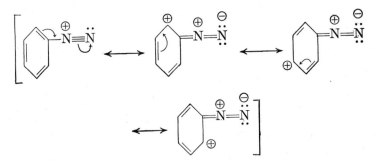

The usual reaction of aliphatic diazonium ions is a decomposition into nitrogen and a carbonium ion (see p. 40):

$$R\overset{\oplus}{-}N\equiv N: \ \rightarrow \ R\oplus + \ :N\equiv N:$$

[4] Hantzsh and Berger, *Z. anorg. Chem.*, **190**, 321 (1930); Klinkenberg, *Rec. trav. chim.*, **56**, 749 (1937).

The kinetics of diazotization [2] and the reaction of nitrous acid with alkyl amines [1] is consistent with this interpretation of the mechanism of reaction.

Reactions of Diazonium Salts. Many of the reactions of diazonium salts appear to proceed by free radical mechanisms. Thus, depending upon the environment of the diazonium salt, it is possible that cleavage might occur by free radical scission (*A*) or by ionization (*B*):

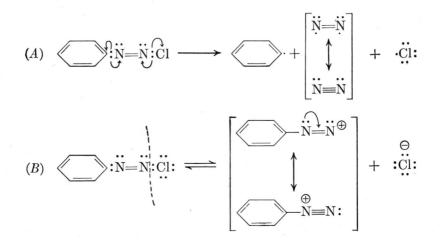

The preparation of unsymmetrical biaryls,[5] the Sandmeyer reaction,[6] the replacement of an aromatic diazonium group by hydrogen,[7] and the reaction of diazonium salts with α,β-unsaturated carbonyl compounds [8] appear to proceed by free radical mechanisms and will not be discussed. Diazonium coupling reactions, however, have the characteristics of ionic processes.

Diazonium Coupling Reactions. The union of a diazonium ion with a phenol or an amine is known as a diazonium coupling reaction. The process appears to be an example of aromatic substitution in which the reactive species are the diazonium cation and phenoxide ion or the substituted aniline molecule: [9]

[5] Bachmann and Hoffman in Adams, *Organic Reactions*, Vol. II, p. 224, John Wiley and Sons, New York, 1944.

[6] Hodgson, *Chem. Revs.*, **40**, 251 (1947).

[7] Kornblum and Cooper, Abstracts of Papers, 116th Meeting of the American Chemical Society, p. 50M, Atlantic City, New Jersey, September 1949.

[8] Koelsch, *ibid.*, **65**, 57 (1943); Koelsch and Boekelheide, *ibid.*, **66**, 412 (1944).

[9] (*a*) Wistar and Bartlett, *ibid.*, **63**, 413 (1941); (*b*) Hauser and Breslow, *ibid.*, 418.

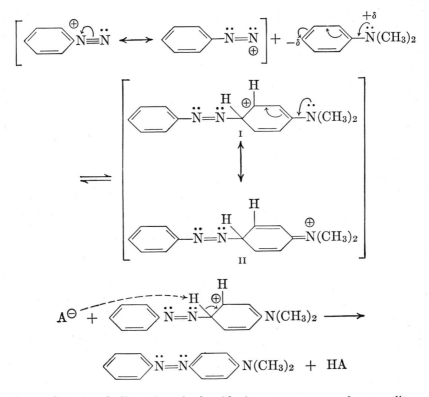

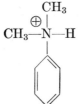

An undissociated diazonium hydroxide is not necessary for coupling since benzenediazonium chloride couples readily with either β-naphthol or sodium β-naphthoxide in anhydrous pyridine solution.[9b]

In the light of this mechanism, several well-known facts concerning diazonium coupling reactions are readily explicable. Sodium acetate or sodium carbonate is usually necessary for coupling to lower the acidity of the reaction mixture and to increase correspondingly the concentration of free base or phenoxide ion. There is little probability of reaction between diazonium and substituted anilinium ions since they are of like charge and the aromatic nucleus of the anilinium ion is deactivated:

With phenol, the phenoxide ion not only has an opposite charge which is favorable for bringing the reactive species together, but also the electron density in the *ortho* and *para* positions is much higher than in phenol itself since there is no restraining positive charge developed in the resonance forms contributing to the stability of the phenoxide ion (see pp. 24, 131). This can be readily seen by comparing formulas III and IV.

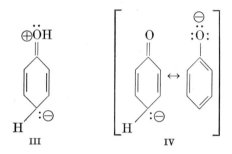

It is also understandable that a *p*-nitro group in a diazonium ion favors the coupling process. Electron-attracting groups increase the positive character of the diazo group and therefore the acceptor capacity of the diazonium ion.

It is interesting that the resonance form II must contribute to the stabilization of the intermediate I to II or no coupling will occur. It is well known that benzene will not couple with diazonium ions, but neither will N,N,2,5-tetramethylaniline (V).[10] In this molecule, the nitrogen

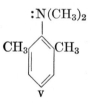

atom cannot enter into resonance with the benzene ring because the bulk of the two *ortho* methyl groups prevents the necessary coplanarity (see the "Steric Inhibition of Resonance," p. 27).

Considerations of this kind also provide an alternative explanation for a number of phenomena which for some time have been attributed to bond fixation (Mills-Nixon effect).[11] Thus the fact that 2,7-dihydroxy-naphthalene couples only in the 1- or the 8-position has been taken as

[10] Nenitzescu and Vantu, *Ber.*, **77B**, 705 (1944).

[11] For a more complete discussion of these ideas, see (*a*) Wheland, *The Theory of Resonance*, pp. 270–272, John Wiley and Sons, 1944; (*b*) Waters, *J. Chem. Soc.*, **1948**, 727; and (*c*) Longuet-Higgins and Coulson, *Trans. Faraday Soc.*, **42**, 756 (1946).

evidence that the dihydroxynaphthalene has the structure

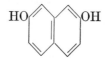

rather than the hybridized resonance form:

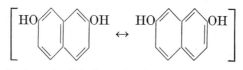

Similarly for 5-hydroxyhydrindene the formula

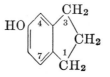

has been suggested as preferable to

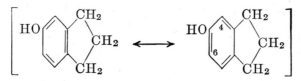

since coupling occurs readily in the 6-position but with difficulty in position 4. This is not the only interpretation, however. The same conclusion would be reached if we assume that the double bonds are not fixed but that reaction simply proceeds through the intermediate most stabilized by resonance. Thus if it is agreed that resonance of the oxygen atom with the benzene ring is essential for coupling, the important resonance structures to be considered are VI and VII for attack in the 1- and 8-position of the dihydroxynaphthalene, and VIII for attack in position 3.

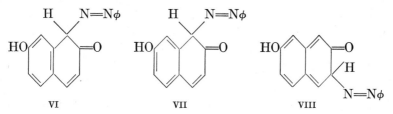

Certainly forms VI and VII will contribute more strongly to the stability of the intermediate than VIII, since both retain the resonance energy of an intact benzene ring. Consequently reaction should proceed preferentially in the 1- or 8-position.

Similarly with 5-hydroxyhydrindene, the intermediate

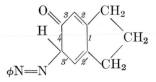

should be more stable than

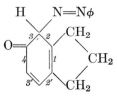

since the effect of a five-membered ring fused in the *ortho* positions of benzene is to compress the bonds labeled *1* and *2* and to lengthen bonds *3* and *4*.[11c] Double bonds are shorter than single bonds, so that this inherent stretching and shortening will tend to favor formation of the upper intermediate.

Obviously these considerations are simply another way of looking at the same problem, but they avoid the seemingly valid objection to the Mills-Nixon interpretation that the resonance energy of these compounds is too high to permit bond fixation.

Diazoamino Rearrangement. When a primary or secondary aromatic amine is used in the coupling process, attack of the diazonium ion usually occurs at the amino group rather than at the nucleus:

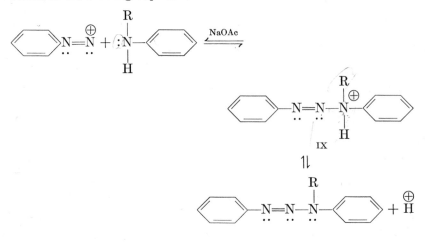

This, of course, is the position of highest electron density. The reaction proceeds to completion by the loss of a proton from the diazoammonium ion (IX). The overall process is a competing reaction with direct coupling, and occasionally it is found to proceed at a slower rate than coupling when the aromatic nucleus of the amino compound or the diazonium ion is particularly reactive.[12]

In acid solution, diazoamino compounds give the product that would have been expected from a direct coupling with the aromatic nucleus:

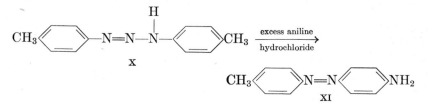

The reaction undoubtedly involves cleavage of the diazoamino compound followed by a recombination step, since p,p'-dimethyl diazoaminobenzene (X) gives p-amino-p'-methylazobenzene (XI) [13] when it is heated with excess aniline hydrochloride:

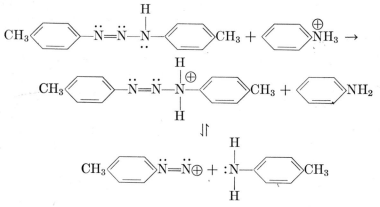

A satisfactory mechanism is the following:

(Continued on next page)

[12] Fieser and Fieser, Organic Chemistry, p. 628, D. C. Heath and Co., Boston, Mass., 1944.

[13] Nietzki, Ber., 10, 662 (1877); see also Kidd, J. Org. Chem., 2, 198 (1937).

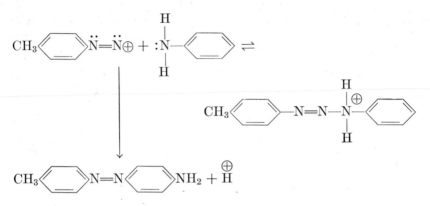

Wolff-Kishner Reduction. When the hydrazone of a carbonyl compound is heated with strong alkali, nitrogen is evolved, and two hydrogen atoms are introduced into the molecule:

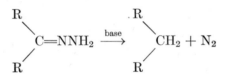

This reaction is usually called the Wolff-Kishner reduction.[14]   In early procedures, sodium ethoxide was the base commonly employed and the reaction was carried out at about 180° in a sealed tube.   A simplified technique, however, has been developed for carrying out the reaction in diethylene glycol solution with sodium or potassium hydroxide.[15]   Little is known concerning the mechanism of the reaction, but two possibilities [14, 16] are shown on p. 275.

[14] For a review of the Wolff-Kishner reaction, see Todd in Adams, *Organic Reactions*, Vol. IV, p. 378, John Wiley and Sons, New York, 1948.

[15] Huang-Minlon, *J. Am. Chem. Soc.*, **68**, 2487 (1946); see also Todd in Adams, *Organic Reactions*, Vol. IV, p. 385, John Wiley and Sons, New York, 1948.

[16] Seibert, *Chem. Ber.*, **80**, 494 (1947).

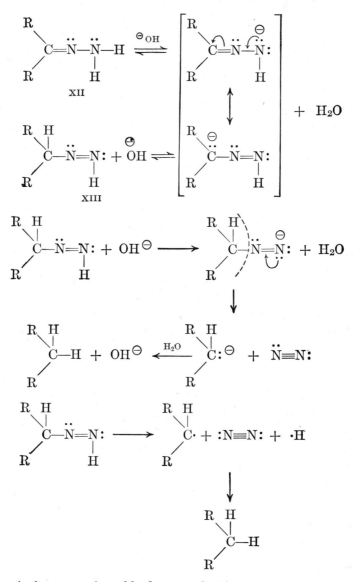

Although the conversion of hydrazones (XII) to substituted diimines (XIII) does not seem to have been realized, the reverse reaction, which probably involves the same intermediates, is well known.[17]   Benzene

[17] See (a) Taylor and Baker in *Sidgwick's Organic Chemistry of Nitrogen*, pp. 432–434, Oxford University Press, Oxford, England, 1937, and (b) Todd, *J. Am. Chem. Soc.*, **71**, 1356 (1949).

azo ethane (XIV), for example, is converted to the phenylhydrazone of

$$\langle\!\!\rangle N{=}N{-}CH_2CH_3 \xrightarrow{\text{NaOH}} \langle\!\!\rangle NHN{=}CHCH_3$$

XIV

acetaldehyde by the action of acids or alkalies. The final step in the reaction may be regarded as an ionic process such as the one shown or as
a free radical transformation.[17b] In support of the latter view it has been
found that p-isopropyl benzaldehyde methylhydrazone (XV) gave p-
ethyl-isopropylbenzene (XVI) in yields of 25 per cent.[17b]

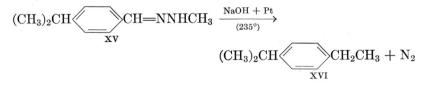

$$(CH_3)_2CH\langle\!\!\rangle CH{=}NNHCH_3 \xrightarrow[\text{(235°)}]{\text{NaOH + Pt}}$$

XV

$$(CH_3)_2CH\langle\!\!\rangle CH_2CH_3 + N_2$$

XVI

With N-substituted hydrazones it is not possible to write the ionic
mechanism shown above for the last step.

CHAPTER 15

MISCELLANEOUS REACTIONS INVOLVING THE MIGRATION OF A DOUBLE BOND

Displacement Reactions at an Allylic Carbon Atom.   It has long been known that reactions carried out with compounds of type I or II

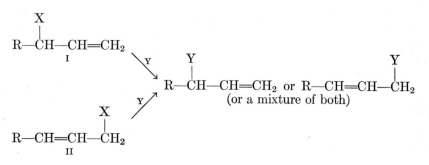

often lead to rearrangement or a mixture of products when the replacement of X is attempted.   Thus, methylvinylcarbinol (III) yields a mixture of 79.3 per cent crotyl bromide (V) and 20.7 per cent methylvinylcarbinyl bromide (IV) on treatment at $-15°$ with hydrobromic and

$$CH_3-CH-CH=CH_2 \xrightarrow[H_2SO_4; \ -15°]{48\% \ HBr \ +} CH_3-CH-CH=CH_2 \quad (20.7\%)$$
$$\underset{\text{III}}{OH} \qquad\qquad\qquad \underset{\text{IV}}{Br}$$

$$+$$

$$CH_3-CH=CH-CH_2 \quad (79.3\%)$$
$$\underset{\text{V}}{Br}$$

sulfuric acids.[1]   Similarly, the reaction of crotyl chloride with potassium acetate in acetic acid gives a mixture of crotyl and methylvinylcarbinyl acetates.[2]

[1] Young and Lane, *J. Am. Chem. Soc.*, **59**, 2051 (1937).
[2] Roberts, Young, and Winstein, *ibid.*, **64**, 2160 (1942).

$$CH_3-CH{=}CH-\overset{\underset{|}{Cl}}{C}H_2 \xrightarrow[\text{(78.6°)}]{\text{KOAc in HOAc}} CH_3-CH{=}CH-\overset{\underset{|}{OAc}}{C}H_2 \quad (84\%)$$

$$+$$

$$CH_3-\overset{\underset{|}{OAc}}{C}H-CH{=}CH_2 \quad (16\%)$$

The most logical interpretation of such results is to consider that the reaction proceeds by the simultaneous operation of two processes.[3]   One is a normal S_N2 type displacement which gives only primary products from primary starting materials and secondary products from secondary starting materials.   The other is an S_N1-like process in which reaction of the intermediate carbonium ion can occur through the resonance structures VI or VII to give crotyl or methylvinylcarbinyl products:

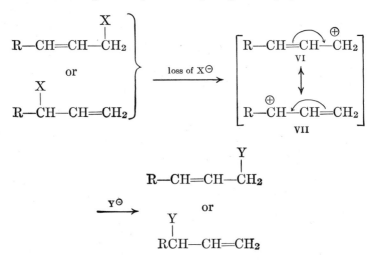

It is a consequence of this concept of displacement at an allylic position that conditions which favor an S_N2 attack should tend to decrease the amount of the other isomer formed.   Correspondingly, conditions which would be expected to produce a preliminary dissociation should favor rearrangement.   In the extreme case, when the reaction proceeds exclusively by ionization into a carbonium ion, the same proportion of products should be obtained regardless of whether compounds of type I or II were employed as starting materials.   These consequences have been very nicely verified for the crotyl-methylvinylcarbinyl system which has already been mentioned.   In acetic anhydride or acetone (solvents

[3] Young and Lane, *ibid.*, **60**, 848 (1938); Young and Andrews, *ibid.*, **66**, 421 (1944).

in which S_N2 reactions would be expected to predominate) no isomerization occurs when crotyl or methylvinylcarbinyl chloride is treated with acetate ion:[2]

$$CH_3—CH=CH—\overset{\overset{\text{Cl}}{|}}{C}H_2 + KOAc \xrightarrow{\text{Ac}_2\text{O; }100°} CH_3—CH=CH—\overset{\overset{\text{OAc}}{|}}{C}H_2$$
$$\text{(exclusively)}$$

$$CH_3—\overset{\overset{\text{Cl}}{|}}{C}H—CH=CH_2 + (Et)_4NOAc \xrightarrow{\text{acetone; }58°}$$
$$CH_3—\overset{\overset{\text{OAc}}{|}}{C}H—CH=CH_2$$
$$\text{(exclusively)}$$

With silver acetate in acetic acid, however, we should expect the route involving a carbonium ion to predominate (see p. 82), and we find, in fact, that the ratio of products is almost the same from either starting material:

$$CH_3—CH=CH—\overset{\overset{\text{Cl}}{|}}{C}H_2 + AgOAc \xrightarrow{\text{HOAc; }25°}$$
$$CH_3—CH=CH—\overset{\overset{\text{OAc}}{|}}{C}H_2 + CH_3—\overset{\overset{\text{OAc}}{|}}{C}H—CH=CH_2$$
$$\text{(60\%)} \qquad \text{(40\%)}$$

$$CH_3—\overset{\overset{\text{Cl}}{|}}{C}H—CH=CH_2 + AgOAc \xrightarrow{\text{HOAc; }25°}$$
$$CH_3—CH=CH—\overset{\overset{\text{OAc}}{|}}{C}H_2 + CH_3—\overset{\overset{\text{OAc}}{|}}{C}H—CH=CH_2$$
$$\text{(56\%)} \qquad \text{(44\%)}$$

An exception to these general principles which has been reported is the reaction of α- or γ-ethylallyl alcohol with thionyl chloride. The primary isomer gives principally the secondary chloride, and from the secondary isomer the primary chloride predominates.[4] It has been pointed out, however,[5] that these results may be explained by an S_Ni type reaction of the intermediate chlorosulfinic ester in which a six-membered ring is involved. Thus for the transformation of α-ethylallyl alcohol (VIII) to γ-ethallyl chloride (IX), we have:

[4] Meisenheimer and Link, *Ann.*, **479**, 211 (1930).

[5] Roberts, Young, and Winstein, *J. Am. Chem. Soc.*, **64**, 2158 (1942).

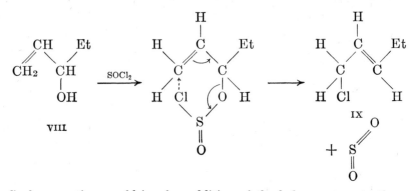

VIII   IX

Such a reaction would involve addition of the halogen atom to the γ-carbon atom of the allyl alcohol, a simultaneous shift of the double bond and elimination of a molecule of sulfur dioxide. The sequence is similar to what must occur when sodiomalonic ester reacts with ethylvinylcarbinyl chloride (X) to give XI. (See p. 92.)

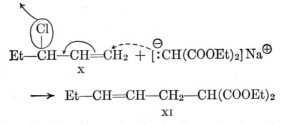

$$\longrightarrow \ Et\text{—}CH\text{=}CH\text{—}CH_2\text{—}CH(COOEt)_2$$

XI

Another closely related reaction is the isomerization of substituted allyl alcohols. This reaction is particularly interesting since the rearrangement of optically active alcohols proceeds with the retention of a high degree of optical activity in some instances. For example, (+) γ-methyl-α-ethylallyl alcohol (XII) forms on standing (+) α-methyl-γ-ethylallyl alcohol (XIII) with 73 per cent retention of optical activity.[6]

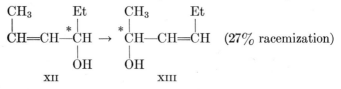

XII   XIII

The transformation is catalyzed by acids, and it appears to be a carbonium ion rearrangement similar to those discussed in Chapter 3 in which the migrating group never leaves the sphere of influence of the electronically deficient atoms which are involved:[7a]

[6] Airs, Balfe, and Kenyon, *J. Chem. Soc.*, **1942**, 18. See also Balfe and Kenyon, *Trans. Faraday Soc.*, **37**, 721 (1941).

[7a] Braude, *J. Chem. Soc.*, **1948**, 800.

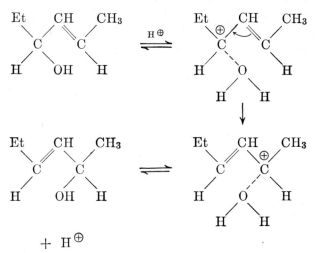

$$+ \; H^{\oplus}$$

As might be expected of a carbonium ion process (p. 41), electron-releasing groups in the aromatic nucleus of phenylpropenylcarbinol (XIV) facilitate its rearrangement to styrylmethylcarbinol (XV).[7b]

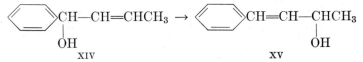

XIV   XV

Alkali-Catalyzed α,β–β,γ Equilibria of Unsaturated Compounds.[8]
When an α,β or β,γ unsaturated carbonyl compound is heated with a strong base, an equilibrium is often established between the two isomers:

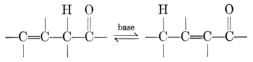

Similarly, allylbenzene is transformed almost irreversibly into propenylbenzene:

and 1,3-pentadiene results from the exhaustive methylation of piperidine, presumably by the isomerization of the initially formed 1,4-pentadiene.

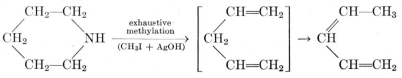

[7b] Braude and Stern, *ibid.*, **1947**, 1096.

[8] For an excellent discussion of tautomerism in which this particular kind is included, see Baker, *Tautomerism*, Routledge and Sons, Ltd., London, England, 1934.

These reactions appear to proceed through the formation of a common carbanion obtained by the attack of the base on a hydrogen atom attached to a carbon atom alpha to one of the unsaturated groups. For the α,β–β,γ equilibria of unsaturated carbonyl compounds, the isomerization may be outlined as follows:

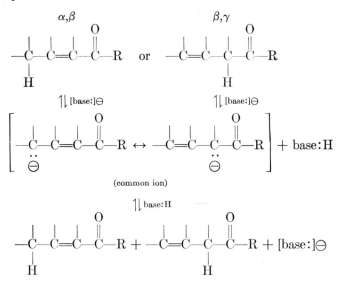

(common ion)

Exchange reactions with deuterium oxide solution support the idea of the formation of a common carbanion. Sodium vinyl acetate (XVI), for example, exchanges hydrogen for deuterium atoms in sodium hydroxide solution containing deuterium oxide.[9] The rate is faster than the rate

$$CH_2{=}CH{-}CH_2COONa \rightleftharpoons CH_3{-}CH{=}CH{-}COONa$$
XVI

of isomerism to sodium crotonate. Sodium crotonate also exchanges but much more slowly,[10] and this relationship is in agreement with the fact that the sodium vinylacetate-crotonate equilibrium is much in favor of sodium crotonate (98 per cent).[11] Under the same conditions propionic, butyric, and isobutyric acid do not exchange. It is also to be expected that the ease with which the intermediate is formed (and therefore the ease of establishing equilibrium) will depend upon the factors influencing carbanion formation which were discussed in Chapter 6 (p. 123). This is illustrated by the fact that acids of the type XVII and XVIII require hot

[9] Ives and Rydon, *J. Chem. Soc.*, **1935**, 1735.

[10] Ives, *ibid.*, **1938**, 91.

[11] Linstead and Noble, *ibid.*, **1934**, 614.

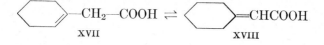

aqueous alkali for their interconversion. Their esters and acid chlorides, however, are more readily equilibrated, and the analogous methyl ketones are so easily isomerized that special precautions must be employed to prevent isomerization during their preparation.[12]

For most organic chemists the position of equilibrium in the α,β–β,γ equilibrium is more interesting than the rate at which equilibrium is established. Indeed a great deal of attention has been directed to this aspect of the phenomenon.[13] The interpretation of all these results is difficult, but many of the data can be correlated by a consideration of hyperconjugation and resonance. Thus, if a common carbanion is involved in the transformation, we should expect that olefin to predominate from it which would be the more stabilized by resonance. Usually the α,β-position will be favored because of conjugation with a carbonyl or nitrile group. The effect of introducing alkyl groups into a molecule, however, will be such as to shift the equilibrium in the direction in which the double bond will become conjugated with the largest number of α-hydrogen atoms (hyperconjugation). A few examples will illustrate the point.

		Number of Hyperconjugation Structures Possible for the α,β- and β,γ-Isomers
α-Alkyl groups	CH_3—CH_2—CH=CH—$COOH$ 62% α,β *(See footnote 14)*	$\alpha,\beta = 2$ $\beta,\gamma = 5$
	CH_3—CH_2—CH=$\overset{\overset{\displaystyle CH_3}{\mid}}{C}$—$COOH$ 81% α,β *(See footnote 15)*	$\alpha,\beta = 5$ $\beta,\gamma = 4$

[12] See Baker, *Tautomerism*, p. 46, Routledge and Sons, Ltd., London, 1934.

[13] Principally by Linstead and his co-workers. For leading references see Adkins in Gilman, *Organic Chemistry*, pp. 1041–1043, John Wiley and Sons, New York, 1943.

[14] Ives and Kerlogue, *J. Chem. Soc.*, **1940**, 1364.

[15] See Baker, *Tautomerism*, pp. 156, 157, and 160, Routledge and Sons, Ltd., London, 1934.

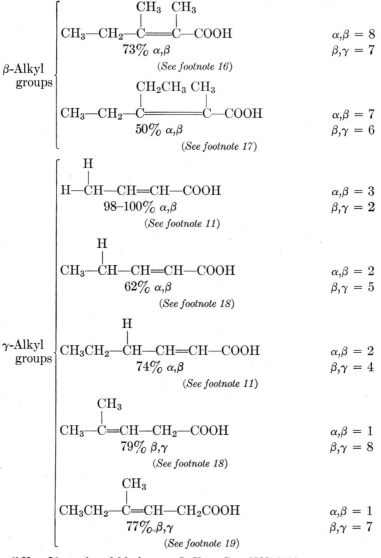

Number of
Hyperconjugation
Structures Possible
for the α,β- and
β,γ-Isomers

β-Alkyl groups

$$\text{CH}_3\text{—CH}_2\text{—}\overset{\overset{\displaystyle \text{CH}_3}{|}}{\text{C}}\text{=}\overset{\overset{\displaystyle \text{CH}_3}{|}}{\text{C}}\text{—COOH}$$
73% α,β
(See footnote 16)

$\alpha,\beta = 8$
$\beta,\gamma = 7$

$$\text{CH}_3\text{—CH}_2\text{—}\overset{\overset{\displaystyle \text{CH}_2\text{CH}_3}{|}}{\text{C}}\text{=}\overset{\overset{\displaystyle \text{CH}_3}{|}}{\text{C}}\text{—COOH}$$
50% α,β
(See footnote 17)

$\alpha,\beta = 7$
$\beta,\gamma = 6$

γ-Alkyl groups

$$\text{H—}\overset{\overset{\displaystyle \text{H}}{|}}{\text{CH}}\text{—CH=CH—COOH}$$
98–100% α,β
(See footnote 11)

$\alpha,\beta = 3$
$\beta,\gamma = 2$

$$\text{CH}_3\text{—}\overset{\overset{\displaystyle \text{H}}{|}}{\text{CH}}\text{—CH=CH—COOH}$$
62% α,β
(See footnote 18)

$\alpha,\beta = 2$
$\beta,\gamma = 5$

$$\text{CH}_3\text{CH}_2\text{—}\overset{\overset{\displaystyle \text{H}}{|}}{\text{CH}}\text{—CH=CH—COOH}$$
74% α,β
(See footnote 11)

$\alpha,\beta = 2$
$\beta,\gamma = 4$

$$\text{CH}_3\text{—}\overset{\overset{\displaystyle \text{CH}_3}{|}}{\text{C}}\text{=CH—CH}_2\text{—COOH}$$
79% β,γ
(See footnote 18)

$\alpha,\beta = 1$
$\beta,\gamma = 8$

$$\text{CH}_3\text{CH}_2\text{—}\overset{\overset{\displaystyle \text{CH}_3}{|}}{\text{C}}\text{=CH—CH}_2\text{COOH}$$
77% β,γ
(See footnote 19)

$\alpha,\beta = 1$
$\beta,\gamma = 7$

[16] Kon, Linstead, and Maclennan, *J. Chem. Soc.*, **1932**, 2452.
[17] Armand, Kon, Leton, Linstead, and Parsons, *ibid.*, **1931**, 1411.
[18] Letch and Linstead, *ibid.*, **1932**, 443.
[19] Linstead and Mann, *ibid.*, **1930**, 2064.

Number of
Hyperconjugation
Structures Possible
for the α,β- and
β,γ-Isomers

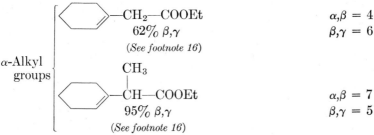

α-Alkyl
groups

—CH₂—COOEt $\alpha,\beta = 4$
62% β,γ $\beta,\gamma = 6$
(*See footnote 16*)

CH₃
|
—CH—COOEt $\alpha,\beta = 7$
95% β,γ $\beta,\gamma = 5$
(*See footnote 16*)

It is evident from these examples that there is only a qualitative relationship between the ratio of the numbers of hyperconjugation structures which can be written for the two isomers and the ratio of the two
at equilibrium. The results also may be interpreted as a consequence of
strain (p. 117). The explanation for the anomaly with the cyclohexyl-
ideneacetic esters is not clear. It is not observed with the corresponding
acids or cyclopentenyl derivatives.

=CH—COOEt $\alpha,\beta = 4$
60% α,β $\beta,\gamma = 6$
(*See footnote 16*)

CH₃
|
=C—COOEt $\alpha,\beta = 7$
88% α,β $\beta,\gamma = 5$
(*See footnote 16*)

An even more facile isomerization occurs when a second activating
group is introduced into the β- or γ-position of an $\alpha,\beta-\beta,\gamma$ unsaturated
carbonyl compound. Itaconic anhydride (XIX) rearranges to citra-

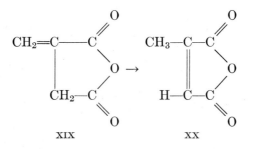

XIX   XX

conic anhydride (XX) on distillation at atmospheric pressure,[20] and treatment of ethyl itaconate (XXI), citraconate (XXII), or mesaconate (XXIII) with sodium ethoxide results in a mixture of the three in which

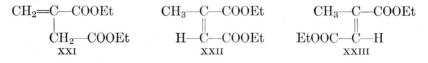

$$CH_2=C-COOEt$$
$$|$$
$$CH_2-COOEt$$
XXI

$$CH_3-C-COOEt$$
$$||$$
$$H-C-COOEt$$
XXII

$$CH_3-C-COOEt$$
$$||$$
$$EtOOC-C-H$$
XXIII

equilibrium favors the α,β-isomers (77 per cent).[21] This isomerization is of considerable practical importance for it is evident that syntheses conducted in strongly basic media may lead to mixtures of products regardless of the ester employed as the starting material.[22]

When a second identical activating group is introduced into the γ-position, as in glutaconic ester, the α,β and β,γ positions are equivalent until an alkyl group is introduced:

$$EtOOC-\overset{\alpha}{CH_2}-\overset{\beta}{CH}=\overset{\gamma}{CH}-COOEt$$
$$\equiv EtOOC-\overset{\alpha}{CH}=\overset{\beta}{CH}-\overset{\gamma}{CH_2}-COOEt$$

When an alkyl group is present, however, that form would be expected to be favored which will allow the greater number of hyperconjugation structures. In accordance with this principle, the stepwise methylation of ethyl glutaconate yields successively XXIV, XXV, and XXVI.[23]

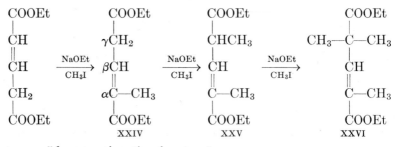

5 hyperconjugation forms α,β
1 hyperconjugation form β,γ

[20] Shriner, Ford, and Roll, in Blatt, *Organic Syntheses*, Collective Vol. 2, p. 140, John Wiley and Sons, New York, 1943.

[21] Coulson and Kon, *J. Chem. Soc.*, **1932**, 2568.

[22] Ingold, Shoppee, and Thorpe, *ibid.*, **1926**, 1477.

[23] Thorpe and Wood, *ibid.*, **103**, 1754 (1913). For a more detailed discussion of the glutaconic ester problem, see Baker, *Tautomerism*, pp. 164–169, Routledge and Sons, Ltd., London, 1934.

The Nature and Reactions of Allylic Grignard Reagents. One of the most perplexing problems associated with unsaturated systems is the interpretation of the nature and reactions of allylic Grignard reagents. The reactions of the magnesium derivatives of crotyl and methylvinylcarbinyl halides have been extensively studied,[24] but still only tentative conclusions can be drawn concerning the nature of these reagents and the mechanisms whereby reaction occurs.

When a Grignard reagent is prepared from a crotyl halide, the resulting ethereal solution appears to be identical with the solution prepared from the corresponding methylvinylcarbinyl halide and magnesium. This solution is usually called a *butenyl* Grignard reagent. Hydrolysis [25, 26, 27] and addition reactions (see p. 288), for example, have repeatedly shown that the products obtained are independent of the structure of the starting material employed. The constitution of this solution, however, is not definitely known (see pp. 188–194). If the butenyl Grignard reagent is essentially covalent it could exist exclusively in the primary form (XXVII), exclusively in the secondary form (XXVIII), or as a mixture of the two:

$$
\begin{array}{cc}
\text{MgX} & \text{MgX} \\
| & | \\
\text{CH}_3\text{—CH}\text{=}\text{CH—CH}_2 & \text{CH}_3\text{—CH—CH}\text{=}\text{CH}_2 \\
\text{XXVII} & \text{XXVIII}
\end{array}
$$

If it is essentially ionic the carbanion would be a resonance hybrid of the structures XXIX and XXX.

$$
[\text{CH}_3\text{—}\overset{\frown}{\text{CH}}\text{=}\text{CH}\text{—}\overset{\ominus}{\overset{..}{\text{CH}}}_2 \longleftrightarrow \text{CH}_3\text{—}\overset{\ominus}{\overset{..}{\text{CH}}}\text{—CH}\text{=}\text{CH}_2] + \overset{\oplus}{\text{MgX}}
$$

$$
\text{XXIX} \qquad\qquad\qquad \text{XXX}
$$

It is impossible to assign a structure to the reagent on the basis of the structure of the products obtained from the addition reactions of the butenyl Grignard reagent until it has been determined whether the reagent is ionic or covalent and whether rearrangement occurs during addition of the reagent to a reactant. A number of experimental facts concerning the butenyl Grignard reagent are outlined below. Except where a mixture is indicated, only one product has been isolated from each of the reactions shown.

---

[24] Principally by Young and his co-workers. For a leading article see footnote 31.

[25] (a) Young, Winstein, and Prater, *J. Am. Chem. Soc.*, **58**, 289 (1936); (b) Young and Eisner, *ibid.*, **63**, 2113 (1941).

[26] Young and Winstein, *ibid.*, **58**, 441 (1936).

[27] Young, Kaufman, Loshokoff, and Pressman, *ibid.*, **60**, 900 (1938).

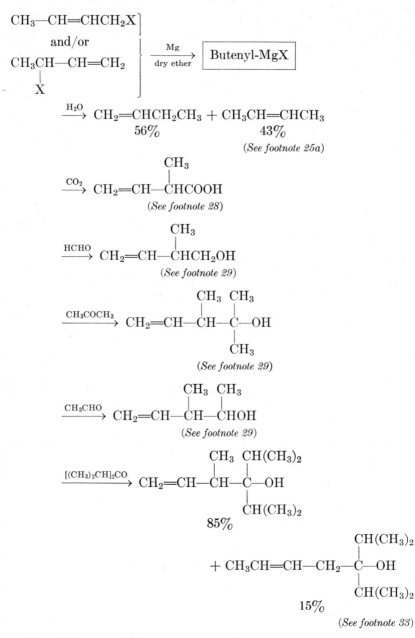

CH$_3$—CH=CHCH$_2$X ⎤
and/or   ⎪ $\xrightarrow[\text{dry ether}]{\text{Mg}}$ Butenyl-MgX
CH$_3$CH—CH=CH$_2$ ⎬
          | ⎪
          X   ⎦

$\xrightarrow{\text{H}_2\text{O}}$ CH$_2$=CHCH$_2$CH$_3$ + CH$_3$CH=CHCH$_3$
                        56%   43%
                                      (*See footnote 25a*)

$\xrightarrow{\text{CO}_2}$ CH$_2$=CH—$\overset{\overset{\text{CH}_3}{|}}{\text{CH}}$COOH
                (*See footnote 28*)

$\xrightarrow{\text{HCHO}}$ CH$_2$=CH—$\overset{\overset{\text{CH}_3}{|}}{\text{CH}}CH_2$OH
                (*See footnote 29*)

$\xrightarrow{\text{CH}_3\text{COCH}_3}$ CH$_2$=CH—$\overset{\overset{\text{CH}_3}{|}}{\text{CH}}$—$\underset{\underset{\text{CH}_3}{|}}{\overset{\overset{\text{CH}_3}{|}}{\text{C}}}$—OH
                            (*See footnote 29*)

$\xrightarrow{\text{CH}_3\text{CHO}}$ CH$_2$=CH—$\overset{\overset{\text{CH}_3}{|}}{\text{CH}}$—$\overset{\overset{\text{CH}_3}{|}}{\text{CH}}$OH
                      (*See footnote 29*)

$\xrightarrow{[(\text{CH}_3)_2\text{CH}]_2\text{CO}}$ CH$_2$=CH—$\overset{\overset{\text{CH}_3}{|}}{\text{CH}}$—$\underset{\underset{\text{CH}(\text{CH}_3)_2}{|}}{\overset{\overset{\text{CH}(\text{CH}_3)_2}{|}}{\text{C}}}$—OH
                            85%

+ CH$_3$CH=CH—CH$_2$—$\underset{\underset{\text{CH}(\text{CH}_3)_2}{|}}{\overset{\overset{\text{CH}(\text{CH}_3)_2}{|}}{\text{C}}}$—OH
                            15%
                                      (*See footnote 33*)

[28] Lane, Roberts, and Young, *ibid.*, **66**, 543 (1944).
[29] Roberts and Young, *ibid.*, **67**, 148 (1945). See also Kiun-Houo, *Ann. chim.* [11], **13**, 175 (1940).

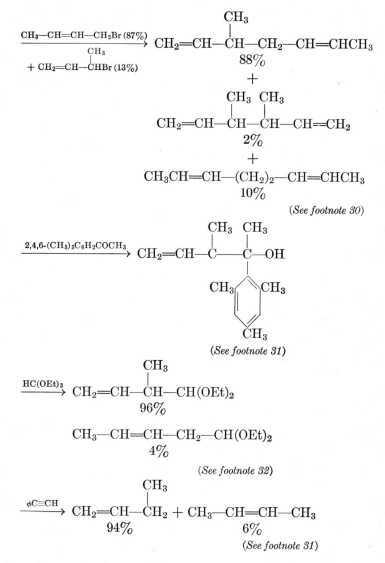

$$CH_3-CH=CH-CH_2Br\ (87\%)$$
$$\overset{CH_3}{\underset{}{}}$$
$$+\ CH_2=CH-\overset{|}{C}HBr\ (13\%)$$

$$\xrightarrow{\hspace{2cm}}\ CH_2=CH-\overset{\overset{CH_3}{|}}{C}H-CH_2-CH=CHCH_3$$
$$88\%$$
$$+$$
$$CH_2=CH-\overset{\overset{CH_3}{|}}{C}H-\overset{\overset{CH_3}{|}}{C}H-CH=CH_2$$
$$2\%$$
$$+$$
$$CH_3CH=CH-(CH_2)_2-CH=CHCH_3$$
$$10\%$$

(See footnote 30)

$$\xrightarrow{2,4,6\text{-}(CH_3)_3C_6H_2COCH_3}\ CH_2=CH-\overset{\overset{CH_3}{|}}{C}\overset{\overset{CH_3}{|}}{\underset{}{C}}-OH$$

(See footnote 31)

$$\xrightarrow{HC(OEt)_3}\ CH_2=CH-\overset{\overset{CH_3}{|}}{C}H-CH(OEt)_2$$
$$96\%$$

$$CH_3-CH=CH-CH_2-CH(OEt)_2$$
$$4\%$$

(See footnote 32)

$$\xrightarrow{\phi C\equiv CH}\ CH_2=CH-\overset{\overset{CH_3}{|}}{C}H_2\ +\ CH_3-CH=CH-CH_3$$
$$94\% \qquad\qquad 6\%$$

(See footnote 31)

All these data are consistent with the point of view that rearrangement occurs during reaction of the halide with magnesium and that the Grignard reagent is mostly in the covalent methylvinylcarbinyl form. Under usual conditions, then, it may be supposed that the reagent

[30] Young, Roberts, and Wax, *J. Am. Chem. Soc.*, **67**, 841 (1945).
[31] Young and Roberts, *ibid.*, **68**, 1472 (1946).
[32] Young and Roberts, *ibid.*, 649.

behaves as a reactive covalent compound to give products:

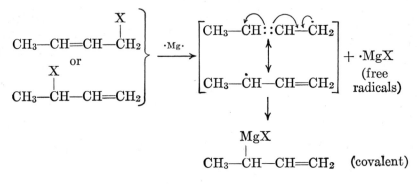

In a polar environment such as water, partial dissociation into a carbanion might occur, the reaction of which could lead to a mixture of crotyl and methylvinylcarbinyl products:

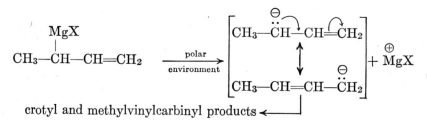

crotyl and methylvinylcarbinyl products ◄───────┘

Although this concept correlates the data moderately well with respect to the position taken by the entering group, there is one very striking characteristic of the butenyl Grignard reagent which suggests that these ideas have oversimplified the situation and that they may even be erroneous. *Butenyl Grignard reagents undergo 1,2-addition reactions to hindered carbonyl groups with abnormal ease.* So easily, in fact, that a mechanism of addition different from the one operative with an alkyl or arylmagnesium halide seems to be indicated. Thus, in the addition of butenylmagnesium bromide to diisopropyl ketone and acetomesitylene, the yields were 89 [33] and 83 per cent,[31] respectively. These results are particularly striking since a butenylmagnesium halide appears to be the only Grignard reagent known which will introduce a secondary group into diisopropyl ketone. Accordingly, it has been suggested [31, 32] that the 1,2-addition of allylic magnesium halides proceeds by a *cyclic mechanism* in which the γ-carbon atom of the organometallic reagent becomes attached to the carbonyl carbon atom:

[33] Young and Roberts, *ibid.*, **67**, 319 (1945).

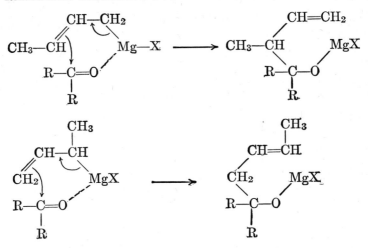

or

From the point of view of this reaction mechanism, the crotyl Grignard reagent must be considered the more stable covalent form since the methylvinylcarbinyl derivatives always predominate from such reactions.

With respect to the cyclic mechanism, a comparison of the reactions of the allylic Grignard reagents and sodium allylbenzene is informative. Since sodium belongs to the first group of the periodic system, an organosodium compound would not be expected to form coordination complexes as does an organomagnesium compound. Consequently, the reactions of sodium allylbenzene should not proceed through a cyclic addition complex, and the composition of hydrolysis products should be independent of the ability of a hydrolytic agent to form a coordination complex. This has been verified with sodium allylbenzene: [34]

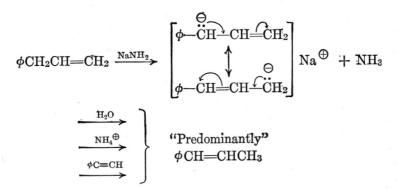

[34] Campbell and Young, *ibid.*, **69**, 688 (1947).

Conversely, if an allylic Grignard reagent reacts preferentially by a cyclic mechanism but carbanion formation is also possible, the nature of the hydrolysis products should depend upon the ability of the hydrolytic agent to coordinate with the Grignard reagent. This is true in the butenyl series (p. 288), where we find that water gives a mixture of 1- and 2-butene, whereas phenylacetylene gives nearly pure 1-butene. These facts are in agreement with the supposition that the reaction of phenylacetylene with the butenyl Grignard reagent (in essentially the crotyl form) involves a coordination complex of the magnesium atom of the Grignard reagent with the electrons of the triple bond.

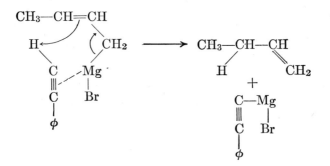

A similar mechanism can be written for the formation of 1-butene from the crotyl form of the butenyl Grignard reagent and hydroxylated materials.

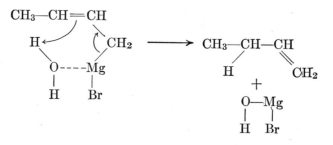

The fact that a mixture of olefins is actually obtained, however, indicates that this cannot be the only mechanism of hydrolysis open to hydroxylated compounds.

The Claisen Rearrangement.[35]   The rearrangement of allyl aryl ethers to allyl-substituted hydroxy aryl compounds is generally known as the Claisen rearrangement. It is now evident, however, that this rearrange-

[35] For excellent reviews, see (a) Tarbell, *Chem. Revs.*, **27**, 495 (1940), and (b) Tarbell in Adams, *Organic Reactions*, Vol. II, p. 1, John Wiley and Sons, New York, 1944.

ment is a specific instance of a much more general reaction involving the allyl group. Thus any vinyl allyl ether (XXXI) or biallyl system (XXXII) [36] may be expected to undergo rearrangement provided that the β,γ double bond of the allyl group is not in an aromatic ring:

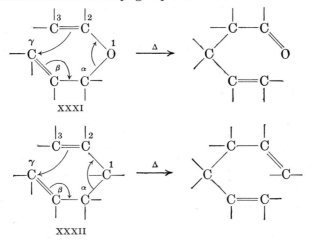

A large number of these rearrangements are known:

Allyl Vinyl Ethers: [37]

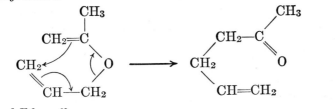

Allyl Aryl Ethers: [38]

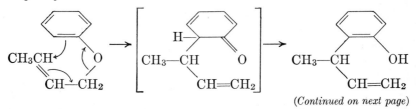

(Continued on next page)

[36] (a) Cope and Hardy, *J. Am. Chem. Soc.*, **62**, 441 (1940); (b) Cope, Hoyle, and Heyle, *ibid.*, **63**, 1843 (1941); (c) Cope, Hoffman, and Hardy, *ibid.*, 1852; (d) Whyte and Cope, *ibid.*, **65**, 1999 (1943); (e) Kimel and Cope, *ibid.*, 1992; (f) Levy and Cope, *ibid.*, **66**, 1684 (1944); (g) Kleinschmidt and Cope, *ibid.*, 1929; (h) Cope and Field, *ibid.*, **71**, 1589 (1949).

[37] Tarbell in Adams, *Organic Reactions*, Vol. II, p. 29, John Wiley and Sons, New York, 1941.

[38] *Ibid.*, p. 45.

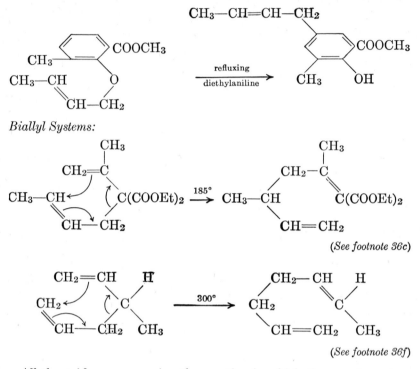

Biallyl Systems:

(*See footnote 36c*)

(*See footnote 36f*)

All the evidence concerning the reaction in which the γ-carbon atom and the atom labeled 3 are united supports the intramolecular cyclic mechanism shown in XXXI and XXXII. The process is first order,[36b, 39] it does not require an acidic or basic catalyst, and no crossed products are obtained when the rearrangement is carried out with a mixture of different starting materials.[36c, 39b, 40a]   Even in phenol solution the reaction is truly intramolecular.   No deuterium can be found in the product when phenyl allyl ether is rearranged in 3,5-dideuterophenol.[40b]

When both *ortho* positions of an aryl allyl ether are occupied, the allyl group will rearrange on heating to the *para* position, usually with no isomerization.   The only known example of *para* rearrangement which occurs with isomerization is the α-ethylallyl ether XXXIII.[41]   Certainly

[39] (*a*) Kincaid and Tarbell, *J. Am. Chem. Soc.*, **61**, 3085 (1939); (*b*) Morse and Kincaid, *Abstracts of Papers*, p. 11M, 102nd Meeting, American Chemical Society, Atlantic City, N. J., September 1941; (*c*) Foster, Cope, and Daniels, *J. Am. Chem. Soc.*, **69**, 1893 (1947).

[40] (*a*) Hurd and Schmerling, *J. Am. Chem. Soc.*, **59**, 107 (1937); (*b*) Fomenko, Miklukhin, and Sadovnkova, *Doklady Akad. Nauk. S.S.S.R.*, **62**, 91 (1948); (*C.A.*, **43**, 602 [1949]).

[41] Mumm, Hornhardt, and Diederickson, *Ber.*, **72**, 100 (1939).

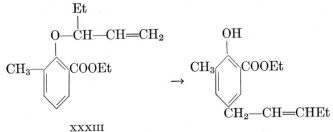

XXXIII

a cyclic mechanism is ruled out for the transformation because of the distance of migration and the fact that the reaction can occur without isomerization of the allyl group.   A free radical reaction is not indicated since *meta* substitution products are never obtained.   Dissociation into a carbonium and an aryloxide ion does not seem likely because a positively charged allyl ion would surely combine with a reactive solvent such as dimethylaniline, and as a result lower the yield of rearrangement.   This is apparently never observed.[42, 43]   The *para* rearrangement is also a first-order reaction.[43]   Thus the reaction seems to be an intramolecular process, but no definite conclusions can be reached concerning the mechanism.

[42] Tarbell in Adams, *Organic Reactions*, Vol. II, p. 44, John Wiley and Sons, 1944.
[43] Tarbell and Kincaid, *J. Am. Chem. Soc.*, **62**, 728 (1940).

AUTHOR INDEX

SUBJECT INDEX

Acetaldehyde, aldol condensation of, 177
  reaction with butenyl Grignard reagent, 288
  relative reactivity of with phenylmagnesium bromide, 156
  relative reactivity of with semicarbazide, 156
  Tollens condensation with, 178
Acetals, formation of from aldehydes and alcohols, 215
  formation of from aldehydes and orthoesters, 216
  sensitivity to acids, 217
Acetanilide, nitration of, 243
Acetate ion, relative base strength of, 112
Acetic acid, dissociation constant of, 12
Acetomesitylene, reaction with butenyl Grignard reagent, 289
Acetone, base-catalyzed condensation of, 178
  reaction with butenyl Grignard reagent, 288
  reaction with halogens, 207
  reaction with hypohalites, 207
  relative reactivity of with Grignard reagents, 156
  relative reactivity of with semicarbazide, 156
Acetophenone, condensation with benzaldehyde, 184
  reaction with halogens, 207
  Schmidt reaction with, 71
o-Acetoxyacetanilide, nitration of, 245
p-Acetylaminodiphenyl ether, bromination of, 240
  nitration of, 240
Acetylaminotoluenes, nitration of, 244
Acetyl chloride, Friedel-Crafts reaction with, 261
Acetylenic carbinols, formation of, 179
Acid bromides, relative reactivity toward Grignard reagents, 90

Acid chlorides, relative reactivity toward Grignard reagents, 90
Acid fluorides, relative reactivity toward Grignard reagents, 90
Acids, freezing point depression of in sulfuric acid, 36
  reaction with carbonyl groups, 35
  reaction with nitriles, 35
  reaction with olefins, 35
  relative ease of carbanion formation from, 127
Acylation, of benzene derivatives, 260
Acyl halides, reaction with aluminum halides, 261
Acyloin condensation, 171
Acyl-oxygen fission, 226
Addition, of HCl to 2-pentene, 33
Addition to carbon-carbon double bonds, 135
  conjugate addition, 141, 148
  free radical, 136
  initiated by anions, 146
  initiated by cations, 141
  ionic, 136
  of alkyl halides, 145
  stereochemistry of, 138, 140
  which involves two reaction paths, 153
Addition to carbonyl groups, acid catalysis, 156
Alcohols, reaction with acrylonitrile, 151
  reaction with nitriles, 173
Aldehydes, freezing point depression of in sulfuric acid, 36
  reaction with acrylonitrile, 151
  relative ease of carbanion formation from, 127
Aldol reactions, 176
Alkali cyanides, in benzoin condensations, 194
Alkanes, isomerization of, 59
o-Alkoxyacetanilide, chlorination of, 246
p-Alkoxyacetanilide, halogenation of, 246

305